THE TATT

This is the story of the handsome Mario – also known as El Rubio the Blond One – and later as the Count of San Mateo. As a youth Mario receives the roughest of educations on the docks and in the bars of Havana – preparation for his designated future role as the Queen of Spain's lover. But when he meets the beautiful Zaydah, bride-to-be of Adan, heir to the throne of Morocco, he is suddenly caught in a vortex of love and passion which sweeps him into mortal conflict with all his blood-sworn loyalties.

There are others, too, who share Mario's charmed and violent destiny. There is Concha, the girl who gives Mario his first knowledge of women; the wise Spanish Moor, Don Baltazar, who foresees the shattering consequences of Mario's passion; the gentle slave, Ramon, who searches for his own different kind of love; and the great Napoleon, with whom Mario must barter for the fate of his adopted country.

Also available in PAN Books

DRUM
MANDINGO
MASTER OF FALCONHURST
SANTIAGO BLOOD
CHILD OF THE SUN
FALCONHURST FANCY

CONDITIONS OF SALE

This book shall not, by way of trade or otherwise, be lent, re-sold, hired out or otherwise circulated without the publisher's prior consent in any form of binding or cover other than that in which it is published and without a similar condition including this condition being imposed on the subsequent purchaser

THE TATTOOED ROOD

KYLE ONSTOTT
AND
LANCE HORNER

UNABRIDGED

PAN BOOKS LTD : LONDON

First published in the U.K. 1962 by Souvenir Press Ltd.
This edition published 1964 by Pan Books Ltd.,
33 Tothill Street, London S.W.1

330 20051 8

2nd Printing 1966
3rd Printing 1967
4th Printing 1967
5th Printing 1967
6th Printing 1968
7th Printing 1969

© William W. Denlinger, 1960

Printed in Great Britain by Richard Clay (The Chaucer Press), Ltd.,
Bungay, Suffolk

Chapter One

THE BOY, El Rubio, was eleven or twelve, he himself didn't know his age, nor did he care. There were so many more interesting things to think about, as he loitered along the Havana waterfront. The thing of the moment was the overripe mango he had just filched. He bit into it and enjoyed the spurt of juice that struck his cheek, ran over his chin and trickled across his small belly down into the top of the ragged garment that served as his *pantalones*. It didn't matter. They were now so torn, so ragged, so full of rents that they hardly served their purpose, scarcely covering either his breech or the posterior parts of his anatomy which showed through them. Otherwise he was quite naked except for the incrustations of accumulated dirt that clothed him from his scalp to the calloused soles of his feet.

A late afternoon's drizzle of warm rain had been falling, and during it El Rubio had sought the shelter of a doorway. Like a cat, he hated water. True, in earlier days he had been in the habit of swimming out to some brig or sailing ship anchored in the harbour. He would circle it like a dolphin, screaming himself hoarse in his endeavour to get one of the passengers to throw him a *centavo*. But he had learned through experience that the larger boys were always able to dive faster and swim better, and that even when he did succeed in getting a coin, they would take it away from him later by force. So he had given up the practice and subsequently there had been little occasion for him even to approach water.

Now that the sun was out again, hot on his naked back, he dallied near the wharves, eating the mango and cursing under his breath. He had just been ejected from the old auction house where they were holding a slave auction, and he was angry – he considered that the whole city of Havana was rightfully his and that he could go where he pleased, excepting perhaps the governor's palace. When the auctioneer had seen El Rubio begging from the planters who were seeking bargains in slaves, he had ordered one of his slave attendants to throw him out, with a warning not to return.

The auction itself had carried little interest for El Rubio.

The slaves offered had been ugly black *bozals*, fresh from Africa and mostly males, while he had counted upon seeing some – at least one or two – young yellow girls, octoroons or quadroons, stripped for the purchasers' examining fingers. El Rubio could not purchase, but he could dream. In his imagination he was able to buy and own slaves, command them, feel and caress them, flog them – in short, use them as he liked. Then, in the rising heat of his imagination, he would enter into all kinds of intimacies with them or, tiring of them, he could sell them and buy others. Although he had not the remotest expectation of ever owning a slave, daydreams cost him little.

As for the Negroes themselves, he had no feeling for them, slave or free. Indeed, El Rubio, despite his yellow hair, his blue eyes and light skin, assumed that he himself was part Negro. His coloration, from which he derived the nickname of El Rubio, the Blond One, was an inheritance from his father – whoever he might have been. Certainly the woman he knew as his mother carried Negro blood; an octoroon perhaps. He had been born free and christened with the name of Mario – although it was a name he seldom heard except from Doña Ana, and then it was usually changed to its diminutive, Marito. As Mario he was almost a stranger to himself. He and his own small world knew him as El Rubio.

He had just turned off the wide roadway which bordered the wharves into one of the narrow canyons that served for streets in colonial Havana, when he felt a tug at his right ear. He had but one thought – the police had finally caught up with him! All his petty thieving, all his fighting, all his little crimes had finally found him out. Terrified, afraid to turn, he advanced one cautious step. The grip held firm but he took assurance from the strange word that was spoken to him.

'Kid.'

He relaxed. It was not the police, but rather some foreigner speaking an unknown word. Mario brushed the hand away from his ear and looked up to see a tall, burly, long-armed man, more blond even than himself. He was roughly dressed and there was a black patch over his left eye. Three days' growth of yellow beard did little to mask the ruddy youth of the man's face.

'What happened to the whore – *la puta* – who used to live here?' the stranger inquired, pointing to a weatherbeaten door.

Mario shook his head. '*No sé, señor,*' he replied, smiling. The strange words conveyed little to him, but *puta* had caught his interest. Anything to do with whores excited Mario. '*Eres ingles? Un marino?*'

The sailor nodded. '*Americano,* kid. And if by *marino* you mean sailor, yes to that. But the *puta* —' He hesitated for a word. '*Dondé* is the *puta*? Where the hell is the bitch?'

Mario understood. If the stranger wanted a whore, there were four in his own house – the whorehouse his mother kept. The sailor grasped the meaning of a few of the words which Mario spouted at him, particularly those which the boy emphasized and repeated – the most emphatic of all being the word *dinero*, which Mario accompanied with an obscene gesture of moving the forefinger of his right hand through the clasped fingers of his left. The sailor reached in his pocket and withdrew a handful of gold and silver coins, and these spurred Mario on to even greater efforts. It did not take long for his gestures to indicate a glowing picture of the girls' outstanding anatomical details, and the sailor, now thoroughly aroused, was eager to be led any place where there were women.

Skipping sideways and backwards to be sure that his charge was following him, Mario turned into San Isidro Street, where two short blocks brought them to the house with the faded blue door which was his home and his mother's modest bordello. Mario pushed at the door, hurried in and beckoned the sailor to follow. He deposited him on a rickety chair in the shabby *sala* and ran to the rear of the house in search of his mother. In a moment he was back, tugging Doña Ana by the skirt, full of pride at having brought home his first client – and one with a pocketful of money.

Doña Ana beamed in satisfaction, her smile of hospitality broadened by Mario's description of the money he had seen. She dusted off a more comfortable chair with the corner of her skirt, motioned the sailor to sit there, fluttered her hand to assure him there would be only a moment's delay, then bobbed through the door, screaming down the hall for the girls. All four of them soon appeared, quite nude except for their professional smiles.

The two older ones were dumpy, with worn-out figures, their skin blotched and purpled, their hair lifeless and greasy. A third was a mulatto wench, young and buxom, but neither her pointed breasts nor the sleek dark satin of her skin appealed to the sailor. The fourth, whom Doña Ana proudly introduced as Concha, was white and young – scarcely beautiful, but new enough to the business to retain some semblance of adolescent virginity. Mario darted over to the sailor, pointed to Concha, and spouted at him in Spanish. This last effort at salesmanship was unnecessary: the sailor was already sold.

The room to which Concha led him was on the second floor, separated from the outside gallery by a sleazy curtain of printed cotton. It overlooked the inner patio, a miserable square of muddy cobbles with an open cistern in one corner and a scraggly *aguacate* tree in the other. Inside there was a straw tick on a roped bedstead covered with a greyish sheet. Concha motioned to the bed and the sailor sat down. Only then did he notice Mario, whose proprietary interest in this, his first customer, had drawn him to the bedroom. Concha did not resent the boy's intrusion – after all, it was only El Rubio – but the sailor cursed him in English and ordered him to be gone. Mario went outside on the gallery, but did not leave. It was too easy to peek through the side of the curtain.

Three hours had passed and now the tropic night shrouded the house. Mario had quit his post at the curtain and had come downstairs hoping for some rice and beans, but Doña Ana had not yet prepared the evening meal. She was listening, waiting for the reassuring creak of the rope bedstead to start all over again. Instead, she was startled by a sudden pounding on the floor. Doña Ana, with Mario at her heels, hurried up to see what was amiss. The tallow candle which she carried showed the two still naked on the bed, the sailor propped up on his elbows, rubbing the sleep out of his eyes and calling for wine.

'*Vino*,' he shouted, '*vino*! God damn it to hell! *Vino!* Don't you understand?' He pantomimed the act of drinking.

They understood the word, but Ana, who savoured wine when she could obtain it, rarely had sufficient capital to stock it in the house for the entertainment of her guests. That was for more elaborate establishments than hers. Besides, her patrons were usually drunk when they arrived, and seldom had more than just enough money to pay for the meagre half hour she allowed them with her women. But if the sailor wanted wine, he wanted wine.

'*Dinero*,' she replied. '*Tienes que pagar primero*.'

He pointed to his trousers on the chair. 'In the pocket.' He patted the side of his bare hip.

Mario investigated the pocket and chose the largest coin, an American gold eagle. His sudden wealth caused him to swagger from the room, run tumbling down the stairs and out the front door to the corner *cantina*. Jorge, who kept the *cantina*, had never seen American gold, but he recognized the approximate value of the coin and questioned Mario as to how he had obtained it. For once the boy told the truth and Jorge, scenting other gold pieces where this one came from, summoned his wife to take charge of the store and accompanied Mario back to Doña Ana's, using as a pretext the weight of the dozen bottles Mario had purchased. With the same generous helpfulness, Jorge helped Mario carry the wine upstairs to Concha's room.

The sailor sat up on the edge of the bed, reached out for one of the bottles and broke its neck by hitting it against the bedstead. He gulped half the contents before handing the bottle to Concha, who finished it.

The wine was sherry of a sort, topaz brown, fiery and potent. It was the best that Jorge had, and its effect was immediate. Although the sailor had wanted rum and had hoped the word *vino* would produce it, this potion satisfied him. Its inner glow produced a burst of generosity and he broke the necks off more bottles, handing one each to Ana, Mario and even Jorge, who had edged into the room and plumped himself down on the edge of the bed. Ana soon grew maudlin, and then Mario broke into uncontrollable laughter, the evening meal was forgotten.

Jorge, taunted by Concho's warm flesh, surreptitiously undid his belt and slipped down his trousers. But the sailor noticed, and his mood quickly changed, anger overcoming his good humour. He picked Jorge up off the bed, grabbed him about the middle, carried him out the door and dumped him over the rail of the gallery into the patio below. Vivid Spanish oaths arose from under the *aguacate* tree which had broken Jorge's fall. He was unhurt but disappointed. No man, particularly a Cuban with his pants down, wants to be disturbed – let alone dropped over a second-story gallery rail.

Dusting his hands and grinning at Mario, the sailor returned to the bed, sprawled himself across the now-sleeping Concha, rubbed his bearded face against her neck and fell asleep. Ana looked across at Mario, who pointed to the sailor's pocket. But she shook her head. She was sure she would get it all eventually, without stealing it.

For a few hours Ana's household slept, but when the sun crept over the escarpment of La Cabaña and started to light up the city, the sailor stirred enough to grope blindly beside the bed until his hand encountered another bottle. The wine of the previous night had dried him, leaving his muscles slack, his skin hot, his head pounding and his temper uncertain. He drank from the fresh bottle and then became aggravated by the snoring of the sleeping Concha on the bed beside him. Without waking her, he pushed her off on to the floor, and when she opened her eyes to stare dumbly at him he hit her and cursed her with words she did not understand.

But, as the wine warmed his stomach and restored his vigour, he regarded her with more favour, relented, and lifted her back again on to the bed, fondling the bruises that his knuckles had caused. She resented the ill-treatment she had received, but when she opened her mouth to protest, he poured the rest of the wine down her throat. This made her feel better, and she bent over him with wine-stained lips to renew his passion.

Mario sidled in from time to time to watch the sweating forms panting on the bed or to steal a swallow or two of wine. Ana walked in boldly to extract money from the sailor's pocket when she believed that he had consumed enough time to warrant another instalment on his bill. Each time she investigated the stock of coins in his pocket, her estimate of what she should receive increased.

So passed that day and the next and the next until all the sailor's gold, as well as all the bottles of wine Mario kept running out to get, were simultaneously exhausted. With the disappearance of the man's money, Ana was faced with the problem of getting rid of him, although he apparently had no thought of leaving. He had no recollection of how long he had been in the house, and was drunkenly complacent as to how long he intended to stay. Unaware that his money was exhausted, and apparently unconcerned over such a triviality, he failed to understand Ana's insistence that he leave at once.

At length, in desperation, she undertook to eject him bodily. Gathering his clothes into a bundle, she flung them down into the dark street, then cajoled him into coming downstairs. He resisted her, not belligerently but firmly, and laughed at her as if they were playing a game. With the aid of Mario and the four girls, Ana succeeded in half carrying and half dragging the mirthful but unsuspecting man to the door. She opened it quickly and gave him a sharp push. He landed, stark naked, in San Isidro Street, unable to get back to the door before it was bolted. Unconcerned about his nakedness, he beat upon the door until his hands were sore, then sat down on the threshold and mumbled curses at the occupants of the house. After a time, he reached for the bundle of clothes, struggled into them, and departed. It was the last the Casa Ana saw of him.

San Isidro Street was a permissive and impersonal thoroughfare and the spectacle of a buck-naked man beating on Ana's door excited no comment, only an amused curiosity. It was noted that his skin was light, his hair was fair and that he was very much a man. It was also surmised that now Doña Ana, her four girls, and her blond brat would probably eat well for a couple of days.

Behind the bolted door of her house, Ana coralled Mario and sat him down facing her in one of the straight chairs of the *sala*. She fumbled in her bodice and took out a little bag full of the gold pieces which she had taken from the sailor. These she dumped in her lap and counted. There were enough to feed the six occupants of the house for a month, as well as to recruit another girl whose virginity her mother had been jealously preserving for a year or more, awaiting Ana's readiness to receive her. The privilege of the first night with her would bring back half of the cost to Ana and she could then dispense with the services of one of the two fat and ageing whores who drew little patronage and less money.

She looked up from the gold and spoke to Mario. Her words were gentle but firm with authority.

'You see, Mario, how fortunate we are. Now we can eat, and with this money we can make more money. It's all due to you. You brought the man here; otherwise we would not have it. *Que suerte, chico!* Now it is time for you to be a man. You must help me. There are many men like this one who just left. They come to Havana on ships and they have been without women, sometimes for months. Their pockets are full of money and they want women, but they do not know where to go to spend the money they have been saving. It is up to you to find them and bring them here. Understand?'

'*Sí, Mamacita.*' Mario seemed to grow in stature as he sat on the hard chair. 'And for doing that, what do I get besides the food I eat?'

She thought for a moment, wondering what would appeal to

the boy most. What reward could she give him that would make him more diligent? Her thumb pointed upstairs. 'There's Concha! Whenever you want her, unless of course she is busy. And . . . there'll be the new girl too.'

'And —?' Mario looked at her expectantly.

'What, more, *chico*?'

'*Pantalones, Mamacita*. I'm getting too big all over to go through the streets like this. Here in San Isidro they are accustomed to seeing more of me than I should show but if I must go to other parts of the town, well. . . .' He poked his finger through a particularly revealing rent in his breeches and waggled it at Ana.

'Keep your nastiness for the whores, boy. Remember I'm your mother. Yes, you shall have new breeches – brand-new ones of white sailcloth, bought from the tailor. But under one condition.'

'And that, *Mamacita*?'

'That you wash yourself with soap and water.'

'All over?'

'All over.'

'It is necessary?'

'*Absolutamente!*'

'Then, *Mamacita*, you go buy the trousers and I shall wash myself.'

'Oh no! You do not get out of it that way. I go to buy the trousers, yes, but while I am gone, Concha and the other girls stand in the patio to see that you are thoroughly scrubbed.'

Mario smiled at her through the grime encrusted on his face. 'That makes it different. Maybe it will be fun. Go, *Mamacita*, and when you return you will not know your Mario.'

With his new white trousers, Mario embarked upon his new profession. It was a pleasant one to him, and as his first client had been a sailor, it was only natural that he should seek more customers along the piers of the waterfront. Most sailors had money to spend and were lavish as long as it lasted. They were avid for women and only too grateful to be shown where they might be found. Therefore El Rubio's advances were welcome – and if he was able to talk to them immediately upon their arrival, before any other panderer had discovered them, he was usually able to inveigle them to the Casa Ana.

Bumboats – the *botes vivanderos* – always went out to meet incoming ships after they had sailed into the harbour between El Morro and La Punta. Mario found that he could get a ride out on them in exchange for working on the oars. Thus he could solicit clients even before they left their ships. Occasionally he had difficulty in making himself understood, Spanish being his only language, but there was usually at least one sailor aboard who could act as an interpreter. When not, Mario would employ the pantomime at which he had become an expert.

Sometimes this was to his own disadvantage; one or another sailor would see in the handsome boy's lewd gyrations an open invitation and, thinking that Mario was selling himself, would offer the boy money for his services in lieu of a woman. The pieces of silver or the handful of coppers would be tempting to Mario, who was by no means ignorant or resentful of the invitation, but he had learned from other boys who had yielded to such bribes that it was painful – at least for the first few times. So Mario declined. Not morality but simple fear deterred him.

As time passed and he accumulated a store of foreign words, he became more professional in his approach. With the increased patronage of the sailors he brought home, Doña Ana's business flourished. Money for food and rent was no longer a problem. Mario even had a room to himself. As the months passed he became an integral part of the Havana waterfront – El Rubio, the pimp.

Chapter Two

IT WAS a good business and El Rubio persevered in it – partly because pimping was something he enjoyed, and partly because of his mother's insistence. The money his efforts brought in belonged to Doña Ana, and only rarely did Mario share it. She provided a home, a place to sleep, and food, which became more palatable as she became more affluent. Most important to Mario, however, was his access to the girls, whenever they were not otherwise employed. This cost him nothing and, in fact, they were only too happy to accommodate him.

As he increased in years and stature they would even have willingly paid him for his services had they been able, for, unlike many clients of the house, Mario never abused them. Indeed, an emotion akin to real love was felt for this stripling, whose youth and air of innocence made each occasion seem like his first, and whose blondness, whose beardless cheeks and smooth body combined to give him an almost feminine aspect. This last, however, was entirely negated by his performance; even as a boy his passion had left no doubt of his virility.

As he grew more adept in his profession, his manner of approach to prospective clients became more effective, his methods of convincing them improved and his technique of selling ripened into a more subtle process. The harsh volubility of his words lessened and he relied more on the sidelong glance, the pantomimic sweep of his hands and an exotic movement of his hips, his eyes swimming in affected ecstasy. He no longer shouted his words, but instead waxed confidential, almost secretive – even though there was nothing very secretive about his business.

He was scarcely aware that he was working, there were no particular duties, no responsibilities, no hours to keep. He was merely satisfying his own curiosity by visiting ships and then incidentally confiding information to sailors desperate for women – any women. As for the money they paid Doña Ana, Mario was not concerned. He had little use for money. A full belly and a bed to sleep in, with a whore for company – these were all he desired. His job was to steer the men to San Isidro Street; Ana's was to take their money for services rendered.

Mario grew and matured. No longer was he a dirty urchin in ragged pants. A golden fuzz began to appear on his face and his voice changed and grew deeper, occasionally breaking on a high note or descending without warning into a low bass. His muscles became firmer and more pronounced, although retaining their boyish roundness. One thing that did not change, however, was the cherublike innocence of his face, which served to cozen and deceive. His eyes took on a darker blue, but they continued to illuminate his perpetual smile.

On an early afternoon during his sixteenth year he was contemplating the business of the evening when, from his vantage point near the *Muelle de Santa Clara*, he gazed across the sun-drenched harbour, to the little village of Casablanca on the opposite side and saw a schooner drift slowly up to the roadstead and anchor. It was a weatherbeaten tub, noticeable only because there was so little other shipping in the harbour. As it swung around on its anchor chains, Mario read the name, on its bow – *Inocencia*. There was little about the ship that looked innocent; she appeared more like a senile, down-at-the-heels, worn-out harridan.

But she was a ship newly arrived in port and she would need fresh fruits and vegetables; the bumboats would soon be going out to her. Most important of all, she carried men who would be wanting women. Mario started walking and then broke into a trot as he hastened towards the broad water steps where the bumboats tied up. He knew he would be welcome on one or another, either as a rower or as a guest. In the past he had occasionally given tips to the owners of the boats – tips which had consisted of a free half hour at Doña Ana's. Now one of the bumboats was just about to leave and its owner, seeing Mario approach, waited for him to run down the steps and jump in.

As they neared the ship, the ladder of the *Inocencia* was dropped over the side and the captain appeared at its top, aglitter in a gold-braided uniform, with a light ceremonial sword at his side. A very large and very black Negro in tattered trousers also appeared and, grasping the captain on one arm, carried him down the ladder and seated him amidships in the ship's boat that awaited them, manned by two rowers, at the foot of the ladder. The captain was a man in miniature – possibly an inch over five feet in height and not exceeding a hundred pounds in weight – and it was apparent that he was fearful of descending the ladder alone. Once the captain was seated, the boat started to move away from the ship's side without waiting for the Negro to reascend the ladder. He plunged into the water of the harbour and swam back towards the ship.

The *Inocencia* was a Brazilian ship out of Pernambuco, its diminutive captain a Portuguese, and it was evident by his full dress uniform that he was on his way to Havana, probably to inveigle a cargo. Mario watched without regret as the captain's boat moved away from the *Inocencia*. The captain would have been immune to his own solicitations; if he were seeking a woman, he would frequent some more elaborate establishment than the Casa Ana – perhaps the Casa Josefina in the *Calle del Sol*.

When the captain's boat neared the bumboat he called to it, waving it back to shore. He wanted nothing in the way of supplies.

The men in the bumboat started to turn it around but, as they were now so near the *Inocencia*, Mario decided to jump and swim the remaining distance to the ship and take his chances on getting another boat back. A few strokes carried him to the ship's ladder. He climbed up it, then made his way to the forecastle to talk with the sailors as best he could. At least the ship was Portuguese, so he would have little difficulty, their language being so akin to his own.

There were twelve men in the forecastle – nine white or nearly white Portuguese and three Negro slaves, two of whom were large, powerful, and black. The third was smaller and much lighter in colour, and walked with a slight limp. He had been branded with the word *bicho* on his shoulder, and it was this which caught Mario's attention. What it meant in Portuguese he did not know, but in Cuba its generally accepted slang use was to designate the male generative organ. To see it branded on the man's back, and to think of him responding to it as a name, sent Mario into gales of laughter.

'*Eres un bicho?*' Mario asked him. '*Un bicho grande o pequeño?*'

The young Negro sidled over to him and laid one hand on his arm with a light, sliding caress. It lingered there just too long for Mario's liking and he shook it off in anger. '*Eres un bicho verdadero,*' he snarled at the black. 'You're well-named – you are a prick.' He turned his back on the slave and expatiated more fully on the girls at Ana's house.

The sailors became interested in Mario's intimate details of the prowess of his mother's whores. Several of them – the ones who had the necessary funds – inquired specific directions to San Isidro Street, with the promise that they would visit Ana's as soon as they were ashore.

In the midst of their conclave the ship's mate appeared, yelling for Bicho and spouting orders for a number of minor tasks to be done. He was a tall, powerful, big-boned man, with a livid knife scar extending down his cheek from the outer corner of the left eye. His body was naked above the waist, save for a greasy woollen cap perched on the back of his head, which was furred with unruly curls of shaggy hair that, together with a growth of stiff black beard, gave him the appearance of some predatory animal. At his orders the seamen dispersed to their various tasks with many a '*Sí, Conho, sí, sí, Conho*' – all except Bicho, who came running up in answer to Conho's call and stood, waiting expectantly.

Conho disregarded the boy, his reason for calling him apparently forgotten in his careful scrutiny of Mario. He sat down on a coil of rope, tipped his head back, stretched his huge legs out in front of him, looked Mario over appraisingly and then winked at him. The sun, shining through the shaggy hair on his chest, picked out the tattoos underneath, evidently marked there when he was younger and hairless. A full-rigged ship sailed from one brown nipple to the other. One arm bore a cluster of crude red roses over the initials, SMUC. A priapic nude male figure covered the entire upper portion of the other arm. Conho smiled and winked at Mario again, then flexed his bicep, causing the male figure to writhe in ecstatic jumps. Mario smiled back, grateful for the mate's good humour. He was uncomfortably aware that he had no immediate transportation back to shore and that it was a lengthy distance for him to swim.

His eyes still on Mario, Conho motioned him closer, then grabbed and hugged him, standing up so that their bodies touched. Even inured as Mario was to evil smells, Conho's animal stench nearly overpowered him. Grinning, Conho pinioned him against the rail with his huge arms, muttering, 'Be nice to Conho, boy, be nice to Conho.'

He ran his rough hands over the smooth skin of Mario's chest and teased him about his youth, declaring that someday Mario would be a man and would grow hair like his own. He made no effort to conceal his activities from the crew and even called Bicho, who was cowering jealously nearby, to help him strip Mario of his pants. The wearing of the wet garment any longer, he solicitously suggested, would make Mario ill. To substantiate this advice, he pointed to the huge black, who had spread his pants to dry on the roof of the deckhouse. Mario saw a certain logic in Conho's words and did not want to resist the man or change his good humour, fearing what might happen if he incurred Conho's anger before he could escape. Fortunately, he felt no particular embarrassment at being naked, accustomed as he was to going about Ana's house in this manner when there were no clients around.

Conho suggested a drink of rum and added knowingly that a good stiff drink would dispel any *catarro* the boy might have caught by wearing the wet pants. Without waiting for an answer, he took Mario by the shoulders and steered him playfully, but firmly, aft to his cabin. Once inside, Mario saw a neat pile of some dozen bottles of rum on the deck of the cabin, within easy reach of the hammock. Another dozen bottles, all empty, rolled about on the floor.

Conho closed the door, reached for a half-filled bottle and upturned it to his mouth. Then he wiped the neck with his dirty hand and passed the bottle to Mario. Mario took a deep drink and handed it back to Conho, but the man waved it away, telling Mario to finish it. He himself reached for a new bottle, opened it, and plumped down in the hammock. As Mario raised his arm to drink, Conho grabbed him and drew him down beside him.

Mario had never drunk so much rum before. Although he had not liked the man who was holding him close, he did not seem to mind him so much now. The fear of him, of what Conho might do, was slowly fading under the haze of alcohol.

Conho pulled Mario a little closer in the hammock and then released him quickly as the door opened. It was Bicho.

Conho reached for an empty rum bottle and threw it, but Bicho dodged, and it shattered against the bulkhead. The slave took in the situation at a glance but did not retreat.

'Captain's come back,' Bicho said, grinning at Mario.

'The bastard!' Conho stood up, drew up his trousers and

fastened them with difficulty. 'Why didn't the goddam *pulgacito* stay away ten minutes longer?'

He gulped down a huge swallow from the newly opened bottle and handed it to Mario, insisting that he finish it. As Mario drank, Conho brushed Mario's hair back from his forehead, and then noticed that the boy's eyes were closing. He leaned over, took the bottle from Mario's hand, and kissed him on the shoulder. Then he tiptoed from the room, taking care to lock the door behind him.

In his cabin, the diminutive captain was divesting himself of his heavy broadcloth uniform. When Conho entered he retreated hastily behind a screen.

'Well, *Senhor Conho*,' he chirruped happily from behind his barrier. 'I have done well in this city of Havana. We have a cargo out to the United States and then another cargo awaiting us there back to Havana. Our voyage should be profitable.'

Conho, who ran the ship entirely without assistance from the captain, suffered his superior this one job. It was the one thing the captain could do better than Conho, for the captain was an educated man and his words could command a respect in shipping circles, that Conho's never could. It was an equable arrangement. While on board, the captain spent most of the time in his cabin and let Conho take command of the ship. And when they were in port, Conho let the captain go ashore to represent them.

'What do we carry, *Senhor Capitan*? What do we carry and where do we pick it up? Shall we move into the *muelle*, the pier?' Conho was never so drunk that he forgot the business of the ship.

'No, it comes out on lighters.' The captain stuck his head out from behind the screen. 'Be prepared to receive it early in the morning, at sun-up. There'll be bananas and coconuts for Baltimore. Largely bananas. I don't know how many, but enough. We'll be paid by the ton. And blacks,' he added, 'a handful of slaves, forty-seven in all, to be landed at Charleston.'

'I thought we were through with blackbirding,' Conho said, scowling. 'Slaves on shipboard are a nuisance.'

'Not these,' the captain assured him. 'They are all broken and acclimated, and forty-seven is not many. It's not like the middle passage, with wild *bozals* aboard, all a-mustanging. We'll have no trouble. These are broken – though of course they'll have to be watched.'

'Aye, aye, *Senhor*,' Conho agreed. 'We'll fetter them?'

'Naturally. We can't have a shipful of beasts running at large.' The captain emerged from behind the screen, dressed in immaculate white linen. 'Some rum, *Senhor Conho*? We'll drink to the success of our voyage, and then I return to Havana. I shall remain ashore overnight and probably for the whole day tomorrow. You'll handle the cargo.'

Conho, never one to refuse a drink, accepted the captain's toast, then hastily excused himself, on a wave of the captain's hand. He was anxious to get back to his cabin. He ran nimbly along the deck, fumbled with the lock and tiptoed in. Mario was still stretched out in the hammock, senseless, apparently dead. Conho looked down at him and was suddenly frightened. If the boy was dead – and well he might be from the quantities of raw rum Conho had forced on him – how could he dispose of the body? Would he be accused of murder? A dead Rubio was the least of his wishes, particularly right here in Havana harbour.

Very cautiously, Conho advanced a step and leaned closely over the hammock. Mario reeked of rum, his eyes were closed and one hand hung limply over the edge of the hammock. Conho applied his ear to Mario's chest, heard the pulsing heartbeat. The boy was alive. Sleeping. In a drunken stupor. With a sigh of relief, Conho knelt on the floor by the hammock and again lowered his head to Mario's chest. He sobbed convulsively as he kissed the sleeping boy.

Slowly collecting himself, Conho rose to his feet, took another drink of rum, and then went out, locking the door behind him. He was just in time to see the big Negro carrying the captain down to the boat. He waved the captain off, then took a turn around the deck. Everything was shipshape; the *Inocencia* was securely anchored and there was only a faint breeze from offshore. He returned to his cabin and Bicho brought in his supper, enough food for two, and left it on the chair. Conho looked at the food, shook his head and pushed it away.

He reached for more rum and then counted the remaining bottles. There seemed to be one missing. That god-damned Bicho! Bicho alone had a key to the cabin, and, Conho well knew, a fondness for rum. He lumbered to his feet and grabbed the slave whip from where it hung on the bulkhead of the cabin. One hand clenched the whip tightly and the other hand sought the latch on the door, his blood pounding as he thought of the welts he would raise on the slave's back. But then Conho hesitated. Tomorrow would be a gruelling day for all the crew. Every man, even Bicho, would be needed to load the cargo. Regardless of how drunk he might be, Conho was conditioned to the discipline of the sea; he was a sailor first and always.

And anyway, he was tired.

He threw the whip down on the cabin floor, removed his shoes and pants, took a last gulp from the bottle of rum, and climbed into the hammock. Still drunk, Mario slept on in a stupor. Even Conho's weight in the hammock and the man's sweaty closeness did not rouse him.

The tropic sun came up with such a sudden bluster that it seemed to shake the land and the sea. Bicho arrived with breakfast and knocked on the door, routing Conho out of the hammock. Mario continued sleeping. The sight of food repulsed the man. His head ached, his muscles were stiff, and his desire for the boy was still unsatisfied. But he was aware of the early arrival of the cargo and the necessity of his being on deck when it came. He gulped down the bitter coffee, leaving the bread and eggs untouched, and groped with his free hand for his shoes and pants. Buckling his belt, he stepped over and regarded the sleeping Mario, then regretfully backed towards the door, turned, and left the cabin.

Mario awoke some time later, surprised to find it already full day. His mouth felt dry and tasted full of bitter cotton. His head was bursting, as if clamped in heavy steel hands. The dingy cabin spun around him as he dragged himself from the hammock and tried to stand. It was impossible. He sat back, his face in his hands, and then succumbed to the support of the hammock. Gradually he forced his head up again and looked over the edge of the canvas. There was a rum bottle standing nearby with about a finger of rum left in it. Mario reached for it, letting the liquor dribble into his mouth. Soon he began to feel better.

Little by little he pieced together the dimly remembered episodes of the previous afternoon, and as the picture unfolded he became indignant, furious, rabid with anger. Although he felt no pain, he was suddenly sure that Conho had ravished him. The El Rubio of the waterfront was far from innocent, but to have been forced into such a thing by a stinking, hairy man, to have surrendered himself unwittingly without even a *centavo* to show for it – *Caramba!* He'd kill the bastard.

His trousers were nowhere to be found. They were not in the cabin. He tried the door and found it unlocked, and, quite unabashed at his nakedness, he walked out on deck. Assuming an air of casual interest, he stood by the rail and watched the lighters arrive at shipside. They contained thousands of stems of green bananas – not the overlarge *platainas* which were eaten as a vegetable in Cuba, but the smaller, more delicate variety which were favoured for export. Following these came the coconuts, packed in bags woven from long grass. These the slaves placed just aft of the bananas in the hold. Conho was busy directing the men, but he had noticed Mario coming out of the cabin and now kept him under close surveillance.

All day Mario hung about the deck, waiting for a chance to escape over the side and return to shore on a lighter. But it was to no avail; he was always conscious of Conho's eyes on him, and of his own nudity. Twice the mate had caught him near the ladder and had pushed him back. 'Taking your pants, boy, was even better than locking you up, wasn't it?' Mario never doubted that Conho's intention was to keep him on board until after the ship sailed – but he was damned if he was going to serve as Conho's bedmate for a whole voyage. El Rubio had taken care of himself in many situations and, although he was apprehensive, he was far from despairing.

As the swift tropic dusk erased the outline of the old morro fort, which commanded the harbour, the cargo of slaves started coming out in rowboats. They were naked and fettered ten to a boat, in addition to the rowers. All were males, a vicious-looking lot, many of them with tribal marks on their faces, arms and upper chests. They were the '*bozals*' – brutes that had survived the middle passage from Africa only to be broken and seasoned in Cuba for sale in the United States where prices, already high, were rising daily.

Their stowage and chaining in the aft of the hold, behind the bananas and coconuts, was a complicated matter. They had to be placed sitting one in front of the other, each man between the legs of the one behind him, and Conho had to be there personally to supervise their correct placement. Before he went below, however, he made sure that Mario was on deck and away from the ladder.

Some half of the slaves had arrived and, although it was now dark, the light from the ship's lanterns illuminated the boats as they came out of the darkness to the side of the ship. As one of the boats, emptied of its load, turned to go back to the city, Mario heard a hail from one of the rowers.

'*Aló, Rubio. Dondé vas? A los Estados Unidos?*'

Mario peered out into the darkness and recognized the face beneath the waving arm. It was one of the waterfront boys with whom he used to dive for pennies. He waved back, gesturing for silence. '*Esperame, Carlos.* I'm coming with you.'

He saw the rowers stop and the boat drift idly by, only a few yards from the ship. A quick look behind assured him that there was nobody near and he vaulted over the rail into the water below, the splash of his dive drowned out by the noise of the boarding slaves. Eager hands reached for him and hoisted him over the gunwale and into the boat, where he lay on the floor under the rowers' legs. The pounding of his heart made him forget his headache and eased the bitter taste in his mouth. He knew only that he was safe, headed once more for Havana and home.

There was nothing in the boat that he could use to cover himself and neither Carlos nor the other men could spare any of their garments without becoming as naked as Mario. Although Carlos volunteered to go to Doña Ana's and get substitute clothes, Mario realized that it would be useless – he had lost the only pair of pants he owned.

When the boat touched the broad water steps, Mario was in its prow, ready to jump ashore. He was far too old to be seen stark naked abroad in Havana, but the streets were unlighted, the night was black, and there were many doorways to duck into if he saw the *guardias* approaching. Avoiding the busier thoroughfares and seeking the darker, narrower ones, he made his way from doorway to doorway until he finally reached San Isidro Street.

Once inside the familiar blue door, he collapsed in Ana's arms. Never before had he realized how much he loved her, how much security she meant to him. Her unquestioning reception of him after such a long absence made him feel guilty, and now, for the first time in his life, he thought he deserved a whipping. It might also take away the stench of Conho from his nostrils and the sick taste of rum in his throat. But Doña Ana was too happy to have him back even to think of punishment – and suddenly the calloused El Rubio of the wharves was a little boy again, whimpering in his mother's arms while her kisses loved away all transgressions.

It was some time before she could get the story of the previous night out of him. But finally, between sobs, it burst forth, in all the bawdy language of his waterfront vernacular. He withheld no detail. He believed he had been raped, and as he talked this belief grew so vivid that it began to produce a physical pain he had not felt before.

Doña Ana was furious – as much as if Mario had been her virgin daughter, instead of a strapping son. And she felt herself fully justified. Was the rape of a son less than that of a daughter? No! She would go out to the ship herself. She would take a knife. She would make that Conho wish he had never been born. She would kill him!

Slowly Mario succeeded in quieting her ravings. He assured her that it was all over, that there was nothing she could do, that he was safe.

Doña Ana regarded him for a moment, and then stood up. She raised Mario to his feet and led him up the stairs. There was only one way to remedy his grief, to re-establish his belief in his own masculinity. She would bed him with Concha.

Mario crept in silently beside the girl and wept himself to sleep in Concha's arms. Once during the night he awoke screaming from a dream in which the hairy sailor was over him, leering at him – but Concha's hands soon brought soothing comfort, and, as Mario's lips sought hers, he knew that he would never again, as long as he lived, desire anyone but a woman.

Chapter Three

MONEY BEGAN to assume important proportions to Mario as he passed through his seventeenth year. Its necessity first came in terms of a razor he saw in a shop window on Obispo Street. It was no ordinary razor, this – with a plain black handle of wood or horn – but one which possessed a handle of beaten silver, studded with mother-of-pearl. Mario lingered daily in front of the shop window, gazing at it through the dusty, fly-specked glass. He could almost feel the smooth coolness of it in his palm, sense the clean-cut swath it would leave on his face. For now the golden fuzz that covered his cheeks had become a beard – bristly on his upper lip and thick under his chin. It was hot, it became sticky with sweat, it itched him, it irritated Concha's smooth skin, but perhaps most important of all, it was earning him unwanted nicknames – *Barba Rosa*, Red Beard, and, even worse, *Macho de Cabrio*, Billy Goat.

There were no razors in the Casa Ana. It was purely a house of women, and anything as masculine as a razor was unlikely to be found among the rouge pots and jars of rice powder that littered the girls' crude dressing tables. That explained the supreme attraction for Mario of the mirror-like blade with the gleaming mother-of-pearl handle. It became an obsession, something he must own for his new manhood. And, as it was to be the sign of his coming of age, it must come from himself, not from Ana or any other woman; a man didn't get his first razor through a whore's sweat.

But the price of twenty-five pesetas, delicately inscribed in violet ink on the card beside the razor, was entirely beyond Mario's present means. One solution would have been to get a job, but this idea he quickly dismissed. It was all right to help row a bumboat out to a ship once in a while, or give the stevedores a lift with a cask of wine, but a regular job with regular hours was emphatically not to his liking. And yet, in one way or another, he had to earn the money to get that razor.

He had, in the past year, grown tall, with long powerful legs and strongly muscled arms. Now he not only brought men to Ana's house but, on busy evenings when the house was full, served also in the capacity of a *fanfarron* or whore-house bouncer. When the sailors drank too much and became surly and obstreperous – beyond Ana's control – it was up to Mario to put them out. He did this easily, seldom fighting with them, and never losing his temper.

Ever since that night aboard the *Inocencia*, he had been careful never to touch rum; and hence, being in full possession of his senses, he was always more than a match for any drunken sailor who started to make trouble. Mario would merely grab one of the man's arms with one hand, twist it behind his back, take a firm grip on the seat of his breeches with the other, wait for Ana to open the front door, and then heave him into the street. And that would be that. After it was all over, Ana or some of the girls would come up and touch his swelling biceps or dig their fingers into his flat belly, murmuring, '*Que hombre!*'

But then they would tweak his callow beard and laugh at him. *Caramba!* The beard must go!

After one particularly boisterous night when he had dispensed with two sturdy schnapps-filled Dutchmen who had tried to throw one of the girls into the patio, Mario slept late – through the next day and far into the hot evening. When he finally managed to pull himself out of bed, he yelled down the stairs for coffee. The new girl who brought it up, a high-cheeked *mestizo* from Panama, was coyly desirous of getting Mario back into bed. But he would have none of her.

He was sick of the dead air in the hot room. Down on the docks it would be cooler. There was always a breeze across the harbour, ruffling the water and making the flags on the ships flutter. He pushed the girl from the room, gulped the hot coffee and dashed tepid water from a copper can over his face.

Dressing was more complicated now. He had a shirt to get on and tuck into his trousers, a belt to fasten and shoes to put on, although the latter were only rope-soled *alpargatas* which tied with a rawhide thong. Once downstairs, he supplemented the coffee with hot bread and a half-dozen eggs that Ana fried for him. Then, as always these days, he lifted her bodily off the floor and kissed her. He never forgot his gratefulness to her the night he had almost failed to return from the *Inocencia*.

It was cooler when he reached the waterfront, but he was disappointed to find that most of the ships that had been there the day before were now gone. The big blunt-nosed tub from Holland had sailed with its drunken Dutchmen; the American brig from New Orleans had loaded its quota of passengers and left; even the small coastwise schooner from Santiago had sailed out between the Morro and La Ponta. There was, however, one new arrival tied up at the San Francisco.

She was the Spanish ship, *Fernando*, a regular caller in Havana on her course from Veracruz to Cadiz. Her red-and-gold banner moved listlessly in the evening breeze as Mario regarded it with sneering disgust. There was never much business on the Spanish ships. The sailors were frequent callers at Havana, knew the city well, and spoke the language; those few who came to Ana's house were clients of long standing and had no need for a guide. Furthermore, they were goddamned Spanish snobs. Mario spat in the direction of the ship.

Well, there was no business tonight. All that was left to do was to sit still and keep cool. As he lounged against the wall, still warm from the day's sun, he fingered the copper *centavos* in his pocket, mentally computed their total and found he had enough for a glass of wine. It was an excuse to sit in a café, so he wandered over to the one that faced the harbour, directly behind the plaza. Here he found an empty table out on the pavement and seated himself comfortably, enjoying the breeze that rattled the palm fronds. He started to think about his problem – the razor and how to get it. Even now he could imagine the cool lather on his face, feel the sharp blade as it sliced through the blond beard. It was so real that he rubbed his hand over his cheeks; but instead of the smoothness he desired, his fingers encountered only bristly stubble.

His wine soon gone, he sat twirling the glass in his hand, regarding the passers-by with a practised eye. He dismissed them as of no promise until he noticed a young lieutenant of the *Fernando*, sweating in his hot uniform. He was scarcely more than a boy, about Mario's own age. He looked young and inexperienced, a fit subject for Concha, who delighted in the quick ecstasies of young lads. Mario shifted in his chair, prepared to follow the boy, but relaxed as he saw him sit down a few tables away and call the waiter. In the lisping accent of pure Castilian speech, he ordered a glass of sherry. When the waiter had brought it, he showed the man a piece of paper. Evidently it contained an address, for the waiter started gesturing and pointing. The young lieutenant followed the meanderings of the dirty finger as best he could, nodded his head as if he understood, then gulped down his wine and left. Mario waited a few seconds, until he was beyond the lights of the café, then followed him.

The lieutenant walked straight up to the plaza and across it, hesitated for a moment and then started up Obispo. As he entered the narrow street, Mario caught up with him. For a few steps they kept pace with each other on the sidewalk; then the lieutenant looked up and smiled at Mario. Mario nodded his head and returned the tentative greeting with an even broader smile. His smile was always engaging. He had never lost the spontaneous grin of boyhood. It was a smile to be trusted, to have confidence in. And the young lieutenant both trusted and confided. He bowed.

'*Buenos noches, señor.*'

'*Muy buenos noches.*' Mario could be polite too, when it suited his purpose. 'You are a stranger here? Off the *Ferando*?'

'*Sí, señor*, to both of your questions.' The soft speech of the lieutenant was in contrast to Mario's harsh Cuban accent.

'And you seek an address?' Mario continued to smile.

'The house of Josefina in the *Calle del Sol*. I have heard of it, particularly of the girl Lupa who is there. One of my shipmates tells me there is no experience in the world like an hour with Lupa.'

'Lupa!' Mario made an obscene gesture. 'Lupa is a bitch and the house of Josefina a stinking hole.' He took the lieutenant's arm. 'Listen, *hombre*, if you want a woman, there is only one place in all Havana – the Casa Ana. Have you not heard about it? Clean, *hombre*, with girls the most refined and the most beautiful in Havana. There's Rosita. . . .' His hands curved over his breasts and down his hips. 'Not yet sixteen,' he whispered. 'And Pepita. No' – he shook his head – 'she is like a flame touching your body, but she is not for a young man like you. For you' – he hesitated a moment to give greater weight to his words – 'for you, Concha.' He went into a detailed account of various ways and means that Concha could devise.

But neither Mario's detailed descriptions nor his eloquent phrasing seemed to sway the lieutenant. He still grasped the piece of paper in his hand and, although he politely allowed Mario to finish, he was not to be deterred. '*Gracias, señor*. I appreciate all that you say and I do not underestimate the delights of the Casa Ana, but tonight it must be Lupa at the Casa Josefina.'

'But you'll not last ten minutes with Lupa. You know her specialty, *hombre*? She uses whips.'

The lieutenant sighed, but continued on his way. 'So I've been told, and that's why I must prove that I can. Idelfonso – he's one of my shipmates, a big hulking brute of a fellow – he makes fun of me. Today he bet me one gold duro that I couldn't stay with Lupa half an hour. Now I must win that bet. The whole ship knows about it, and if I fail I'll never live it down. I'm to meet Idelfonso at the Casa Josefina. He came ashore early this afternoon and went there to reserve Lupa for me.' He threw out his chest and forced his lips into a grim line. 'It is a matter of honour, *señor*.'

Mario nodded in understanding. He felt sorry for the boy and wished that he could take his place in the coming contest, but the mention of a gold duro had put other thoughts in Mario's mind. He gazed down at the fellow through half-closed eyes. A plan was beginning to form – not entirely definite as yet, vague and uncertain. 'And what time are you due at Josefina's?' he asked.

'At ten, *al punto*.' The lieutenant pulled a watch from his waistcoat pocket.

Mario put out a restraining hand to hold him in front of the light that streamed from a corner *cantina* and looked down at the watch. The delicately filigreed hand showed only nine o'clock and, more important than the hour, Mario saw that it was a gold watch. 'But you have an hour, *Teniente*. Would you take some advice from a stranger?'

'You hardly seem a stranger, *hombre*. I feel I know you.'

'Then listen! I know this Lupa. As I said, she's a bitch. You've got to master her, and no man can do that when he's cold sober. Stop, let us sit here a few moments while you fortify yourself with a few fingers of rum. It will give you courage to face Lupa.' He took the lieutenant's elbow, guided him into the *cantina*, and pulled out a chair for him at the table. He'd never been in this café before. The waiter was a stranger, a slouching half-blind old man with a grey film of cataracts over his eyes. Mario ordered a single drink.

'Will you not drink with me, *amigo*?' the lieutenant asked courteously.

Mario hesitated. 'I rarely drink, but it would be an insult to refuse your invitation. *Dos copitas de ron*,' he yelled through the deserted *cantina* to the man behind the bar. The waiter brought a bottle and two glasses and Mario poured a big one for the lieutenant and a small one for himself. 'To your success with Lupa, and may you win the wager.'

He waited for the other to down the rum and then poured him a second, but none for himself. 'You'll need it, *Teniente*. Now listen to me. I've heard how this Lupa works. She keeps the whip under the mattress, and just when you think everything is going fine, she reaches for it. In a moment she's on top, clawing, kicking, biting and then slashing with the whip. There are some who like it. But if you've never tasted the whip, especially in the hands of Lupa, you'll be a sorry sight tomorrow! So, listen! At first, while she's quiet and docile and loving, let your hand stray under the mattress and get the whip yourself. Then you can teach that bitch, Lupa, a lesson, and win your gold duro and the respect of this Idelfonso bastard.' He filled the glass again, waited until it was finished, then called the *mozo* for the bill.

The lieutenant reached in his pocket and drew out a handful of gold pieces, gave one to the waiter and took his change in silver. The glint of gold and the flash of green light from the emerald on his finger were inventoried by Mario along with the watch. He helped the lieutenant up from his chair, steadied him on his feet, and as he passed the waiter he said, 'Take it easy, lean on Jose.'

'Jose?' The lieutenant grinned in drunken amiability. 'Is that your name? Jose?'

Mario nodded in assent and got him out on the street.

'Take me to the Casa Josefina, *amigo*,' the lieutenant pleaded. 'The rum has made me dizzy and I have forgotten how the man told me to go. But you will take me, Jose?' He reeled against the wall.

'Yes, I'll take you, *amigo*. But not that way.' Mario shook his head. 'That's not the way to the *Calle del Sol*. It's this way.' He pointed in the opposite direction. 'And if you want to make time, I know a short cut. Come, or you'll be late. This way.'

Mario propelled him down the narrow street and turned a corner into another, darker street. They hurried along for a block, then into another street, this one hardly more than a slit between the blank walls of houses. There was no vestige of light here and they proceeded arm in arm in the soft darkness.

'Damn!' Mario stumbled and caught himself by the lieutenant's arm. 'I tripped over my shoelace. Wait until I tie it.'

He kneeled down, fumbled with the thong which tied one *alpargata* and withdrew it. The lieutenant was a step ahead of him. Mario clasped the ends of the thong in his hands, then raised his arms slowly. Quickly his hands descended over the other's head, the thong cutting into the fellow's throat. Mario's powerful hands pulled the cord tight and twisted until he felt the weight of the body slumping to the ground.

He loosened the thong and heard the soft thud as the body dropped to the ground. Still clutching the thong in his left hand, Mario's right sought the trouser pocket and emptied it of its gold. The watch slipped out of the waistcoat pocket into Mario's own pocket. The ring was a little more difficult, but Mario put the boy's finger into his mouth and, when it was slippery with spit, the ring came off easily. The whole operation took only a few seconds.

Mario stepped over the body and walked quickly to the end of the alley. There was nobody in sight. Without undue haste he traversed the dark streets until he was back in the plaza, where he sat down on a bench and threaded the lace back into his shoe. From there it was only another short block to the waterfront and he was back again in familiar territory. He stopped at the same *cantina* where he had first seen the lieutenant. Some of his friends were playing dominoes at one of the tables and he looked on as a spectator, his hand in his pocket feeling the smooth hardness of the gold while his mouth protested that he had no money to play.

The next day, Mario approached the shop in Obispo Street. The razor was still in the window, and Mario sauntered inside. But he had not been raised on the docks of Havana for nothing. To pay twenty-five silver pesetas for a razor would have aroused suspicion. There were safer ways of doing it. He pulled fifteen pesetas, carefully tied in a grimy cloth, from his pocket and laid them on the counter. Then he made a deal with the proprietor. He would buy a plain razor for ten pesetas and he would leave a deposit of five pesetas on the pearl beauty in the window if, and he smiled most engagingly at the proprietor, the señor would not sell it, would wait until Mario had earned another ten pesetas. Then he would return the plain razor for credit, add another ten pesetas and, with the five on deposit, he would buy the razor he wanted.

The man nodded in agreement; he was an Andalusian and he loved a complicated barter. Did Mario have a job? Oh, most assuredly! He was a stevedore on the docks. When the proprietor looked at the bulging muscles under the thin shirt, he believed him; and when he saw Mario's sprouting beard, he realized his need for a razor. Poor fellow! He must have been saving a long time to get one.

Mario stopped twice on his way home. At one store he bought a new pair of white pants and a new shirt, and at another a new pair of shoes, similar to those he was wearing. It would not look well to blossom forth in too-gaudy finery the day after a lieutenant of Their Most Catholic Majesty's Navy was found garrotted in an alley in Havana. Although there was nothing to connect Mario with the crime, it always paid to be careful. The watch and ring were not even hidden in Mario's house. They were carefully concealed in a crack in the stucco wall in a dark corner of La Machina wharf.

Once back in the house, Mario had Concha heat a big copper pan of water for him. With a bar of Castile soap which he borrowed from her, he worked up a thick lather and spread it over his face. The razor scraped the lather from his face and left it pink and smooth, shining with cleanliness, good to feel beneath his fingers. Then he surprised even himself. He set the copper pan of water on the floor and stood in it. Concha got up on a chair and poured more water over him while he soaped his entire body. Then she helped him scrub himself, rinsed off the soap with more water and brought him a towel.

For the first time in his life, Mario felt the joy of being clean. His skin tingled, and it was a pleasant sensation, one which he decided he would enjoy every day. Concha liked it, too. Her lips nuzzled to the dampness of his smooth chest and her hand slid over his moist belly. Then she laughed and gave him a little push towards the stairs.

From that day on, waterfront robberies and occasional killings increased. Sailors from foreign ships stumbled out of dark alleyways, gasping for breath, their pockets rifled. Those were the lucky ones. Others remained in the alleys until they were discovered in the morning. Sometimes when their bodies were lifted up, there would be a clotted mass of blood on the cobbles beneath them, or there would be a thin red line around their necks, under their swollen, purple faces.

Little by little, Mario's clothes became better in cut and quality. The white trousers were of finer material and tailored to hug his thighs without a wrinkle. He no longer wore *alpargatas*, but shoes of leather. Yet who would suspect El Rubio, whose mother's whorehouse was now prospering? If Ana was suspicious, she held her peace. If Mario visited the church more often than usual and lighted candles at the altar, who would question his reason for so doing? Nobody but Mario himself.

The tinkle of silver in the alms box in the church did little to assuage his conscience. He never liked to kill, he only wanted his victims' money. The bastards were foolish to resist. What mattered a few pieces of gold or silver, compared with life itself? But when they did resist, there was only one way to save himself. That was the only reason he pulled his knife from its sweaty leather sheath under his armpit, or stretched the thin catgut of a guitar string around their necks. Each time it happened, he swore it would be the last; but a man needed things.

He was grown up now. *Muy hombre!* A man had to have money of his own – not money doled out by his mother, but money he gained himself. Copper *centavos* were not enough for Mario; he needed silver and gold pieces that rang out with a sweet, metallic music when he threw them on the table to buy wine for his friends or on a shop counter to buy a fan for Ana, a mantilla for Concha, or a trifle for some other girl.

Chapter Four

THE LILAC shadow of a rustling palm frond, etched by the sinking sun, slowly lost the sharp edges of its serrated outline on the white stucco wall of the hotel which faced on Havana's new and fashionable Prado. The walls of the building slowly changed from blinding white to dusty rose. Then, as the light completely vanished in the swiftly onrushing darkness of the tropic night, the wall once again took on another whiteness, this one slightly luminous, almost phosphorescent.

The sounds of the evening *paseo* in the Prado were gradually dying as the last of the carriages swung out from the monotonous circle of the street and headed for home. The sweating coachmen yearned for the moment when they could shed their heavy, gold-embroidered velvet coats. The fond mothers with marriageable daughters sitting beside them on the satin seats of their *volantas* welcomed the darkness of the side streets and the opportunity to relax the set smiles which had illumined their faces during the hour of the *paseo*.

A little breeze, which carried a tang of salt and the faintly bitter smell of seaweed, channelled itself between the grim bulks of El Morro and La Punta fortresses, picked up the warm aroma of roasting coffee, the sooty fumes of charcoal fires, and the stench of decaying refuse in the gutters, wandered over the dirty cobbles of the narrow, twisted streets and entered the windows of the hotel on the Prado, rattling the slats of the jalousies in a second-floor bedroom. It pushed its way into the room, stirred the damask draperies into slow undulations, then penetrated far enough to ruffle the tightly curled grey hair of the man who was sitting at the writing table.

The lines of his face deepened as he threw his pen down angrily, searched in his pockets for a tinder box to light the candles, and found none. A string of ripe Spanish curses ripped through the silence of the room. He pushed himself up from the chair with impatience, crossed over to the door and grabbed at a somewhat soiled bellcord, which at one time had been embroidered with gold. He yanked at it, feeling the scratch of gold threads as his hand slipped along it.

Somewhere far below in the echoing corridors of the hotel, a bell tinkled faintly. Its feeble noise increased his impatience and he pulled at the cord again. This time he was rewarded by a louder jangle. The bullioned tassel of the cord had come off in his hand. He looked at it for a moment in disgust, then flung it to the floor, where it sprawled on the tiles like a flat black tarantula. With one hand cupped around his ear, he stood poised at the door listening.

When, after a moment of waiting, he heard the clatter of leather heels on the marble tiles below, he recrossed the room, pulled the chair out from the desk and slumped his heavy body into it. The shadows in the room distorted his huge form into a grotesque outline, making him appear ill-shapen and deformed. He was a large man, tall and heavy with the corpulence of good living, and he overflowed the baroque chair. In the darkness, he seemed ready to pounce, like some jungle animal which has already flexed its muscles yet remains immovable, waiting for its prey. There was no hint of relaxation in his pose; it was taut, strained, filled with nervous impatience.

The uneven footsteps rapidly ascended the stairs, stumbled, caught themselves and clattered along the tiled balcony, then stopped and hesitated for a moment in front of the door of the room. Before a knock could break the stillness, the man in the chair lifted his head and called out.

'Enter, Eugenio! Enter!' When the door opened, he bellowed, 'Lights, man! Do you expect me to sit here in this damned darkness without even a candle? Curse you, Eugenio, for a lazy ill-formed bastard.'

The servant limped slowly across the room, glancing at his master from under lowered lids. He cupped his hands over a spark as it glowed on the tinder, blew it into a flame, then lighted a candle. From this single burning taper he lit others, until the massive candelabrum on the desk blazed with a dozen lights.

The man blinked his eyes and shaded them with his hand. The flickering lights illumined his face, painting dark shadows in the cruel creases that ran down from the wide nostrils down past the full lips. They brought dancing highlights into the large blue eyes and gilded the once blond moustache which was now streaked with white.

'Your pardon, Excellency,' Eugenio said. 'I was but entering the hotel when I heard your bell ringing. I came as quickly as I could.' The voice was humble – seeking pardon, excusing itself.

'Even those useless legs of yours should be able to fetch a package of snuff from around the corner in less than two hours. Do better, *estupido*, or else. . . .'

The servant's mouth opened to speak, but the other cut him off impatiently.

'Do not interrupt, Eugenio. You know you're a stupid fool.' He smiled, but it was a bitter smile, without humour. 'You'd have to be, to have stayed with me these many years. God alone knows why you do.' He turned towards the desk, fumbled for the discarded pen, then dismissed the servant with an impatient gesture. 'Get out! See if you can remember to serve my dinner on time. Watch the wine that it is properly chilled, and keep that damned cook from bobbing into the room to see if I am satisfied. He reeks of garlic.'

Instead of leaving instantly, Eugenio stood dumbly beside the desk. He took half a step away, then gathered up sufficient courage to return. He shifted his weight from one foot to the other, clumsily, for his feet were badly clubbed – ugly monstrosities in their patched and stretched leather shoes.

'Idiot!' The other looked up from his writing. 'Didn't you hear me? Go!'

'I was late, Your Excellency.'

'Yes, yes, I know.'

'But why was I late?'

Lines of anger were beginning to form on the older man's face. His pen caught in the paper, spattered ink over his writing. He flung down the pen, tore the sheet in half, crumpled the pieces in his hands and threw them on the floor. His eyes travelled up Eugenio's waistcoat until they reached the white face and bulging eyes. Not trusting his voice, he pointed to the door.

'But I found him,' Eugenio leaned stiffly forward, his eyes anticipating some rewarding commendation. 'Our journey has not been in vain. I've found him, Your Excellency. I'm sure I've found him. I know it's he.'

'Eugenio!' The man rose and clapped the servant on the back. The bitterness of anger left his voice. He retreated a step, shaking his head in doubt. 'But no, you're too damned stupid. I can't believe you.'

'But I did.' Eugenio's voice rose with the pride of accomplishment. 'I not only found him, but I know who he is and where he lives.'

'Then why are we waiting? Let us go and see him. Come! Shall we call a carriage, or is it near enough to walk?'

'Patience, Don Mario. I think, before we leave, I should tell you what I have managed to find out about him.'

'*Bueno, entonces*. Proceed!'

'He's called "El Rubio" – the blond one. That's because he has the same blond hair that you have. His are the same blue eyes as yours, rimmed with the same black lashes. As a matter of fact, he is yourself as you were thirty years ago. He's tall as you are, maybe even taller, with the build of a *toro bravo*, a thick, strong neck, massive shoulders and slim hips. In Spain he would have made a great *torero*, but here in Havana he is nothing but a petty *ladron*, a little criminal who snatches a purse here, slips a knife into a sailor's back for a thin wallet there, and pimps for a household of disreputable whores for what he cannot steal.'

'Engaging young rascal, what?'

Eugenio nodded slyly.

'But then, I suppose that is what I would have been had I been brought up differently. Maybe it's what I've always wanted to be and didn't know it. But go on, Eugenio.'

'He has a bad reputation, Don Mario. He would as soon kill you as look at you, if he thought he would gain a *centavo* by doing so. Yes, the boy has a bad reputation, all of which I found out by some discreet questioning and a few pieces of your silver while he was drinking a glass of rum. After he had finished, I followed him to his house and saw him go inside. Then I inquired about him from others who lived on the street, greasing their tongues with a few more of your silver coins. They told me his name was Mario.'

'The same as my own.' Don Mario smiled. 'How old is he? You called him a boy.'

Eugenio shrugged his shoulders. 'Who knows? Perhaps twenty, maybe eighteen. *Quien sabe?*'

Don Mario made a mental calculation. 'I was in Havana in 1776. It is now 1798.' He looked up at Eugenio. 'Could he be twenty-two?' He waited for Eugenio's nod, then walked across the room to the large *guardaropa* which stood against the wall, opened the doors wide and took out a cane of dark polished wood. With a twist of his powerful hands, he disjointed the handle, pulled out a thin blade of Toledo steel and cut the air with it. The descending swish of the blade brought a smile of satisfaction to his face.

'Then perhaps, Eugenio, we would be wise to take this with us. I doubt if this young Mario would care to cross swords with me.'

Eugenio forced a smile to his pale lips.

'Not if he knew you were the Marques de la Frontera Baja.' He shook his head. 'Nobody would want to cross swords with Your Excellency.'

Eugenio scuffed across the room, fumbled in the wardrobe and produced one of the half-moon hats which the French Directory had already made popular in Europe. He handed it to the Marques, who adjusted it to just the right angle in front of the mirror, then snuffed the candles. Once again the room darkened, and in that moment of darkness before the door to the hall opened, the Marques laughed. It was not a pleasant laugh, but it served to let Eugenio know that once more he stood in his master's good graces. He waited for the Marques to pass through the door, then closed it slowly behind him and followed his master down the hall.

Chapter Five

A FULL MOON had already risen when Mario, Marques de la Frontera Baja, and Eugenio left the hotel; and it was the same moon, shining full on his face, which woke Mario, El Rubio, from his brief nap in the small bedroom of his mother's brothel in San Isidro Street. Still half asleep, he tentatively stretched out one hand and inched it slowly across the bed, but his fingers encountered only the rumpled dampness of the sheet. The girl must have left while he was sleeping still. Well, let her go! He couldn't even remember which one had been with him. As if it mattered, anyway! He closed his eyes to keep out the glare of the moon, sighed and sought the oblivion of sleep again. But it was no use. The wet sheet stuck to his back and he heaved his body over on his side, causing little rivulets of sweat to channel down his shoulders. The heat in the room seemed a concrete thing – a solid cube, shaped to fit the outlines of the room and occupying every inch of space.

A deadly inertia possessed him as he lay there thinking. What did life hold for him – for Mario, El Rubio? He had pondered the question many times lately and the answer had always been the same. Nothing, except the gallows! Nothing, except that someday he was fated to step out into the bright sunshine with nothing but thin air under his feet and a rope which would choke him dead around his neck. Some night – any night – the *guardias* would surely catch him. They would discover him in some dark alley near the waterfront, searching the pockets of a dead sailor, who still wore Mario's knife planted in his back.

But a man must eat; he must dress himself; he must have rum and tobacco. And, of course, women. But that was something he did not have to pay for, not as long as *Mamacita* kept a supply of girls in the house – all of whom were willing, nay, even more than willing, to accommodate him. He had only to express the wish. Then there were others, many others, who were also willing, and willing to pay good money, too.

However, he was tired of it all – this life of his. He wanted to make the afternoon *paseo* in the Prado, riding on his own horse, escorting *Mamacita*, lolling back on the silken cushions of her *volanta*; a *Mamacita* with diamond rings on her fingers. He wanted a pair of skin-tight white trousers like those the young bloods in Havana were importing from Spain. He wanted a blue coat with long tails and gold embroidery on the collar. He wanted a jewelled snuffbox but, even more than the snuffbox, he wanted to open it with a casual snap and offer it to someone in Havana who really mattered. Then he wanted a pale, fragile woman whom no man had ever had before.

But each year the chances of getting these things seemed more remote. When he was fourteen they had all seemed possible of achievement; even at eighteen he had not despaired. But now, at twenty-two, he realized with an awful finality that they were all impossible. How could El Rubio, the son of a mulatto who kept a brothel on San Isidro Street, even aspire to such things? No, the streets of Havana must remain his life, as they always had been. He was El Rubio, respected if not loved by all along the waterfront. He was proud of his strength, proud of his manhood, proud of himself but . . . he wished he were dead. If it were not for *Mamacita*, he might as well be. *Mamacita!* The fat, foolish little woman whose love had guarded him when he was little, and whose love he returned.

It was time to get up. Slowly and with effort, he raised himself to a sitting position, dropped his legs over the side of the bed and shook the matted hair out of his eyes.

'Get up, Mario,' he counselled himself. 'Get up, shave, take a bath, dress and have something to eat. Then out on the streets again, *hombre*. Who knows what might drop into these hands tonight? *Quien sabe?*'

He stood up, lit the tallow taper on the table beside his bed, rummaged for his razor in the drawer of the table, opened the door and stepped out into the hall. Then he stopped as he heard the sound of men's voices. This in itself was not an unusual occurrence, except that these voices came from outside the door rather than in the house. Usually men did not linger talking on *Mamacita's* doorstep. They entered quickly, afraid of being recognized on the sidewalk. The voices stopped and he heard a number of quick raps on the door, followed by the click of *Mamacita's* little heels as they pattered along the tiles. He heard the door open, heard her gasp in surprise, then heard his own name – El Rubio – mentioned in a masculine voice.

The *guardias* at last! His first impulse was to run back to his room, snatch his trousers from the floor and crawl out the window. But, as he listened, something in the man's voice below told him it was not the police. The smooth Castilian was far too perfect and precise, the phrases too well chosen and the accent too pure. He walked to the head of the stairs and leaned over as far as he could without being seen.

'I'll call him,' he heard *Mamacita* say. There was a tremor of fright in her words. Her heels tapped along the floor and she came up the stairs.

When she reached him, Mario bent over and whispered, 'Who is it?'

Mamacita was puffing from the stairs. Her little round face above her little round body was lined with anxiety as she looked up at her son. The smoothly oiled hair, parted in the middle, with red combs scattered through it, glistened in the light of Mario's candle. She shook her head in indecision.

'I'm not sure,' she whispered, 'but I'd better make some excuse, say you're out – gone away. It bodes no good for you or for me, my son.'

'*Señora*,' the man called from below, 'is the boy there? We have not all night to waste.'

Mario silenced his mother with a wave of his hand.

'*Señor*,' he called down the stairs, 'the boy is indeed here and I am that boy. But, *señor*, it will take me a few moments to dress.' His hands reversed his mother's position on the stairs and forced her down a step or two. 'My mother will attend you in the salon. I shall be below in a moment. I take it your business is important, and is with me?'

'Most important, and with you.'

'*Un momento, señor, un momento, nada mas.*' Mario sent *Mamacita* down the stairs, rushed back to his room, grabbed his soiled clothes and put them on quickly. This might indeed be an interesting night. Who could tell what the *caballero* below might want? The voice sounded as though he would be able to pay well for whatever service he required. Some of these rich men.... He smiled in anticipation of imagined gold pieces.

When Mario came in, the two men stood up. One of them, the club-footed man in rusty black, Mario dismissed with a hurried glance. But the other one, the big one in the fine clothes! This was not a mirrored reflection, Mario assured himself, for the man in front of him was older. He had a moustache and grey hair. But it was a mirror, nevertheless – a mirror of time – for as Mario beheld the man, he saw himself as he would appear in the next two or three decades.

The stranger advanced a step across the room and held out his hand. Mario remained standing in the doorway. The man took another step towards him and, as he came nearer, Mario saw lines in the man's face which he hoped would never appear in his own. Mario had robbed, he had killed, and he had wasted his young years in dissipation; but, although he had been cruel, he knew he had never been as cruel as the man facing him. Mario had killed but he had never tortured; he had robbed, but he had taken only money, he had never stolen a man's soul; he had already made a good start on squandering his youth in dissipation, but in so doing he had degraded only himself, not others.

The man advanced slowly across the room and stopped in front of Mario.

'I am the Marques de la Frontera Baja' – he bowed slightly – 'but recently arrived from Spain.'

Mario looked at him closely.

'If you, *señor*, are the Marques de la Frontera Baja, then tell me, *señor*, who and what am I?'

'A good question.' The Marques' lips closed in a tight, satisfied smile. 'Although there is a little matter of proof, which I expect to receive from this woman' – he inclined his head towards Mario's mother – 'I hardly think it necessary. My eyes do not deceive me, *jovencito*. What they see in you is all the proof I need.'

'I repeat, if you are the Marques de la Frontera Baja, then in the name of God who am I?'

The Marques took his snuffbox from his pocket, flipped open the glittering lid and took a pinch of snuff. He proffered the box to Mario with a gallant gesture.

'You, my lad, are undoubtedly my son, and that makes you, at least as long as I shall live, the Conde de San Mateo. It's a most euphonious name – Mario, Conde de San Mateo. I should know. I used it when I was your age, before my father died. Perhaps, after my rather hard usage, the name is a bit tarnished, but undoubtedly you can dull it even more, if the reports I have heard about you are true.'

Mario felt the strength ebbing from his legs. He swayed a bit in the doorway, but the Marques stretched out a hand and led him to a chair.

Chapter Six

MARIO'S SUDDEN shock of surprise turned into repressed excitement as he watched the Marques, Eugenio and his mother seat themselves on the stiff, uncompromising chairs of Doña Ana's tawdry little salon. After a moment of strained silence, Ana excused herself, went to the front door and bolted it. Business at the Casa Ana would be suspended during the Marques' presence in the house. Mario sat immovable, staring intently at the man he was trying hard to realize might be his father.

He tried to visualize himself as Mario – no longer with the familiar cognomen 'El Rubio' – but Mario, Conde de San Mateo. A count no less! A nobleman of Spain, the son of a grandee! Frontera Baja. . . . He knew that name! *Seguamente!* He had heard it often, for not only was it the greatest name in Andalusia, but it was always mentioned in close proximity to that of the King and the illustrious Godoy, Prince of the Peace. And, according to the way the name 'Godoy' was spoken, it was even greater than the King's – greater than all the other names in Spain.

Mario turned towards his mother, looked at her wordlessly for some confirmation of the Marques' words.

'It's true, Maricito,' she whispered, lowering her head until he could see only the little scarlet combs in her black hair. 'It's true. You are indeed his son. I recognized him when he appeared at the door.'

'But you *are* my mother!' He was emphatic in his assertion.

'No!' The Marques' words cut through the hot air like a whiplash. 'Never! I've sired no sons through half-breeds such as she. The woman is no relation to you, none whatsoever.'

'*Señor!*' Mario's voice had an edge of anger. 'She is my mother. Therefore to me she is a saint. Watch your words. I'll have nothing said against. . . .'

'A *mestizo*,' the Marques repeated, 'and the keeper of a cheap brothel for which you are a panderer. Bah! Let's face the facts. Undoubtedly she has her good points. I knew her once to be both honest and intelligent. But remember this, young Mario.

43

A Marques of Spain does not father sons from a mulatto wench. Bastards perhaps, and bastards they remain. Bastards, such as you are now, but never a son as you shall be. From now on we shall dismiss this woman you have called "mother". Forget her! She has served her purpose. We have yet to listen to her little story and after that, as far as I am concerned, she can continue on her merry way to hell.'

Mario's hand stole furtively under his shirt. His fingers encountered the handle of the thin blade, nestling under the damp hairs of his armpit in its sheath of chamois. He bit his lips as he felt the rising blood of anger flush his cheeks. His slow, calculating gaze paced the distance between himself and Frontera. His left foot moved stealthily forward along the tiles, seeking a firm purchase on the floor, while the right foot, slipping from its loose shoe, inched under the chair, with toes spread wide to give him momentum.

Without warning, he sprang half across the room, the blade of his knife glancing high in the air as it started on its downward plunge. But in the quickness of his sudden temper, he had not figured on the Marques. Without moving from his chair, the old man had transformed the innocent-looking cane on which his hands so casually rested into a streak of flashing light. It came down across Mario's wrist, making him drop his knife to the floor, where it spun in quick circles across the tiles. Mario looked at blood in disbelief spurting from his wrist, unable to comprehend that the blood was his own. Doña Ana ran to him, muttering little animal cries, but the Marques did not move. Instead, he simply laughed.

'You little bastard! And you really are a bastard. Do you think you can outwit me? Ask anyone in Spain about Frontera Baja, and everyone will tell you that, although they hate him, they respect him, for he is the best swordsman in all Europe. But' – he shook his head in grudging admiration – 'I must admit that you are quick. My praise should flatter you, boy. I'll grant you one thing – with anyone other than myself, you might have been successful.'

Mario slumped back on his chair as Frontera glanced contemptuously at Ana. 'Woman, find cloths!' he commanded. 'Bind up the boy's arm and, for the love of God, stop snivelling. It's only a flesh wound and will heal quickly.' He watched her run from the room. 'And as for this' – he picked up the knife at his feet – 'I'll return it to you, my son. A little more experience and you might some day be as good as I, although the sword is much better than a knife. It permits fighting at longer range. You see, I didn't have to move from my chair to disarm you, so I had the advantage.'

He drew a linen handkerchief from his pocket and carefully wiped the sword blade before he inserted it back in the cane. Then he threw the bloodstained kerchief to Mario, who bound it around his arm. Frontera patted the handle of his cane. 'By all means, my son, practise with the rapier. A knife no longer becomes you. It is the weapon of thieves and footpads. Prowess with the sword becomes a gentleman. Cultivate it.'

Ana returned in a few short moments. She was still weeping, but she had brought a copper pan of hot water and some clean strips of linen. She went to Mario, but the Marques' words stopped her as she wrung a cloth out of the water. 'Let Eugenio do it,' he said. 'He has had much practice in surgery and he knows how to bind up a wound so that there will be almost no scar.'

Mario extended his arm for Eugenio's expert ministrations. Strangely enough, now that the first sudden flash of anger had passed, he felt no particular resentment against this man Frontera. Instead, there was a growing sense of admiration. He recognized his new father's superiority; he admired the way he had met the situation – coolly, with no fuss, no unnecessary exertion. It was as though he had merely crushed an intruding cockroach on the floor with his heel.

'And now,' Frontera went on, watching Eugenio's deft hands as he washed and bound Mario's wrist, 'if we can be spared any additional dramatic interludes, I'll be brief and conclude my business here. You, *señora*, stop me if at any time I am wrong. In 1776, exactly twenty-two years ago, I came here to Havana on business connected with my father's two big plantations in Santa Clara Province. We were desirous of purchasing a third plantation which separated the two belonging to us. This one belonged to Don Jorge Hernandez, whose wife, Octavia, was still in her teens, while Don Jorge was already in his eighties.' He glanced at Ana. 'Am I correct?'

She stifled her sobs long enough to answer him. 'Old Don Jorge had sons and daughters twice as old as my mistress.'

'And you, Ana, were her maid?'

She nodded assent.

He turned again to Mario. 'Unfortunately Don Jorge did

not desire to sell his plantation. In fact, he refused the price I offered, so other means had to be employed to get it. Now you, young Mario, would probably have felt that the knife was the best solution, and you would have made a clean little hole in Don Jorge's back. Alas! That was not the best way. Instead, I figured out it would be far better to disgrace Don Jorge and far easier to let him kill himself. So I seduced his wife.'

'You were evil and wicked!' Ana burst out.

'Oh, it was not a difficult job.' Frontera laughed. 'The girl was ripe for picking. Marriage to old Don Jorge had not changed her status as a virgin. She was most willing – most willing indeed. Well, the seduction bore fruit.'

Mario glanced quickly from Frontera to Ana and then back again. 'You mean that I am all white? I do not have any of *Mamacita's* coloured blood? I am not a *mestizo*?' There was sudden, eager pride in Mario's question.

'Most certainly! I told you I fathered no *mestizo* son. And as for Doña Octavia, your mother, she was a Villareal – a good family. But to go on. When Don Jorge could no longer blind himself to your mother's condition, when all the world was taking full advantage of the situation to fit horns on his head, there was a frightful scene. Don Jorge kicked his wife out without a penny to her name, and he kicked Ana out along with her. Then he proceeded to kill himself, and I was able to buy the plantation at my own price. Ana and her mistress came weeping to Havana, to my doorstep. Octavia seemed to think I would marry her. I didn't; but, being a man of honour, I gave her money.'

'But not enough, Señor.' Ana raised her head and glared at him. 'Not enough for the doctors and the medicines we needed when my poor little lady lay dying after the child was born. Not enough to save her. She died and left him behind. I raised him and I called him "Mario" because I knew that was his father's name.'

Frontera shrugged his shoulders, as though he had shaken the burden of Mario, Octavia and Ana from them many years ago.

Ana tried to control her sobbing. 'Many is the time we have been hungry together, Mario and I. Many is the time I pretended that I had eaten so he would have the one crust of bread we had between us.'

'Most admirable of you, I am sure, and most unselfish.' Frontera bowed in mock flattery. 'But all that is over. You both look particularly strong and well-fed at present, so we can forget the past. But don't misunderstand me. I am not here as a repentant father, nor through any sense of recently awakened paternal affection. I care nothing for this young man, except as he serves my purpose. I ask no love from him, and he will get none from me in return. We shall not fall on each other and cry "dear father" and "beloved son". Not at all! I understand exactly what he is – a petty thief, a pimp for third-rate whores, and probably a murderer as well, for he displays a close acquaintanceship with his knife. That does not matter. I intend to acknowledge him as my son. Surely nobody can deny the resemblance between us. So I shall legitimatize him – make him my heir.'

'Can you do that?' Mario leaned forward in his chair and looked at Frontera doubtfully.

'And why not? There is only one law in Spain today, and that is the word of Godoy. And who is Godoy? A lout of a man who wields a fleshly sceptre that is the only thing in Europe which will satisfy our sluttish Queen – and seemingly it serves equally well for our stupid King. Yes, Godoy possesses so much manhood that he rules Spain today. But who put Godoy where he is? Answer them, Eugenio.'

'It was you, Your Excellency.'

'Quite right.' He leaned forward in his chair, holding Mario's knife by the very tip and presenting it to his son. 'One day, while driving near my estates outside Granada, I stopped to water my horse at a mountain pool. There were some youths swimming in the pool, one of whom I particularly noticed. Good God! One had to notice him; one could not take one's eyes off him. Although only in his teens, he was magnificent. More stallion than man. Monumental! Colossal!' Frontera measured an exaggerated distance with his hands. 'I knew at once that I had found the answer to our dear Queen's restless search. So I took this young Godoy with me, trained him a little in the arts of love, and presented him to Queen Maria Luisa at the Escorial. You know the rest. Even here in Havana, you know that today Godoy is Spain. Therefore, Godoy will do as I say, and Mario will be my son – my legitimate son in the eyes of Spain and the world.'

Mario nodded slowly. He sought his father's eyes and for the first time he smiled at him and was rewarded by an answering smile. He reached under his shirt and replaced the knife

Frontera had handed him. His wrist had almost stopped aching and he was beginning to enjoy himself.

'And when I am your son, *padre mio*, what then? Why do you suddenly want a son after all these years?'

Frontera reached over with his cane and lightly tapped Mario's bare toes. It was almost an affectionate gesture. His thin-lipped smile broadened.

'A most discerning question. Direct and to the point. I'll answer, but not so directly and not so exactly to the point. Forgive my circumlocution. Yes?'

Mario nodded as his father continued. 'When you know me better, you will realize that I have love for nobody. I hate everyone. But there is one person I hate more than all the rest, and that is my younger brother, Eliseo, Conde de Camporeal. And he hates me. He wishes my death because he knows that if I die childless, all I have will become his. Consequently he has continuously plotted against me. There have been Moorish assassins in my house in Granada; Italian assassins in my house in Rome, Spanish assassins in my house in Madrid. I have been served poisoned wine, and there have been ambushes at night in dark streets. I am becoming a little tired of seeing the grinning face of death at every turn. That is one of the reasons why I came to Cuba – not the only reason, for my estates here need looking after – but I sought also a little tranquillity, a breathing space from death. Then Eugenio here, who is capable of more deviltry even than I, reminded me of you.'

Eugenio slowly shifted his misshapen boots. A grimace of self-satisfaction spread over his flat face.

'It seemed a good idea.'

'It was! Certainly it will be more difficult for my brother to kill two of us than me alone. With you on hand, Mario, it will avail him nothing to get me out of the way. Therefore, he must forget me for a while and concentrate on you. And therefore, I shall recognize you as my son and flaunt you in Eliseo's face with the fond hope that he will kill you before he kills me. That, *hijo mio*, is why I shall recognize you as San Mateo; it is my only reason. If your blood stains the cobbles of some dark alley on a moonless night, it will not affect me half as much as though it were my own.'

Mario stood up and stretched out his bandaged hand. 'A most worthy display of fatherly affection. So I am to be the pigeon who is to have its throat slit to save yours. *Bueno!* Perhaps it is better to have one's throat cut by a grandee of Spain than to have one's breath stopped by a hangman's rope. I have little choice. The gallows or the assassin's blade. I'll choose the latter. So let us shake hands, my dear father.'

The Marques hesitated, then reached out his own hand. 'For a moment, Mario, I seem to feel something like affection for you. But don't worry, I shall conquer it. Now I shall leave you. Having found you, I must make some plans – many plans. The only thing I demand of you at present is absolute obedience. Promise me that you will do exactly as I say, and do not be surprised at anything that may happen. Whatever comes will be a part of my plan for you, so accept it without question. Do not leave this house for the present, and allow nobody to enter here. The fewer people in Havana who know that Mario, El Rubio, the waterfront rat, and Mario, Conde de San Mateo, are one and the same, the better. *Hasta luego*, my son. You will know what to do when you see this.' He slipped a massive gold ring, engraved with a heraldic shield, from his finger and handed it to Mario for a brief inspection. Then he slipped it back on to his own finger.

Ana ran before them, and unbolted the door. Without another look at Mario, Frontera Baja and his servant passed out into the street.

Chapter Seven

THERE WAS very little sleep in the Casa Ana that night. The street door, locked and bolted, presented an unaccustomed and most inhospitable blankness to the prospective customers who sidled up to it. Mindful of Frontera's cautioned secrecy, Ana herded her girls into their rooms and forbade them, on pain of dismissal from her house, to so much as open their doors.

Mario sat downstairs with her in the little salon till well past midnight. A desire to talk – to know more about himself – kept him plying her with eager questions and she, alternately sobbing and smiling through her tears, told him the story over and over again until he finally became convinced that it was all true and that he actually was the son of Frontera and the ghostly figure of Octavia Villareal.

Ana's tears were genuine, for she loved the boy with a frustrated love which had had no other outlet. Now the very unselfishness of that love was forcing her to part with him, regardless of her own loneliness. Whether he would ultimately benefit from this separation, neither she nor Mario could answer. Both of them distrusted Frontera – Ana from experience and Mario from intuition – but both of them were forced to admit that he had been, if nothing else, overwhelmingly honest with them. Through the man's own admission, he had not come seeking the affection of a son; a shield for his own life and a sacrificial victim to his brother's greed were all that he desired. He had promised nothing but temporary wealth and almost certain death, and, although there was much for Mario to gain, Ana's love for him and his for her weighed heavily in the balance against the position he would occupy as Frontera's son.

Nevertheless, as the candles guttered into pools of liquid tallow and smoking wicks, it was settled that Mario would go with Frontera. They climbed the stairs to their rooms – Ana to a night of grieving sorrow, Mario, with the resilience of youth, to sleep. And this night he slept alone. The knowledge of his new identity had suddenly placed him above the drabs of Ana's house. He had become a different Mario, more fastidious and circumspect, and now he was able to people his dreams with *señoritas* far above the class of Ana's girls.

The realization that he was actually a count of Spain, even though tonight he slept in Havana's poorest brothel, was projecting him into a world which he had never thought of attaining. For him this night marked the end of the Casa Ana and all that it contained – with the exception of the little woman in the next room whom he still thought of, and always would think of, as *Mamacita*, his mother.

Dawn had no more than entered the room and dissolved the shadows from Mario's sleeping figure when he was awakened by a banging on the door below. In his sudden transition from sleep to wakefulness, he confused the present sounds with the knocks of the night before, and he thought that Frontera had returned to tell him it was all a mistake.

But as he untangled his thoughts from the web of sleep, he realized that it was now morning and the clamorous banging on the door below was much more emphatic and forceful than that of the soft-handed Eugenio of the night before. He swung his legs over the side of the bed, searching with his toes for the white cotton breeches on the floor. With difficulty, he slipped them on and stumbled out of his room. Then, completely awakened by the continuous clamour, he raced down the hall, passing Ana's door as it opened to disclose her standing anxiously in the doorway.

He took the stairs with a downward leap and rushed to the front door. The little-used bolt gave him trouble and it took some time to push back. The moment the bolt was slipped, the door was pushed open so violently that Mario had to retreat a step to avoid being crushed against the wall. He caught a quick glimpse of several men outside, in addition to the two now in the hall, one of whom closed the door while the other backed Mario up against the wall. The muzzle of his musket made an icy circle against Mario's chest, and he knew in an instant that all his plans for the future were ended. For the two intruders were dressed in the olive-green and black of the Havana *guardias* – the Spanish constables who so frequently terrorized the San Isidro district. Mario had pictured this scene many times in his more tortured dreams, but this time it was no dream; it was all too real.

They had come! A confusion of half-formed thoughts rushed through him, one superimposed upon another. They were here! The *guardias* had him at last, and at the very moment when he had thought himself free of them forever. Now he would never be anything else but El Rubio, soon to be a shapeless lump of meat, dangling at the end of a rope, kicking his feet in a futile dance of death.

Now he would never know what it would mean to be San Mateo; to ride in his own carriage, to wear tight white trousers and a blue coat embroidered with gold; to ogle the pretty girls in the *paseo*. Too late! But at least he had had a few hours of hope. He had enjoyed that one small dream of what life might have been.

The taller of the two men, wearing a gold-and-scarlet cockade in his cap, pushed the other behind him and lowered his gun. The butt of the musket swung high in the air and caught Mario on the side. He slipped and fell; his body sprawled across the stairs. In spite of the pain from the blow, he wondered if he had a chance to escape. He could leap up the stairs, out through a window and across the roofs. But no! The musket of the officer was again pointing at him. There was no choice. He could do nothing. Even if he could overcome the two men in the hall, there were at least a dozen outside the door, all in green-and-black uniforms.

'Juan Gomez, Captain of His Majesty's Guardias,' the tall man barked. 'I have an order for your arrest for the murder of the American seaman Jones of the brig *Tremont*.'

Mario did not answer. Why protest his innocence? Of the many crimes he had committed, he could not recall robbing or killing an American seaman. Perhaps he had. Who knows? There was nothing he could do but hold his hands helplessly in front of him and let the man clamp the irons around his wrists. But Gomez, pushing him roughly along the wall towards the street door, had not reckoned on Ana. She had been watching from the top of the stairs and now she landed in the lower hall, a screaming, snarling fury, kicking and clawing at the officer until the second constable had to put her away and pinion her arms against the wall.

'There, there, *señora*.' The voice of Gomez was strangely soothing. 'Why make such a fuss about it? There's nothing you can do to help matters now. Save your strength to visit him later in prison.' A slight nod of his head caused the other constable to release her. Ana crumpled into a heap on the floor as Gomez spoke to the other man.

'Go outside and tell the others to back the cart up to the door. Tell them I have the murderer in irons, but don't forget to tell them that he is a dangerous character, this Rubio, and warn them to have their truncheons ready if he makes any trouble. Go now, and close the door behind you. I'll give the woman here a chance to say *"Adios"* to her son.'

The other opened the door and sidled out. In the brief moment that the door was opened, Mario heard the shouts of a crowd congregated outside. He knew that he was already condemned by San Isidro Street even before he stood trial. All of his friends in the neighbourhood would be only too glad to testify against him, hoping thereby to save their own hides and ingratiate themselves with the authorities. He looked up at Gomez and blinked. It was hard to believe, but it was true. The man was actually smiling and patting Ana on the shoulder.

'We have only a moment.' He spoke softly to both of them. 'Here!' he thrust a clenched hand toward Mario. 'Take this! It should mean something to you. I've been told to show it to you, but nobody must see me do it.'

Mario lifted up his hands, heavy from the manacles, and opened his fingers. He felt the warmth of the constable's hand on his and then he felt something else – something round and smooth. When the constable withdrew his hand, Mario stared at the bright object in his palm. *Madre de dios!* It was the very ring that Frontera had shown him the night before! Ana saw it too and gasped, then flung her arms around him.

'Thank God! It's all right now, Mario,' she assured him. 'I'm beginning to understand.'

'And I too, *Mamacita*.' He felt as if every muscle in his body had lost its wound-up tenseness. 'The poor El Rubio must disappear, and how better can he disappear than to be arrested and condemned to die. So that's the way it is going to be! Well, let them hang El Rubio. The lousy little bastard had it coming to him. Who cares? Let this stupid El Rubio disappear forever – just so long as San Mateo sails for Spain.' He slipped the ring on to his finger, but Gomez shook his head and reached out his hand.

'I must take it back,' he explained. 'You cannot keep it.'

'It has served its purpose.' Mario was loath to relinquish it, but he handed it over. 'Well, *Capitan*, shall we go?'

Gomez made a secretive motion with his fingers to his lips. 'One thing more. We must make this look convincing. You must put up a fight. You are a dangerous criminal – a murderer – and you must not go too willingly. So put up a struggle, but be careful how you use those iron bracelets. I have no desire to have my face slashed to ribbons. Now, Rubio! Start struggling. I'll open the door and call for help.'

Mario started yelling with well-feigned anger and fright. He flailed his chains against the wall and cursed Gomez with all the gutter garbage he had accumulated from a life in the streets. Ana joined in with incoherent shrieks of pain and sorrow, and Gomez drowned them both out with answering curses as he opened the door. As Mario writhed and squirmed, striking out blindly with his steel-shod wrists, he managed to elude the hold that Gomez had on his slippery body and run headlong into the street.

Someone reached out a foot and tripped him, and he fell to the pavement. He heard a man's mocking laugh, and then a dozen upraised truncheons of heavy, leaded wood made a swift descent on his head and body. It was all over in a minute and then Mario's half-naked body sprawled in the gutter – a mass of bruises, with blood streaming from his wounds.

'That's enough!' Gomez ordered. 'Save something for the trial. You're not to kill him now.'

The residents of San Isidro Street made a gasping semi-circle around the unconscious Mario. Ana, who had never stopped shrieking, ran from the door and flung herself across Mario's prostrate body, kissing his lips, her matted hair falling across his chest. Gently the neighbourhood women lifted her up and tried to console her, while not so gently the *guardias* picked up Mario's body and heaved it into the waiting cart. Gomez jumped up behind and glared down at the crowd.

'No matter how many times we come here,' he growled, 'no matter how many of you we cart off to the *carcel*, you monkeys still think you can get away with it. This one thought so too.' He pointed to Mario's blond head dangling over the edge of the cart floor. 'He thought himself smart enough and big enough to outwit us. But he wasn't. Now we've got him, and in a few days you'll hear that the great El Rubio has sucked his last breath of Cuban air. Take a good look at him, because the next time you see him he'll be dancing on air.'

He signalled to the driver and the suddenly silenced crowd

parted to let the cart pass down the street. The solicitous neighbour women supported Ana into the house. The door closed behind her and her sorrow.

Then San Isidro Street shrugged its soiled and sweaty shoulders and drifted away. It was time for morning coffee and, for those who didn't have coffee, there was at least an exciting topic of conversation. El Rubio, the stupid fool, had finally got his! He'd lord it over them no more. It was the end of him. But in the crowd there were some who remembered the strength of his honey-coloured limbs, the smoothness of his skin and the pressure of his lips. These few allowed themselves a passing moment of regret.

Chapter Eight

THE COLD dampness of the rough flagstones sent a creeping chill along Mario's naked back. He returned to consciousness by tortuous degrees. First he tried to turn over on his side, but a sharp pain in his thigh and a series of fiery explosions in his head prevented him from moving. As he became accustomed to the semidarkness, he slowly recognized the striped pattern of the barred door, and realized that he was in the grim old *carcel*.

How he had always feared the place! Even the sun-baked outside of the old building had always seemed a repugnant omen of disaster. He had always crossed to the other side of the street whenever his wanderings in the city brought him near it. Now he was actually inside it, and it was far worse than he had ever imagined. Only the returning reassurance of the gold ring he had momentarily held in his hand that morning prevented him from crying out; from standing up and clinging to the barred door, shaking it with senseless fury; from finally collapsing in a hysterical frustration of wordless shrieks.

All this, he kept reminding himself, was merely a part of Frontera's plan for him. The Marques could ill afford to have it known that his son had been a pimping waterfront thief. So now he must obliterate that part of Mario's life, for ever, and present a completely different personage as his son and heir. The old Mario would be dead – and, although Frontera had implied that it would not be long before the new Mario would be dead also, at least the new one would die as a *caballero*. But all that was in the far distant future. It was the immediate present that concerned him now, and for the immediate present he was in prison, alone.

He raised himself partly upright on one elbow and inspected the cell. There was little enough space – no more than necessary. The whole cell measured little more than his own body in length and hardly as much in width. One side supported a rough plank shelf, strewn with a matted mass of mouldy straw. Over in one corner a battered tin bucket leaned against the dirt-encrusted wall.

That was the full extent of the furnishings, but as his eyes became more accustomed to the dim light, he could make out a web of finely written words, names, and phrases, interspersed with a weird variety of obscene drawings, scrawled on the walls. Former occupants had expressed their longings and desires. There, together with their uncomplimentary opinions of the King of Spain, the Captain General of Cuba, and the local *guardias* and prison turnkeys.

He managed to pull himself up to the wooden bed and then, resting his elbows on the boards, he lifted himself erect. An instinctive desire to flee caused him to stumble over to the grating, press his face as far as possible through the rusty bars and peer down the length of the corridor. There was little to see. A barren vista of stone floor and peeling plastered walls stretched bleakly to the left, interrupted only by a uniform rank of grated doors similar to his own.

At the end of the corridor there was a row of iron bars, and through it a splash of sunshine painted the floor with vibrant light. The pool of light was comforting. At least he could tell whether it was day or night. He seemed to be entirely alone – a small island of life in the heavy silence that deadened the corridor. No other face appeared at any of the doors; no welcoming hand preceded a friendly arm through the bars; no voice greeted his anxious '*Oye, hombres, que pasa?*' He was entirely alone, without any of the comforting sounds of fellow humans.

How long he remained mutely standing there, he had no way of knowing. There was nothing to indicate the passage of time except the almost imperceptible movement of the pool of light at the end of the passage. He watched it for a while as it crept across the floor from one wall to the other; then he went over to the bed and dropped down upon it. It was a relief to stretch out, and his thoughts began to take on more coherence.

He realized that his whole existence now depended on one man – Frontera. With that realization came a round of fearful fantasies. Suppose Frontera had merely wanted to get rid of him and the whole story was some diabolical subterfuge! Suppose Frontera forgot him and he was left to rot in this miserable hole. Frontera might die overnight or be called away from Havana, find a new mistress who consumed all his attention, break his leg or be wounded in a duel.

As each dismal idea presented itself, Mario came to know the dumb, chilling fear of helplessness and hopelessness. Suppose – oh, suppose! But from the very depths of his tortured imagination he slowly climbed to the warmth of self-consolation. Why suppose any more? There were always two sides to every situation. Far better to take the known surety of the ring Gomez had shown him that morning as proof positive of Frontera's good intentions. Better to picture himself as the Count of San Mateo and let that thought inspire a whole series of delightful fantasies as to what he would be able to do when he had finally achieved that position.

Here indeed were comforting thoughts. His daydreams drifted on and at length became wholly inspired by a particularly obscene drawing scratched on the wall exactly on a level with his eyes. Its crude outlines gave form to the mental picture he was composing, and gradually he relaxed and closed his eyes. As his breathing deepened the drawing became a colourful actuality. He slept, and when the jailer came to his cell a smile had stencilled itself on his face.

The harsh grating of a key in the lock awoke him and an instinct of self-protection caused him to sit upright, bracing his back against the angle of the corner. Beyond the jailer's indistinct face there was another. The long black habit and the monkish cowl could not entirely hide the flat features of Eugenio. Mario sprang up with confidence.

'A confessor to see you before your execution,' the jailer muttered.

'My execution? God help me, man, I haven't even had a trial.' Even Eugenio's reassuring presence could not stifle Mario's fear.

'Some never do, and you're one of those.' The man seemed to take a sadistic pleasure in this statement. 'Those that are in the condemned row have only one more step to take.' His arm came up as he pointed to the sunny door at the end of the hall. 'Through there. But from there on, there are three different paths. If they are traitors to the king' – he made a quick motion at his throat – 'they get the garrotte.' He spat on the floor. 'And if they are thieves, they get a circle of hemp around their necks. But murderers, now' – his little eyes gloated over Mario – 'that's a different story. You're a murderer, they tell me.'

'So they tell me too,' Mario answered.

'Then you'll have a big fuss made over you. You'll be shot! Ah, that's something to see. All the public is invited in for that one. They'll tie you up to a post over against the wall and wrap a blindfold around your eyes. Then the drums play soft and slow and the troops come marching in, all dressed up in their best uniforms. Twelve of them – the best marksmen in His Majesty's Army. Six of them kneel down in front and take aim at you, and six remain standing in back, their muskets all in a line with your heart. "Fire," says the captain, and twelve shots ring out as one. And what do you do? You jump around like a frog on a hot stove when the bullets hit. Wham! You go up in the air, frontways, sideways and every which way as far as the rope on your hands will let you. Funny? Makes me laugh to split my sides. Ah, but I love shootings and seeing how those boys can dance.'

The monk entered the cell and held up his right hand, more to silence the man than to make the gesture of benediction.

'That's enough,' he said. 'Now leave us. Lock the door of the cell when you go, and then return in half an hour.' He waited silently for the jailer to leave.

'Well, Mario,' Eugenio began, 'you see we have not forgotten you. You'll only be here a few days. Let's see. Today is Tuesday – that means the rest of today. Wednesday, Thursday, and Friday. You are to be executed on Saturday.'

'What do you mean, "executed"?' The cold fingers of fear choked off Mario's words.

'Just what I said. On Saturday morning you'll walk out through the door that fool jailer was talking about. You'll be tied to the post and blindfolded. You'll hear those twelve soldiers come marching in, their boots rattling over the cobbles to the beat of muffled drums. You'll hear the captain shout "fire" and you'll hear the shots.'

Mario shrank back on the planks. 'So! That's the way it is. The whole thing has been a trick. I die after all.'

Eugenio pushed the cowl back from his forehead. 'Die? Who said anything about dying? Oh no! You did not let me finish. You hear the shots and you perform a certain number of wild gyrations, and then you sink to the ground unhurt.'

'Shot but unhurt? And how can that happen?'

Eugenio smiled. 'In your case there will be no bullets in the guns, only powder. The captain has had his instructions. In each hand you'll hold a little glass vial filled with pig's blood.

These you will break in your fingers, and as you twist around the blood will stain your clothes. Immediately after the shots are fired, the captain will walk over, quickly examine your body and pronounce you dead. He'll throw a cloth over you to hide the fact that the bloodstains are not authentic. Then, as far as the city of Havana and all of Spain is concerned, Mario El Rubio is dead. There will be a box waiting, and you'll be put into it and the lid will be nailed on; but there will be holes in the box so you can breathe. Soldiers will load it on a cart and take it to the cemetery. On their arrival, they'll find that the grave has not yet been dug, the grave diggers will just be starting. So the soldiers will leave the box and depart.'

Mario leaned over and rested his elbows on his knees. He peered up at the shadowed eyes above him. 'Are you sure everything will be all right? Just one bullet in those guns and I'll be a dead pigeon.'

Eugenio's glance withered him. 'When His Excellency and I plan anything it *always* works out all right. Those so-called grave diggers will be men from our plantation. We'll have a closed carriage behind the cemetery wall. They'll pry open your coffin and you'll get out, slip into the carriage and be taken to a house the Marques owns in Vedado. There you'll find a complete wardrobe waiting for you. There will be a slave to help you dress. Your luggage will be all packed. You'll shave, dress in your new clothes and take the same carriage back to the San Francisco pier. The *Tres Castillos* sails for Spain that afternoon and the young Conde de San Mateo, his valet and all his luggage will be on board.'

Mario leaned back, put both hands behind his neck and stretched his head backwards. He found that his headache had miraculously disappeared. Eugenio grinned under the shadowing cowl, went to the grating, glanced up and down the corridor to make sure that nobody was coming, then came back and stood in front of Mario. He opened the long black monk's habit to disclose a number of packages and bundles suspended from a belt around his waist. There were several bottles of wine, a roast chicken, a goodly part of a Spanish ham and a loaf of bread. One small package contained bandages and ointment for Mario's wounds. Another held soap, towels and an excellent razor.

'Be sure to shave on the day of your execution,' Eugenio warned. 'We want everyone who knew you to identify you positively. There must be no question that it was El Rubio who was shot.'

When these things had been hidden under the bunk, Eugenio motioned for Mario to stand up. He drew a tape measure from an inside pocket and took out a scrap of paper and the stub of a pencil.

'I've still one very important thing to do,' he muttered with the pencil in his mouth. 'You must be measured for clothes. It will take a dozen tailors, working day and night, to complete your wardrobe, but the magic of the Frontera name and a plentiful supply of the Frontera money will accomplish it.'

He measured Mario in detail, marking down the figures on the scrap of paper. As he drew the tape around Mario's hips, his fingers passed over the dried blood on the boy's trousers.

'You've been hurt, my boy. Come!' He pulled Mario over to the door where the light was better and undid his trousers. They slithered down his legs and Eugenio bent over to examine the wound. His eyes strayed from the bruise for a moment, then returned to it. 'It's nothing but a skin abrasion. A little ointment will heal it.' He rose as Mario gathered up his pants, and fastened them.

Eugenio stood for a moment lost in thought. He nodded his head slowly as if in full agreement with some unspoken conviction of his own. He smiled in self-satisfaction then turned to Mario. His smile broadened.

'Even better than we had dared hope for. . . .' His words trailed off into unspoken thoughts.

Mario looked at him for an explanation, but Eugenio changed the subject. 'His Excellency has some plans for you which he will explain himself; he intends to see you before you sail.' His smile disappeared and his eyes narrowed to thin slits under the overhanging eyebrows. 'Much may happen in the next few days that will be unpleasant. But have no fear. You will be on board the *Tres Castillos* when she sails. That I promise you.' His narrowed eyelids opened and he looked straight at Mario. 'It is most important that you be on board. The Duke and Duchess of Almendares are sailing on that ship and His Excellency will be anxious for you to make a good impression on Her Grace, the Duchess.'

'A duchess? Me with a duchess?' Mario stared at Eugenio in wild disbelief.

'And why not? The Count of San Mateo, particularly you

as the Count of San Mateo, will be a fit companion for Her Grace. You see' – he lowered his voice to a confidential whisper – 'she is a friend of the Queen's and, if I know the Duchess, she will be only too willing to pass on certain information about you to the Queen. That, too, is a part of my master's plan for you.'

Chapter Nine

EUGENIO HAD told Mario that his incarceration would be just a trifling matter of a few days – the rest of Tuesday, Wednesday, Thursday, Friday and that small part of Saturday morning before the execution took place. The offhand manner in which Eugenio had said it had made it sound as though those few days would be really nothing at all – a swift interim of passing time. True, in Mario's old life, such a paltry number of days would have quickly fled. He would have slept away the hours of sunshine and prowled the streets of the waterfront during the night. They would have been days of freedom. But in the grim, dark confines of the Havana *carcel*, every hour stretched itself into a semblance of eternity.

The lewd inscriptions on the wall were all he had to read, and he read the legible ones until he knew them by heart. He would have liked to add some of his own artistry to the walls, but he had nothing with which either to write or to scratch. Eugenio's bottles of wine, while they lasted, gave him a few stupefying hours of drunken forgetfulness, which helped. He did not suffer from hunger, for the food which Eugenio had brought him was more than sustaining. This was fortunate, it being impossible to stomach the watery messes slopped in a tin dish by the turnkey and shoved through the door. The latter, whose name turned out to be Paco, seemed disturbed at Mario's apparent lack of appetite.

'You must eat,' he urged. 'You'll need your strength for Saturday.'

He cautioned Mario in the manner of a solicitous herdsman fattening a shoat for Easter. But when Mario asked why, Paco was at a loss for words. An execution was a bit of an event in his existence and he was determined to get the last full measure of sadistic anticipation and pleasure out of Mario's forthcoming death by discussing it in all its horrendous details. Unable to turn a deaf ear, Mario was forced to listen. But he seldom replied, for there was always the gnawing fear – hidden as far as possible in the back of his mind – that something might go wrong and Paco's dismal prognostications would turn out to be altogether too true. In spite of the slow passage of time, Mario found he preferred to be alone, even with the torture of his own thoughts, than to suffer Paco's ill-omened forecasts.

Eventually the darkness of Friday night came and Mario, worn out by having lived so long in such a few days, managed to fall asleep at dusk, not to awaken until he heard the key grate in the lock. Then he sat up, fully awake. This, then, was the moment he had been both dreading and anticipating. This marked the culmination of all his agonized hours of patient waiting – the threshold of death or freedom, either the beginning or the end. He dreaded to turn and face the door, but when he did so and saw Eugenio's face behind Paco, framed by the monkish cowl, his spirits rose. He looked again and saw beyond them two other men, both in the scarlet and gold of Spanish uniforms.

The latter proceeded immediately to bind Mario's hands behind him. Paco, his lips pursed in experienced contemplation, examined the knots closely.

'Tighter, men,' he advised. 'That will never hold when the bullets hit him. The rope should be drawn right into the flesh.'

'The knots will serve their purpose,' Eugenio interrupted. 'And now leave us for a few moments. This man has a right to confess his misdeeds and consecrate his soul to God.' He pushed them out of the cell with a motion of his hands, then came closer to Mario and whispered, 'A few last instructions. Here are the vials of pig's blood. Keep them hidden in your hands. When you hear the shots, squeeze your hands together. The glass is fragile and will break easily. Usually, when bullets strike a man, they come with such force it raises him off his feet. Jump up in the air as far as you can, throw yourself sideways, then drop to the ground on your belly if you can. Remember this: if you move a muscle when the captain walks over to pronounce you dead, or after that until the soldiers get you in the box, our game is up. His Excellency your father has arranged everything else. This part, and this part only, depends entirely on you. Can you do it?'

'I've had practice in keeping still.' Mario thought of the times he had stealthily stalked an unsuspecting victim, freezing motionless against the shadowed walls in case the man happened to turn around. 'Don't worry about it. Is all else arranged?'

Eugenio deemed it a question unworthy of an answer, but he allowed his lips to curl in the semblance of a smile. 'The *Tres Castillos* sails this very afternoon. The second-best cabin on board has already been reserved for the young Conde de San Mateo. Even now some of his luggage is on board. Need I say more?'

Mario nodded, then turned his head to listen. The iron-shod boots of the soldiers sounded on the flagging. 'The soldiers are returning.'

Eugenio, who seemed well-versed in almost everything, commenced an undertone of mumbled Latin. His hands traced the sign of the cross in the air; then he turned, opened the barred door wide and signalled to the soldiers to take Mario. They entered the cell with quick and efficient motions and grabbed his arms. Mario could feel the iron grip of their fingers pressing into his flesh. They started down the hall.

It was not necessary for Mario to pretend fright. He did not have to borrow the skill of an actor. In spite of Eugenio's reassurances, his reactions were exactly the same as though he knew he had only a few more minutes to live. He felt his knees turn to water, and a hollow emptiness spread inside him, through which he could feel his heart pounding. He knew that his legs would never carry him, but then legs were hardly necessary as the strong grip of the soldiers under his armpits propelled him along the hall. They stopped for a moment before the grated door while Paco unlocked it and flung it open.

After the days spent in the dim obscurity of his cell, the full blast of brilliant light blinded Mario and he was unable to see at first. After they had progressed a few steps from the door and his eyes became accustomed to the sun, he noticed, through half-shut lids, a crowd of people in the prison courtyard. As he walked through the glittering brightness, he heard the steady roll of muffled drums. The soldiers hesitated for a moment to adjust their steps to the slow rhythm of the death march, and then, step by step, with Mario's feet dragging on the ground between them, they carried him across the walled courtyard.

They stopped before the clumsy stump of iron-ringed stone, where the soldiers produced another length of rope and proceeded to tie his hands to the iron ring which was to hold him upright. Then they left him, standing there alone in awful, final isolation. The fear which had been ever-present since his arrest now took full possession of Mario, and he tried to scream out protests of his innocence. But his words were barely more than whispers. Saliva dripped from the corners of his mouth and his throat was dry and burning. He tried to swallow but found he was unable, because of the swelling lump in his throat.

Mario's eyes swept over the distant sea of heads. Here and there he recognized the grinning faces of those whom he had once called friends. All of San Isidro Street, except little Ana, seemed to be there. They were imprinting his every movement on their memories, the better to make themselves authorities on his manner of dying. It would be their main topic of conversation for days to come, and they did not want to be cheated of a single moment. Ay! Ay! This was a *fiesta* for them, a drama, better than the theatre, a colourful episode in their drab lives.

The tempo of the drums quickened and a squad of soldiers slow-marched from the yawning black shadow of a gateway into the sunshine of the courtyard. Stepping in measured cadence to the slow roll of the drums, they crossed the cobbles and drew up in two rows, about twenty-five paces from Mario's post. He heard the captain bark an order and saw the martinet mechanics of the twelve soldiers presenting arms.

Then he saw the captain walk slowly down the ranks and examine each musket. This, Mario knew, precluded the possibility of a single ball's remaining in the guns. A small feeling of relief began to quiet his fear. When another command to shoulder arms had been barked out, the captain walked with military stiffness over to Mario and produced a clean white cloth from a pocket underneath the tail of his coat. Without looking at Mario, he tied it around his eyes, then whispered one word. Once again Mario took heart, the one word was 'Frontera'.

Light filtered through the bandage, but Mario could see nothing; he could only listen and try to picture, from the sounds that came to him, what might be happening. A command cracked out and he heard the scrape of feet as the front row of soldiers knelt. The drums started again – a long succession of muted rolls. Another command from the captain, and Mario knew that they were aiming their muskets at his heart. A procession of vivid images flashed like coloured tapestries across his mind. He saw himself as a little boy, seeking consolation by burying his head on *Mamacita's* lap as he recoiled from the first wallet he had stolen and brought home. The image of the Portuguese sailor he had knifed paraded slowly before him. Once again he felt the ecstasy of the first woman he had ever slept with. . . . And then, suddenly, as he contemplated her beauty, he heard the command 'Fire' and the immediate, deafening rattle of musketry.

With all the strength he possessed, he twisted his body sideways, remembering that he must crush the glass vials in his fingers and managed to rub his hands across his back. His feet left the ground and he forced a violent contortion of the muscles of his belly, then, his head slouched on his chest, he slumped slowly towards the ground, as far as the ropes that secured his hands would allow. He tried to turn his body as much as possible so that his back, splotched with pig's blood, would face the spectators.

He was aware of footsteps approaching him, heard the ropes being sawed with a knife, and when they parted he allowed his body to tumble to the ground. Hands rolled him on his side and he smelled the pomade of a man's hair and felt the bristles of his beard as an ear was placed against his chest. There was a creak of leather from the boots as the man stood up. Then words rang out: 'In the name of Their Most Catholic Majesties of Spain, I pronounce this man, called El Rubio, dead.'

So he was dead. But still the sun filtered through the bandage over his eyes, and his wrists ached from the ropes. At last, after moments of agony from resisting the desire to move, a welcome, enveloping blackness blotted out the light in his eyes as he felt the folds of a blanket settle over him. The protective folds eased his agony and he knew that he was hidden from the staring, inquisitive eyes of the throng.

'Don't move,' he cautioned himself, 'because if you move a muscle, you're done for.' Then, disobeying his own command, he tentatively moved one finger. The drums sounded once again and the footsteps of the soldiers retreated, growing fainter as they marched across the courtyard. After that came loud bursts of laughter and animated chattering as the crowd followed them out. Then . . . nothing but silence and the sound of his own heartbeats, until he felt himself lifted up from the ground and dumped into a box that had the clean, hot odour of freshly sawed wood. The sound of hammers over him told him that the cover was being nailed on.

Now, after his rigid discipline over his muscles, he was free once more to take a long, deep breath. He gradually shifted his shoulders until he found a more comfortable position in the box and, after he felt himself being lifted up, he discovered he had sufficient room to move his arms and take the bandage off his eyes. The lifting up and the subsequent scrape along the bottom of the box must mean that he was in the cart. Yes, he could hear the wheels starting to turn. He edged sideways to where a streak of light penetrated a hole in the box. Looking through it, he was able to see the cobbles in the patio disappear as the cart drove out into the streets.

It was close and hot inside the coffin and the springless cart jolted the box so that he had to brace himself to keep from knocking his head on the cover. But it was over and he was still alive. He wanted to laugh. *He* was alive but El Rubio was dead. Even now, in San Isidro Street, they were saying 'El Rubio was' instead of 'El Rubio is'. He allowed himself to smile. No need to think about El Rubio any more. Everything had gone off perfectly, just as Frontera had planned it. His father! Mario felt a wave almost of affection for the man he had seen only once. If one were to have a father, it was well to have a clever one – and nobody could say that Frontera was not clever.

The cart jolted on through the narrow streets of Havana, and Mario was happy. If anyone had ever told him that the happiest moments in his life would be spent in his own coffin on his way to the cemetery, he would have crossed himself in disbelief. But that was how it was – exactly how it was. He'd never been happier before; no, never.

At last the wheels came to a stop and he felt the box being lifted down. It slipped and one of the soldiers let out a string of curses, only to be reprimanded by another, who reminded him that death, even that of a criminal, was a holy thing. The other grumbled but steadied the box, and Mario felt it reach the ground safely. An angry muttering of conversation started, which developed into an argument between the soldiers and some strange new voices.

The grave wasn't dug? Well, why in the name of God wasn't it? They'd had their orders to see that the coffin was buried, but how could they bury it when there was no hole to put it in?

Why should soldiers of Their Majesties be expected to wait for a bunch of goddamned lazy black niggers to take their own goddamn time digging the goddamn grave! Better to see to it the next time that it was ready and waiting.

Another voice interrupted, this one softer and speaking with some authority, apologizing and suggesting that there was really no reason why the soldiers should wait. A few more spadesful of dirt and the grave would be ready. He, the unctuous voice promised, would see to it that the coffin was properly buried, so why should soldiers stand around waiting in the hot sun when there was a shady little *cantina* just outside the cemetery walls, with excellent wine and a couple of pretty wenches to serve it? He, the voice continued, would buy the wine; he was sure the soldiers would rather drink than wait.

Mario could almost see the soldiers smiling. Their anger evaporated in a profusion of *gracias*. Someone clucked to the horse, and the cart rolled away. Mario waited and then saw the entering wedge of a crowbar come between the boards. He listened to the welcome screech of nails as the boards were ripped off, and in another moment the hot sun was shining on his face. Then a shadow passed over him as a man leaned down. Mario looked up to see Eugenio, in the dirty shirt and soiled trousers of a workman, bending over him, extending a hand to help him out of the coffin.

'Your Excellency.' Eugenio grinned as Mario stood up. 'Your Excellency.' He even bowed. 'This way, the carriage is waiting behind the wall.' As they left, Mario looked back and saw one of the slaves renailing the lid on the coffin, while others were hip deep in the grave, throwing out dirt.

Mario hurried behind Eugenio to a small gate in the cemetery wall. A smart black coach with drawn shades was waiting on the other side. Eugenio opened the door and with another 'Your Excellency' helped Mario in and climbed upon the box. They started off and Mario parted the curtains to look out on the receding wall of the cemetery. What were those words that Eugenio had said? 'Your Excellency.' This time he had not meant Frontera. He had meant. . . . By God! He had meant Mario himself. 'Your Excellency.' It sounded good – very good

Chapter Ten

THE TUMULTUOUS events of the early morning were already receding into the background of Mario's memory when the coach swerved off the narrow country road, made a quick turn between a pair of crumbling stone gateposts, and drove up an avenue of tall royal palms. At the end stood a large house nearly obscured by a dense tangle of shrubs and a thick grove of rubber trees. Their deep shade gave a sinister air to the deserted-looking villa.

During the drive, Mario had perched gingerly on the very edge of the seat. He was ashamed of his grime-encrusted breeches and he had tried to keep them as much as possible from the pale rose velvet of the upholstery. But, as the coach stopped, he leaned back against the seat and raised the curtain as far as it would go. A destination had at last been reached.

Eugenio was already on the ground and had the door of the coach open. He helped him down, and, with a quick, furtive glance along the driveway to make sure that they were unobserved, he hustled Mario up the steps of the house, across a pillared portico and into the entrance, whose huge carved door had mysteriously swung open from the inside.

It was dark in the hall, and damply cool. A strange musty odour pervaded the house and, as Mario sniffed it, he felt sure that the place had been closed for years and only recently opened. What furniture he could see was shrouded with dusty cloths. The tiles of the floor were powdered with a fine white dust, and what was evidently a chandelier hung swathed in ghostly sheets, suspended in mid-air like a bundle of soiled laundry.

The door closed noiselessly behind them and Mario was suddenly aware that he and Eugenio were not alone. There was another man whose form emerged from the shadows near the closed door, but as he was dressed in black and his hands and face were black, it was almost impossible to distinguish him in the dim light which filtered through cracks in the boarded-up windows.

Eugenio addressed the man with authority. 'The Conde has

arrived, Ramon. Conduct him to his room. I shall go to the kitchen and prepare some food for him.' He looked up at Mario. 'This is Ramon. He'll take good care of you; that's what he's here for. He is your own slave, your personal property. Follow him and let him suggest what you will do.'

Eugenio left them, was swallowed up in the shadowy reaches of the hall. The slave beckoned and Mario followed the outline of his shoulders – a deeper black against the overall dim greyness. They passed several closed doors; then the man stopped, reached his hand down, turned a latch and waited for Mario to precede him.

Where the hall had been dark and inhospitable, the room that Mario now entered was brilliantly lighted by the sun which streaked through the two tall windows. Here the furniture had been uncovered and the floor scrubbed. Mario noticed that the room was richly furnished in an elaborate style. There were carved and upholstered chairs, a bed, draped and canopied in yellow damask, fragile-looking tables which supported branched silver candlesticks, and a huge wardrobe of carved and gilded wood.

As he stood in the centre of the room, blinking his eyes in the strong light, he got his first real look at the man who had brought him here. The latter was a tall, well-formed Negro, a few years older than Mario – possibly a little under twenty-five. He was dressed in sombre black: a long tight black coat with a flared skirt, knee breeches, black silk stockings and black shoes. A narrow band of snowy white linen at his neck accentuated the blackness of his skin.

Large, dark brown eyes met Mario's squarely from under stencilled black brows. The nose, although wide nostrilled and Negroid, was finely carved; the lips, full and purple, were well-formed, and there was a close skullcap of wiry black hair that showed the fine shape of his head.

'I am Ramon,' the man said, and smiled, showing a row of teeth as dazzling white as the thin line of linen at his throat. 'Your father, the Marques, won me with a turn of the dice yesterday and now, so I am told, I belong to you. It seems that I am the only slave in Havana whom your father deemed worthy to serve you.'

'How is that?' Mario found himself smiling back. He felt at ease, as though some immediate bond other than ownership had been established between them.

'Because your father says that I am the only one who can teach you much that you should know.' Again the teeth showed in a wide grin. 'I was valet to His Excellency the Captain-General, and your father wished to buy me but the Governor refused. He said there was not enough money in Havana to pay for me. But your father had other ideas.'

'Apparently he always has ideas of his own.'

'Yes. He started throwing dice with the Governor. First they played for duros and then, as the stakes got higher, the Marques started doubling, and he always won. After the amount had reached a fantastic sum, the Marques said, "Everything I have won against your slave Ramon" and what could my master do but take the challenge? Again the Marques won, and so I am now here to serve the Conde de San Mateo.'

He came across the room and stood before Mario. 'May I?' he asked, and at Mario's nod started to disrobe him. His fingers recoiled as they touched the filth of Mario's breeches, but he stripped them off and let them fall to the floor, then kicked them across the tiles. 'We'll burn those later.' He shook his head dolefully. 'And a good riddance that will be. Also, it will mark the end of El Rubio.'

'You know?' Mario asked anxiously.

'I had heard of El Rubio before – the name is not unknown in Havana. And I had heard of his execution, as who has not? It was proclaimed throughout the streets of Havana for all of the city to know. However, your father took me somewhat into his confidence and explained matters a little more fully. He knew that he could trust me.'

Mario felt relieved. Now there would be no necessity for him to keep up a constant pretence before this man who was going to be his slave. If he should ever revert to El Rubio, in diction or in action, the other would understand.

He glanced down at his body. Its filth appalled him and for the first time he was conscious of its disgusting stench. Ramon beckoned him to follow into an adjoining room, where a sunken tub of warm water steamed with the heady perfume of lemon verbena. Mario stepped in and sank down into the warm water, letting it envelop his body, soothe and caress it. In the moist fragrance, he could forget the horror of the last few days and revel in merely physical comfort.

He relaxed while Ramon hurried back and forth, assembling a collection of bottles and small porcelain jars, then knelt beside the tub and scrubbed Mario with a handful of the fragrant verbena leaves. As he scrubbed, the dirt of the prison sloughed off and Mario could sense his skin becoming alive once more, glowing pink under the brisk massage. When everything was finished to Ramon's satisfaction, he helped Mario out of the tub, enveloped him in thick towels and seated him on a chair.

He whisked up a thick lather, spread it over Mario's face and deftly shaved him – a far different process from the laborious scraping Mario had performed the night before. With scissors and a comb, he tackled Mario's damp hair, cutting it short in the new French manner so that a lock hung in an inverted 'V' over his forehead. There followed various pomades from the several jars, and a vigorous brushing of his hair until it shone like burnished gold.

His fingernails were pared and carefully shaped; the bruises on his feet were tenderly treated; and every inch of his body was massaged, patted, oiled, rubbed, perfumed, creamed and polished. After what seemed like an interminable time, Ramon appeared satisfied and, like an artist who has just completed a masterpiece, led Mario, towel-draped, into the other room. Mario remained standing while Ramon opened the door of the wardrobe and brought out a dressing gown of thin India silk, which he laid over Mario's shoulders.

Then Ramon led him over to the bed, turned down the sheets, plumped up the pillows, and whispered, 'Rest, my master.'

The smooth linen sheets and the soft mattress were a sensuous delight after the mouldy straw and the hard boards of the prison, and even a far cry from the thin, lumpy mattress, the coarse cotton sheets and the sagging ropes of Mario's bed at the Casa Ana. His clean body slid down into the cool whiteness. He felt the light caress of the silk across his shoulders, sank his head into the downy softness of the pillows, closed his eyes and listened drowsily to Ramon tip-toeing about the room.

He was far too contented even to exert the necessary effort to raise his head when he heard the door open, but he surmised it was food, for he smelled the aroma of coffee. When Eugenio balanced the big silver tray on the side of the bed, Mario realized that he was ravenously hungry. He ate everything Eugenio had brought, finding the eggs more golden, the ham more tender, the bread whiter, and the way it was all served far more appetizing than anything he had ever eaten before.

Eugenio left with the ravaged tray and once more Mario was alone with Ramon, who quietly closed the jalousies, shutting out the sunlight. Mario punched his pillow into a more comfortable position and turned on his side, stretching his legs down into the cool sheets. His eyes closed, inviting sleep, only to open wide at the click of the door latch. He turned over slowly to see Ramon crossing the room, his tall shoulders bent over the heavy burden in his arms. As Ramon approached the bed, Mario was able to see the light cloth covering around the bundle move. Then he heard a sob.

Ramon threw back the linen sheet that covered Mario, laid the bundle beside him and unrolled the cloth to expose a nude girl whom he pushed, not ungently, close to Mario.

'You have had no woman in the *carcel*, my master, and this one will supply your need. She is a slave of your father, fresh from the *finca*, kept chaste for his relish; but he is sacrificing her virginity to you. He was right in thinking you might need her.'

Mario looked down at the girl and saw in the tea-rose perfection of her skin, which darkened very slightly under her pointed breasts, almost no trace of colour. She was young, possibly not more than fifteen, slender and delicately made, with a heart-shaped face whose perfection was marred now by puffed and swollen eyes, red from crying. His excitement, which had enlarged rather than shrunk since his bath, welcomed her now with increased vigour. Although he had been startled by her entrance, his amazement did not deter him from drawing her slender body close to his own. He looked up and nodded to Ramon, who regarded the couple with proprietary interest for a moment, then turned and departed through the same door from which he had entered.

Mario's lips were greedy to seek those which were beneath his. But after he had kissed her, he relaxed the pressure of his mouth long enough to question her. 'Why do you weep, little one? You have no cause to cry. Look, *chiquita*, I, Mario, am going to show you the greatest joy you have ever known. You are most fortunate, so why are you crying?'

'The man, he spanked me.' Her sobs and the closeness of Mario's lips caused her to hesitate between her words.

'Ramon?' Mario was angered. 'Shall we have him flogged? Here before you, where you can watch it?'

She shook her head.

'Why did he spank you?'

She pulled her head back from his questing lips. 'Don't whip Ramon, *señor*. It was my fault, *mi culpa*.'

'Your fault? Nothing as pretty as you could be at fault.' Mario kissed her again and this time she responded. He could feel the tip of her tongue between his teeth.

'I was afraid to come. Afraid of you,' she whispered. 'Afraid I could not please you.' She parted the long smooth black hair from her eyes and gazed back at him. 'But now I am no longer afraid.' Her hand reached up and touched him tenderly on the cheek, then lingered there. He grabbed her other hand and forced it down between their bodies. She uttered a small cry of alarm at what it encountered and struggled to withdraw it, but Mario pushed it back and held it there.

'It is nothing to fear, *chula*, nothing at all.' Mario gripped her wrist firmly as he drew her face to his. The tension in her imprisoned arm relaxed and her stiffened fingers became possessive. She bit his exploring tongue.

'I do not fear any longer.' She laughed. 'It was foolish of me. But, *señor*, I have never been kissed before, nor did I know what made a man a man. Ah, but it is a wondrous thing. My mother kept me for my master's pleasure, and now you are my master. Pleasure me, my master.'

Mario abandoned her lips and courted the hard crimson nipples of her breasts. She sighed, then uttered a tiny whimper as his teeth closed gently together. Her whimpering did not deter Mario. Nothing could stop him now. His gentle wooing exploded into a fierce carnality. The days of continence in the *carcel* were finding relief in the powerful thrust of his heaving loins, and he was deaf to the whimperings which turned into the shrieks of a girl who was rudely becoming a woman. The fire within him flashed through his whole body, only to be quenched suddenly and furiously as the dam burst and his pent-up flood quenched the flames. It was over. He had conquered, but in his victory he had gone down in defeat.

'I hurt, master,' the girl wailed, knowing that she had been forbidden to protest whatever he might do to her. 'Please, my master, do not do it again.'

'I never shall,' he murmured sleepily, 'and no man ever shall again. It is a pain you feel but once in your life. From now on it will be only a pleasure.' His head drooped and he dozed off into sleep, his weight a burden upon her which she bore uncomplainingly because she dared not disturb him. In his sleep, his body rolled to one side.

She breathed deeply, then turned and regarded him, wide-eyed, examining him in detail as he snored beside her, marveling at the difference in the hard muscularity of his body and the yielding softness of her own, thrilling at the gold blondness of his hair, the straight line of his nose, the nipples which lay like copper coins against the whiteness of his chest, and the entire display of masculinity which she had never seen before. She edged closer to him, pillowing her head on his heaving chest, but did not close her eyes. In spite of the pain she suffered she was gloriously happy.

Mario did not know how long he slept but, unknown to him, Ramon was patiently watching the clock. Exactly on the hour he entered, threw open the *persianas* and flooded the room with light. Mario blinked, opened his eyes. 'What do you want?' he muttered, resentful of Ramon's intrusion.

'You must rouse yourself, my master. The appointment with your father will not wait. We dare not be late.'

'Oh, go to hell!' Mario took offence at the smooth urbanity of Ramon's words. 'I'm going to take her once more. Once more, do you hear?' Mario sat up in bed the better to defy Ramon, then slumped over the staring girl, his face buried in the smooth roundness of her belly.

Ramon shook his head. 'His Excellency will be impatient, my master. We have no time to frivol. Come, arise!' Ramon's words, although softly spoken, carried authority.

'Arise! Are you commanding me, slave?' Mario blazed with anger. 'Let us understand one thing and understand it now. No man has ever commanded me before and I shall not start by taking orders from you. I said that I would have this woman once again and I shall have her once again. Now go or remain – I don't give a damn – but take her I shall, whether you are here or not. But if you do not want a flogging later, leave.'

Ramon bowed his head, but when he lifted it he was smiling down at Mario. 'It was not meant as a command, my master, but in truth we have little time. It is your father who has made the schedule, not I. As for me, I would willingly let you stay all day and all night too, for the ocean you must cross is wide and three weeks will be a long time.'

Mario responded slowly to the wide-toothed smile. It was impossible to be angry with this soft-spoken black.

'Ten minutes, then, Ramon.'

'Ten minutes, my master.' He walked across the room and closed the door gently behind him.

The girl was even more ardent than before, but for Mario his performance was vaguely unsatisfactory. He could not blame his bedmate nor, for that matter, himself. Time was on his mind, and no man can perform satisfactorily when one part of his brain is mentally ticking off the minutes as he tries to achieve satisfaction. He was tempted to rebel at Ramon's haste. Why should he heed a slave's demand? The black seemed more the slave of his father than of himself, and Mario felt cheated of authority. Why shouldn't he lie abed, dally with the girl until he could rouse himself no longer, then sleep, exhausted and satiated, with her in his arms until he should again wake and find relief, time without end? Let his father wait and the slave go to the devil.

In spite of his mental turmoil, he achieved his desire, just as the door opened and Ramon entered. 'You've had your ten minutes, my master, and it is now past the allotted time. We must make haste. You know His Excellency. He is not a patient man.'

Mario opened his lips to reply. The sentences of defiance had already formed themselves in his brain and were on their way to his tongue, but the look of patient resignation in Ramon's face halted them. Mario nodded his acquiescence, gathered his silk robe about him and accepted the other's dominance.

He stood up, wondering how he would be dressed, but was more than satisfied when he saw Ramon open the wardrobe door and walk across the room with the exact type of white pantaloons Mario had so much admired and envied on the dandies of the *paseo*. He noted also the short coat with the long tails of sky blue, embroidered with gold, together with all the other things that Ramon carried – the small cloths of fine linen, the socks of thin French lisle, the black shoes that were only a whisper of leather, the shirt of embroidered lawn and the stock of heavy dark silk.

As Ramon handed them to him, one by one, he put them on, but his big fingers were unaccustomed to the tiny buttons and clumsy with the small buttonholes. So in the end it was Ramon who dressed him, from the thin-soled shoes to the satin stock. It was Ramon who eased the coat on over Mario's wide shoulders so it sat there without a crease or wrinkle in the broad sky-blue back; Ramon who produced the handkerchief and scented it with *Eau de Cologne*, Ramon who pulled the two belts to make the fit of the pantaloons even more snug over his hips, and Ramon who turned him around like a tailor's dummy to see that everything was perfect. At last Ramon led him across the room to a tall mirror which hung on the wall.

Mario looked and gasped. Surely this could not be he – this close-cropped youth who stared back at him, this fashionable young buck with a forelock of gold hair on his forehead, whose shaven cheeks glowed pinkly under their light tan. Could he possibly be so tall and well-built as that stranger who stared back from the mirror, whose shoulders stretched so broadly under the gold tracery of embroidery? For the first time, Mario became acquainted with the Conde de San Mateo. He shook his head in puzzled bewilderment and turned to Ramon with a quick word of appreciation.

'*No hay de que*,' the slave answered. 'If the results are satisfactory, it is no credit to me. You supplied the flesh and the Marques the clothes. I have but put them together, and yet' – he grinned – 'I do feel that the result is one we can all be proud of.'

Mario regarded himself in the mirror again. He saw something more than the new clothes and the new haircut, in the reflection that regarded him. An entirely new look in the mirrored eyes had replaced the furtiveness he had been accustomed to seeing there. He saw a prouder lift to the chin, a different set to the shoulders. These things did not depend on the new clothes or on Ramon's efforts. This man – this new man – looked clean and honest, and deep in his heart Mario realized that this was indeed the case. Ramon had scrubbed away more than dirt from his body; he had scrubbed his soul a little bit, too.

As Mario stared into the mirror, he saw the door open behind him and Eugenio enter. Eugenio took a quick glance in the mirror and acknowledged the result with a satisfied look at Ramon.

'We must hasten now.' He turned to Mario. 'His Excellency is waiting for us at the hotel in Havana, and we dare not be late. He has timed your arrival perfectly and will be waiting downstairs in the public room. You must enter and embrace him for all of Havana to see. You are his son. You have been all your life at the *finca* in Santa Clara. You have just come to Havana to sail on the *Tres Castillos*. Can you play your part?'

Mario hesitated a moment. 'I hope so. I shall try to acquit myself so that the Marques will not be ashamed of me.'

'Do not try too hard,' Eugenio cautioned. 'Just be natural.'

Before his departure, Mario turned to Eugenio, pointed to the girl on the bed and asked, '*La chica?* She is a slave, *verdad?*' And, at Eugenio's assurance, he questioned further, 'Mine or my father's?'

'Yours now.' Eugenio spread his hands in a gesture that depreciated her value. 'She is ruined for the purpose for which your father had her raised. But get no ideas in your head, Conde. You cannot take her to Spain. However, if you wish, she shall be kept for your return. We can see to it that she will have no other man while you are away.'

Mario regarded the girl. 'I wonder if I shall ever return to Cuba.' He was thinking aloud. 'El Rubio died today. The dead do not return.' He shook his head as though to dispel his thoughts and then spoke to Eugenio. 'Must she go through life waiting for me to return?'

'But she cannot go with you on the *Tres Castillos*.' Eugenio was firm on that point. 'His Excellency would not permit it. He has other plans for you that do not involve a coloured wench. It is out of the question.'

'I was merely thinking of the three weeks aboard ship.'

'You may find other doors that will open to you – doors that will be wider and easier of access even than this one.'

'Then, if she is mine even though I may not take her with me, I can dispose of her. Take her to the Casa Ana. There she will not be denied the joys I have taught her today.' He grinned. 'Although I could have been a better teacher if I had had more time.'

'It shall be as Your Excellency wishes. Tomorrow she will be delivered to the Casa Ana.'

'With the message to my mother that it is my farewell present to her.'

Ramon held open the door of the coach for Mario to enter, and this time the brightly gleaming leather of Mario's shoes did not look out of place on the varnished steps. He recalled the bruised feet, dirty and discoloured, which had stepped on them only a few hours before. What changes a few hours could make! They could turn a man, condemned to execution, clad only in a torn and filthy pair of cotton breeches, into a *caballero*. They could turn a petty criminal into a grandee of Spain – an El Rubio into a Conde de San Mateo.

This time Mario sat squarely and comfortably back on the rose velvet upholstery and gazed out the uncurtained window as Eugenio mounted the box and Ramon climbed up behind. The carriage started. Mario was returning to Havana – this time to the Hotel del Prado.

Chapter Eleven

WHEN THE coach stopped, halfway up the Prado, in front of the hotel, Mario looked out through the coach window, over the heads of passersby, through the tall pillars that framed the entrance, and noticed that there was a crowd of men in the foyer of the hotel. For a moment he was possessed with a wild desire to flee – to quit the coach and all that it stood for and run as fast as his feet would carry him to the familiar obscurity of San Isidro Street and the easy informality of the Casa Ana. He stifled the desire in the remembrance of his new identity and braced himself for his first appearance in public as Frontera's son. He leaned back against the cushions and waited for Ramon to descend from the footman's box in the rear. The door swung open and Ramon's upstretched hand appeared to steady him as he descended.

Somewhere in the crowd inside, he knew that Frontera was standing, waiting for him. And he also knew that, regardless of what the man might be doing or with whom he might be conversing, Frontera had his eyes on the coach. Mario sensed that any undue haste would betray his nervousness, so he turned casually to Ramon and instructed him to tell Eugenio to wait, then walked leisurely across the pavement, hoping that his deliberate steps would not betray the conscious effort he was making to place one foot in front of the other.

As he walked between the pillars and entered the big, open salon of the hotel, he became aware that there was a sudden lull in the conversation, and that many were regarding him and speculating on who he might be. His pride in his new appearance led him to hope they were commenting on what a fine-looking fellow he was. The possibility gave added strength to his courage, and he walked with more deliberately casual tread across the black-and-white marble tiles.

Then he saw Frontera. His father! The man who had done all this for him! He was standing in front of a tall mirror on the far side of the room, talking to an elderly man who was almost as distinguished looking as Frontera himself. Mario's glance crossed with that of his father across the distance of the room, and he welcomed Frontera's smile. To Mario it seemed anticipatory, whole-hearted, even affectionate. He watched Frontera hurriedly excuse himself from the man to whom he was talking and start across the floor, quickening his steps as he drew nearer.

Should he stand still or continue on to meet his father? Mario hesitated a moment, then went forward and opened his arms, noting that Frontera did the same. They met and he felt Frontera's arms clasp him around the shoulders and he heard him say, 'Mario, Mario' with a rising inflection which certainly denoted both expectancy and joy.

'*Padre mio!*' The words came suddenly and naturally from Mario, without forethought or preconceived planning. His arms lingered for just the right moment in the familiar *abrazo*. Then he felt his father's hand, heavy on his shoulder, leading him over to the man with whom he had been talking. Mario caught a fleeting glimpse of himself and his father in the tall mirror and he was satisfied. Their eyes met in the reflection and the quick look told him his father was relieved, and also that he approved both of Mario's appearance and his conduct. There seemed to be a pride of possession in Frontera's bearing which Mario felt could not be entirely feigned.

The speculative eyes that had regarded Mario as he entered the hotel were now all the more curious as he and Frontera walked across the room. Mario was glad the Marques was speaking in casual, inconsequential phrases which could be heard by those about them.

'Welcome to Havana, my son,' the Marques was saying. 'I hope you had a pleasant journey. But the heat! It is unbearable! Didn't you suffer in the coach? I've been waiting for you for over an hour. I thought you might be here a little earlier.'

'The heat slowed the horses.' Mario's words were as casual as his father's.

'But you're here now. And what a pity that you must leave so soon. *Qué lástima!* We'll hardly have a chance to see each other.' He stopped in front of the man he had excused himself from a moment before. '*Señor* Castanedo, may I present my son, Mario, Count of San Mateo. He has but just arrived from the *finca* at Santa Clara and sails this afternoon for Spain.'

The white-bearded gentleman in the old-fashioned brocaded coat bowed low and, as Mario returned the bow in the same courtly fashion, examined him closely through a gold lorgnette which he perched before his eyes.

'Your son, Marques?' He shook his head. 'Your son? I never knew you had a son, but he is certainly the image of you. I might think I was seeing you as I did when you were here in Havana some twenty years ago.'

'Thank you, Don Julio.' Frontera seemed pleased. He regarded Mario and nodded his head slightly. 'He's not a bad-looking boy, is he? But I see so little of him. He's always at one or the other of the plantations in Puerto Rico, or Santo Domingo, or Mexico or here in Cuba. Alas, he is so wedded to the soil he never comes to Havana, so I see my son all too seldom. . . .'

'Which does not diminish the deep affection I have for him.' Mario finished his father's sentence and was rewarded by a look of approval.

Don Julio had completed his inspection and lowered the *impertinentes*. 'A fine boy, a fine boy, Marques. And yet' – he drew in his upper lip and shook his head – 'It's strange I didn't know about him. Indeed, it's most strange.' His forehead creased in puzzled lines.

'Yes, indeed strange that you didn't know, Don Julio. But you do now and, if you will excuse us, we will go to my rooms. The boy must be on board in another hour, so we shall have but little time to be together.'

The puzzled look still remained on Don Julio's face as he bowed again. Mario and his father walked away. Every few steps they were interrupted by greetings, and Mario was introduced again and again to the different groups.

'My son, the Conde de San Mateo, *señores*.' Frontera hardly stopped as he passed from one group to another. 'My son Mario, Ignacio. My son Mateo, Don Juliano. My son Marito, Pancho.' Mario noticed that his own name varied with the degree of intimacy of Frontera's acquaintanceship. To some he was presented as the Count, to others as Mario. To some Frontera used the name without the title, and to one in particular he had called Mario by the endearing diminutive. Through it all Mario bowed and smiled and shook hands whenever the occasion demanded, until they started up the broad marble stairs. Halfway up, Frontera smiled and whispered, 'Good job, boy.'

It was Ramon who opened the door of Frontera's suite.

Frontera seated himself in the tall chair by the desk and waved Mario to a smaller chair facing him.

'This man is yours.' He indicated Ramon with a wave of his snuffbox. 'I went to considerable trouble to obtain him for you, because he is the only slave in Havana who has the necessary knowledge to teach you what you need to know.'

'And what do I need to know?' Mario looked at Ramon out of the corner of his eye. The slave was standing stiff and straight, his heels together, facing Frontera.

'What do you need to know?' Frontera leaned forward. 'A million things, my boy. Big things, little things, important things, superficial things. So many, many things that you will need to know in order to move in your new society.'

'Am I so stupid?' Mario flared.

'Let's not say stupid. Just ignorant. You'll find the Escorial and the Alcazar somewhat different from the Casa Ana, and you'll find the women of the Spanish Court a decided contrast to the girls of Ana's house. That is, in some ways.' Frontera curled his lip in a wry smile. 'In other ways you'll find them very much the same. However, pay attention to Ramon. He'll teach you how to dress, the right clothes to wear at the right time, the right sort of jewellery to put on, the correct way to handle a knife at table, the most elegant manner in which to take a pinch of snuff, and the right gesture with which to offer it. He knows, even though he is a slave. Indeed, no grandee of Spain knows more about what it takes to make a gentleman than he does.'

For the first time he looked directly at Ramon. 'I'll put him in your hands, slave. Polish him, smooth off his rough edges and fit him to be the son of the Marques de la Frontera Baja. But' – his long thin finger pointed at Ramon to emphasize his word – 'above all, guard him. I'm investing a lot of money in this new son of mine, and I don't want my investment turned into a rotting carcass by my brother's assassins the very first day he arrives in Spain. Now go, Ramon. Prepare yourself for the voyage. Everything is packed?'

'Yes, Your Excellency.'

'Good. We shall be leaving presently. I shall accompany Mario to the *muelle*. It is only fitting that a fond father should wave goodbye from the pier. After that, he'll be in your hands. Watch over him.'

When the door had closed behind him, Frontera reached for

a string of round amber beads, which glowed with topaz light, on the desk and drew them slowly, one by one, through his fingers. He touched each individual bead, caressed its round smoothness and passed it along the silken string with a faint click. He saw Mario staring at his hands and shrugged his shoulders by way of apology.

'A custom I learned from my Moorish friends.' He smiled as he indicated the beads. 'And now, Mario, my son – for after all, you are my son – let us get matters understood between us. Here we sit, you and I, a pretty picture of fond filial devotion and beaming parental affection, even though it cannot possibly exist between us.'

Mario bit his lips and leaned forward in his chair. His hands started to move but he restrained the gesture and sat back. For some reason he had wanted to touch his father, clasp his hand, feel some sort of physical bond between them. Instead he merely phrased a question. 'Why not?'

'Because you do not know me for the rascal that I am and I know you for the rascal that you are.'

'But,' Mario protested, 'I have been doing a lot of thinking these last few days. The Havana *carcel* is a good place to think; that's all one can do in prison. The more I thought about myself as El Rubio, the more I hated myself. Then my thoughts of you became more than mere admiration. . . .'

The Marques clicked three of the beads from his left hand to his right. His attention was riveted on the jewels in his fingers and he kept his eyes away from Mario. There was a curious catch in his voice when he finally spoke.

'I have been thinking also, Mario, and I must admit that most of my thoughts have been about you. I have been arranging many details, and you have been concerned in most of them. Fortunately they have worked out well. But' – he raised his head and regarded Mario – 'I must confess that no degree of affection has entered either into my thoughts about your or my machinations to bring you here. And yet. . . .'

Mario did not interrupt. He sensed that his father was seeking exactly the right words and that they were difficult to choose.

'And yet, when you walked into the hotel this afternoon and I looked across the room at you, I suddenly felt a most unusual sensation – something I have never felt before. I have always been a proud man, but, this afternoon when I saw you, I seemed to possess a strange new pride. I saw that you were tall and straight and fine-looking. I felt that you might be a credit to the Frontera house and, God knows, there have been damned few in our family that ever have been. I realized you were a part of me – formed by me. I thought of the seed I so carelessly planted years ago, and I looked at you and marvelled. I was proud, and when I introduced you to old Don Julio I did it intentionally, because he is the greatest old gossip in Havana. I knew he would spread the news faster than a pack of old women, and I wanted him to. It pleased me to have a son, and I hope he tells all of Cuba about Frontera's boy. But now I find this feeling of pride almost ceases to be pride. Who knows, it might be called love. But never having experienced such an emotion before, I am quite unprepared to classify it.'

Mario extended his hand slowly toward his father. Frontera drew a quick breath, lifted his own hand and struck Mario's down.

'Damn, boy! A father and son do not merely shake hands like a couple of strangers.' He stood up, half lifted Mario from the chair, and encircled him with his arms. When he spoke his voice had lost the edge of sarcasm which up to then had seemed so much a part of it.

'My son!' The words were spoken quickly, but they were full of meaning.

Then Frontera sat down again. 'I rather think we understand each other, Mario. No more words are necessary.' His hand reached out and tapped Mario's knee lightly. 'And now, some last-minute instructions.'

'Whatever you say, my father.'

'You are sailing on the *Tres Castillos* for more than one reason. My friends, the Duke and Duchess of Almendares, will also be on board. I want you to know them, because I want you to use them. He's a superannuated old fool who does not particularly like to wear horns but always seems to find them fastened to his head. He drools all over his shirtfront and is never sober. She, on the other hand, is young, fairly beautiful, extremely passionate, and, most important of all, she stands next to Godoy in importance at court. She has influence with both Carlos and Maria Luisa. Make love to her if you want – you'll probably have little choice, after she sees you.'

'That's one thing Ramon will not have to instruct me in,' Mario said with a smile.

'No, I rather imagine not – at least if all reports are true. Apparently you are well-equipped for making love. So charm the Duchess and then use her. Through her you can, if you play your cards right, climb up the ladder even more quickly than you could with just my help.'

Mario nodded.

Frontera went on slowly. 'I had first thought of going to Spain with you, but I now think it would be premature. I still have some unfinished business in Cuba, and I should prefer you to be much wiser than you are now before I personally present you as my son in Spain. Ramon will teach you much, but there are some things that he cannot help you to learn. Therefore, I have already written to my old friend Moulay ibn Hussein, who is known as Baltazar Ruiz, in Cadiz. The letter went off by ship yesterday, so he should receive it before you arrive in Spain. He is a Moor, and a very learned man – one of the few really good men left in Spain. He has been the representative of the Sultan of Morocco for so many years in Cadiz that he finally adopted a Spanish name. You might even call him a Spanish Moor – after all, we Spaniards of Andalusia are really Moors, even though we have been Christianized for centuries. They say, and truthfully, that a Spaniard is nothing but European Moor.'

'With light hair and blue eyes?' Mario asked.

'That's the Basque blood on my mother's side.' Frontera smiled. 'But about Don Baltazar. I'm sending you to his home in Cadiz to remain for six months, and then we'll proceed to Madrid together. You can read, I hope.'

'Yes.'

'Good. Don Baltazar will choose the things for you to study. You must know something about geography, history, literature – enough so you can carry on an intelligent conversation. And, above all, you must lose that atrocious Cuban accent.'

Mario nodded silently.

'Cram all the knowledge you can into that handsome head of yours,' Frontera said. 'During that time, the papers will be drawn up and your legitimacy recognized. Of course, my brother Eliseo will hear all about it. He'll get word from Havana, or the Duchess will tell him when she lands. So be on your guard at all times. Don't leave Don Baltazar's house alone. Learn to use the sword, but in learning to use it, don't forget El Rubio's proficiency with the dagger. And now, my boy, we must leave. Ring for Ramon. Tell him to have Eugenio waiting at the door. We'll make a grand exit for all of Havana to talk about – father and son, Frontera and San Mateo, two rascals who have suddenly found out they are not such damn villains as they have always considered themselves to be, for surely neither of us can be all bad if we have affection for each other.'

Ramon came and opened the door and they walked out. When they reached the head of the stairs, Frontera stopped for a moment. 'I've seen to it that Ana will be taken care of,' he whispered as he put his arm across Mario's shoulder. They walked slowly down the stairs. Mario thanked him with a nod and felt his father's hand tighten on his arm.

News spreads quickly in Havana and the salon below was even more crowded than it had been before. At the sound of their footsteps on the stairs, every face was lifted. Frontera leaned over the balustrade and waved down, then smiled and gestured to Mario, who repeated his father's greeting.

They walked slowly across the tiles to the waiting coach, leaving an excited buzz of conversation behind them. Everyone eagerly sought out old Don Julio, who, it appeared, had known Mario since he was in his cradle. He could not, he confessed, understand why nobody else knew that the Marques de Frontera Baja had a son. He of course had always known about young Mario of San Mateo, and he naturally had expected that everyone else had, too.

Chapter Twelve

THE SLOW, rhythmical pitch of the ship rocked Mario like a cradle. Through the open ports, a cool salty breeze stirred gently through the cabin. Mario dozed long into the late afternoon of the first day after sailing. It was a quiet lull of peace to disperse the awful uncertainty of the prison and the horror of his cell, the slow death march out into the blinding sunshine, the hot smell of new lumber from the fresh boards of his coffin, and the uncertain excitement caused by his new role as Frontera's son. He was exhausted, and content to lose himself in sleep. Occasionally he would half awaken to an awareness of Ramon near him and see the slender black fingers smooth the sheets and plump up the pillows. Then he would turn over drowsily and luxuriously, and sleep again. Blessed sleep!

Havana was receding fast behind him and he found he had few, if any, regrets. Now Spain beckoned, and Spain held great promise for the future. To be sure, there might be the shadow of a sword over his head, but why worry too much about the future? His Uncle Eliseo might die before Mario arrived, or any of a thousand eventualities might happen. But it was sufficient for the present to revel in the quiet, and submit to Ramon's ever-watchful attention.

Later, he blinked his eyes free from sleep and surveyed the little room which was to be his home for many days to come. The walls were richly panelled in some dark wood, which caught dappled reflections of light on its polished surfaces. A thick red Turkish carpet covered the floor, and polished brass hurricane lamps swung from brass stanchions. Propped up on the brass-railed top of the chest there was a picture – a miniature richly framed in gold and diamonds.

Mario raised himself on one elbow, stretched out his arm to reach and examine it. Could it be a picture of himself? No, it was Frontera, painted when he was about Mario's age, for the costume partook of the more elaborate richness of some twenty years previous. But the face, the nose, the lips and, most of all, the eyes were Mario's. He held it in his hands a long time. The likeness of the painted image to himself gave him a feeling that he actually belonged. It was a definite proof of his present identity. He had needed this additional assurance.

His eyes were open now and sleep had finally departed. He watched the small door at the side of the room open noiselessly and saw Ramon tiptoe in from his own cabin, a tiny one that connected with Mario's. When Ramon saw Mario wide awake, he relaxed his caution and smiled a greeting as he came over to the bed. Just as he was handing Mario the same silk dressing gown that he had worn the morning before in Vedado, a soft rap sounded on the door.

Mario flung the gown around his shoulders as Ramon answered it. He heard a few mumbled words which terminated with Ramon's '*Gracias.*' The door closed and Ramon crossed to the bed and handed a note to Mario, the paper fancifully folded into a cocked hat, with the name San Mateo on the outside. Mario pulled both ends and it popped open. Inside, there were a few lines of bold writing under a ducal coronet.

> 'The Duke and Duchess of Almendares request the presence of the Count of San Mateo for dinner this evening at nine o'clock in their cabin.'

Mario looked at it uncertainly, then handed it wordlessly to Ramon.

'You must answer it,' Ramon said, nodding his head. 'I shall take the answer to the Duke's cabin.'

'But what shall I say?'

'Only a line is all that is necessary,' Ramon advised, 'just write, "The kind invitation of Their Graces, the Duke and Duchess of Almendares, is most gratefully accepted by the Count of San Mateo".'

'That sounds damn silly. Why don't I say "The Count of San Mateo will be glad to dine with you"?'

'Oh no! Never!' Ramon shook his head with grave warning. 'You, my master, are only a count, which is a most exalted position, to be sure, but it is as nothing compared with that of a duke. In Spain – except for the members of the Royal Family and Manuel Godoy, Prince of the Peace – a duke ranks above everybody else. Therefore you must mention a duke's name before your own, and you cannot possibly say "you" to him. You must always address him as "Your Grace".'

'Your Grace, Your goddamned Grace,' Mario mimicked. 'And what do you call me?'

'Your Excellency.' Ramon bowed in Mario's direction. 'It is used for both marqueses and counts.'

'My Excellency! I like it. It makes me feel good. I suppose from now on I shall hear it a lot.'

'Yes, Your Excellency.'

'But sometimes I'm going to want to hear just plain Mario. Ana used to scream it across the patio and up the stairs to wake me. The girls in the house were always calling "Mario, Mario" and the boys in the street would yell out "*Que tal, Mario?*" I shall not miss never hearing "El Rubio" again, but I'd still like to hear "Mario" once in a while.'

Ramon's voice was noncommittal. 'Undoubtedly Your Excellency will meet someone of your own age in Spain who will be permitted to call you Mario.'

'But until then, my good Ramon? Must I always be "Your Excellency"? Couldn't you forget once in a while and say "Mario" just to make me feel at home?'

Ramon hesitated. He could hardly bring himself to say the name. His sense of propriety was outraged.

'Come on, Ramoncito. Try it once.'

'Mario.' A little shudder passed over Ramon.

'That wasn't too difficult, was it?'

'No, my master.'

'No what?'

'No, Mario.'

'That's better, Ramon. Let's get a few things straight now. This is the first time we've had a chance to talk together. I've never owned a slave before, but now you're my slave. If you're not a good one, I'll strip the clothes from your back and lash you until your flesh is nothing but a mass of bloody meat. Understand?'

'Yes, Your Excellency.'

Mario smiled. 'That was the right answer that time, Ramon. I had just reminded you that you were my slave and I am your master, so in that case I most certainly am Your Excellency. But Ramon, I'd far rather have you for a friend than a slave, and I'd far rather be your friend than your master. When we arrive in Spain I shall need a friend far more than I shall need a slave. After all, Ramon, we're about the same age, and we've been thrown together through no fault of our own. You're here through the throw of a die, and my reason for being here is not much different. We're more or less partners in whatever adventure lies ahead of us. Be my friend, Ramon, and there'll never be any welts on your back. If I merit your friendship, will you give it to me?'

This time there was no hesitation on Ramon's part.

'You already have it, Mario.'

'That's better! Thank you, Ramon. Now, take the note to Their Graces, and I'll get up.'

'Stay there, Mario. I'll return in a moment and get everything ready for you.'

'You need not urge me overmuch.' Mario sank back comfortably into the pillows and closed his eyes again. He heard Ramon return, then followed his footsteps around the cabin with half-closed eyes. He watched him open the wardrobe and study the long line of suits that hung inside. Ramon chose one carefully – a black suit of lustrous mohair.

After a rather difficult bath in a small round tin tub, followed by Ramon's careful application of the razor, plus the usual scented pomades, Mario was slowly and carefully dressed. Although he could only see his face directly in the small mirror, by looking down he was able to see the faultless fit of the coat and the breeches. Even the shoes were different from those he had worn yesterday. He couldn't help but recall the days when he had been forced to stay in bed while Ana washed his one pair of white cotton pantaloons.

He waited until the hand of the gold watch which Ramon had placed in his pocket pointed to exactly five minutes off nine before he left. As he opened the door to walk the few steps down the companionway which led him to the Duke's room, he experienced once more the feeling of panic which had seized him when he arrived at Frontera's hotel. Who was he to be having supper with a duke and a duchess? Would he know how to eat, how to talk, how to conduct himself? Damn it! He would try. He lifted his shoulders a little, threw out his chest, raised his chin, and walked straight ahead.

Although they were a duke and a duchess, nevertheless they were just people, and after all . . . what was it Frontera had said? 'An old man who drooled on his waistcoat and a young and beautiful woman.' So, what difference did it make? If a duke could drool on his shirtfront, Mario could use the wrong knife; and if a duchess was young and beautiful, she might enjoy some things he had to offer, even if his accent was more Cuban than Castillian. He found himself in front of the door and rapped sharply.

An elderly manservant in dark plum-coloured livery opened it and ushered him inside. If Mario's cabin was adequate, this was indeed palatial. The Duke even had a small salon, and there was a table set for three in the centre. The servant motioned to a chair, and Mario sat down while the man rapped softly at each of two doors. One of them opened almost at once and a woman came out. She was young, at least under thirty, and, as Frontera had said, she was extremely beautiful.

Mario rose to his feet and bowed low as she walked across the cabin. He seemed to know that, as she presented her hand to him, he was supposed to kiss it. He did, but after the kiss he allowed his lips to remain a fraction of a second longer, and the hand was not withdrawn. Instead, it pressed against his lips so warmly that he could feel his teeth cutting into his lip; then, when it was slowly taken away, he looked up to see the Duchess smiling quizzically at him.

She was tall, nearly as tall as he, with the bearing of a woman who, if she had not always had her own way, had been willing to move heaven and hell to get it. The swaying candles gilded her hair with shifting blue highlights. A rose flush illumined and warmed the olive skin. Long black lashes partially curtained dark brown eyes under two brows which looked like pencilled wings. Mario saw that her lips were large, red and moist – full and ripe. She wore a white gown, high-belted in the Empire style, with a band of gold under her round breasts, displaying a purple-shadowed valley where the bodice was cunningly dropped. As she walked between Mario and the light of the candles, he could swear that she wore nothing under the filmy gauze.

Even greater than the surprise of her beauty was the shock of her voice when she spoke to him. It was far from the affected Castillian lisp that he had expected. To his amazement her voice was coarse, loud, and demanding – as shrill as though she had been selling *aguacates* in the streets of Havana. It reminded him of Ana's girls except that, where they had tried to affect a certain artificial gentility, the Duchess of Almendares seemed to take pride in the harshness of her voice and the vulgarity of her accent.

'Mateo!' she exclaimed. 'Damn you for a wily fox! Where

have you been hiding yourself? Your father told us that you would be on board and, since you were such a boor as to neglect to pay me your respects, I had to summon you. *Dios Mio!* Is that the way the next generation of Fronteras is going to act? If so, God help Spain.'

'My apologies, Your Grace.'

'My Grace and be damned to you. There's no grace about me. Think you that I am going to be "your-graced" on this sea-going hell hole for two weeks or more? Goddamn it, no! I'll have you pitched overboard first, or do it myself. Nonsense! We'll dispense with formality here and now.'

'Exactly what I told my slave only a few moments ago. I have a liking to hear my own name once in a while.'

'Which is?' She came closer to him and her eyes were on a level with his own.

'Mario.'

'Ah! The same as that libertine who calls himself your father. Mario! Well 'tis fitting that the name be carried on, but your father would never have waited a whole day to find *me*.' A wave of her hand dismissed the subject. 'As for names, my fond parents wished the name of Rosa on me. Bah! Rosa! For me? I detest it. And I detest roses too – soft, insipid fat blossoms that you can crush in your fingers.'

'But they have thorns to protect themselves.'

'And who, in the name of God, wants to be protected? No, the thorns are to scratch other people with. I love to scratch.' She smiled. 'Perhaps I shall scratch you some time.'

He pulled back his cuff and offered his bare arm to her, but she only laughed and squeezed it gently with the tips of her fingers. 'I'll not scratch now, Mario. That time may come later. But – we were talking of something else. Ah yes, my name. My friends – and there are damn few of them – call me by a Moorish name which I like. Cleora.'

'And may I call you that?'

'You'd better, if you want my friendship.' She sat down just as the other door opened and a man entered. This could only be the Duke, Mario surmised, for he fitted Frontera's description exactly. He was an old man and already nearly stupid with drink. A sour, winey odour came into the room with him.

Again Mario bowed and again he said, 'Your Grace' and this time he was rewarded by a suspicious, bleary look and the Duke's question.

'Where did Frontera rake you up? A son! A man sprung full-grown from Frontera's forehead like Minerva from her father Jove. Holy Mother of God! Must we believe in another miraculous birth? If you're his son, where have you been all these years, and why haven't you been at Court?'

Mario thought fast. The answer that he gave now must establish a credible story that would survive in Spain. 'My mother was Cuban, Your Grace, and she and my father were not particularly compatible. So he left for Spain and I remained in Cuba with her. I have lived mostly on my father's plantation in Santa Clara, although for the past few years he has had me pay visits to his plantations in Puerto Rico, Santo Domingo and Mexico. Now, since the death of my mother, my father wishes me to go to Spain and take my place as his son.'

The Duke's lower lip protruded in disbelief, but he said nothing. At a signal from him, the manservant entered and they sat down to dinner – a most excellent dinner, beautifully served. The Duke ate little, although his wine glass beat a continuous tattoo on the table, noisily demanding that it be refilled. The Duchess listlessly moved food around on her plate. Only Mario did full justice to the meal.

'But where have you been since we all came aboard?' The Duchess had not forgotten her unanswered question.

'I have been sleeping. I was very late setting out from Santa Clara, which necessitated my driving all day and all night. As a result, after I fell into bed last night, I knew nothing until my slave awakened me this afternoon to hand me your note. May I be forgiven?' His eyes met hers across the table.

'Possibly.' She gave him back a veiled and questioning look. 'Just possibly, if you promise not to waste so much time sleeping again. It is such an uninteresting occupation.'

'To sleep?'

She glanced quickly at the Duke, then leaned across the table and whispered, 'Damn it, no! To sleep alone.'

Mario stole a glance at the Duke and saw that the old man was already nodding in his chair and, exactly as Frontera had prophesied, a stream of saliva was creeping down his chin, ready to fall on his shirtfront.

'Come, let us walk on deck.' She pushed back her chair. 'That' – she pointed to her husband – 'is not a pretty picture to contemplate and, in truth, I am sick of looking at it. There are pleasanter things to consider.'

'Such as?'

'The blackness of the night enfolding the ocean. The blackness of the night enfolding me. The blackness of the night half obscuring a face close to mine with warm lips, seeking my own, and strong arms wrapped closely around me.'

They closed the door behind them, and paused for a moment in the companionway.

'Then let us go on deck, Cleora, and consider these things.' Mario's lips were close to her ear. 'Perhaps you will find more than you bargained for, Cleora.'

'I've sought much in my life, but never found enough to satisfy me.'

'Then let us hope that tonight you will not be disappointed.'

As they walked down the hall, she halted him, took his arm and with restless fingers pulled back the cuff of his coat, baring his arm as he had done previously. One sharp, pointed fingernail tore through his skin, leaving a thin thread of blood on his arm. He felt her lips press against it and when she raised her head her mouth was redder than before. The tip of her tongue circled her lips.

'Your blood is hot, Mario.'

'It is only warm now, Cleora. I suspect that the darkness of the night will heat it.'

She pointed over his shoulder to the closed door of her cabin. 'Now,' she demanded, 'knowing what is inside, do you wonder why I hate the sound of those damnable words, "Your Grace"?'

Chapter Thirteen

MARIO STRETCHED with satisfied exhaustion, and then nestled in his cheek more closely to the warm flesh beside him. That which had been so wildly provocative a few ecstatic moments before was now comfortably soothing. The one guttering candle hissed in its nearly consumed wax and scattered a dim and dancing light around Mario's cabin. Even as he fought to regain his breath, he was aware of the little, low, moaning sobs of the woman beside him, and he could feel the hard pinnacles of her breasts pressing against him, as his arm drew her closer and his fingers found refuge in the hollow of her shoulders. With his one free hand, he gently lifted her face until his lips felt the warmth of hers, and he whispered, 'Cleora.' In response, the lashes on her cheeks raised slightly, her soft moaning subsided, and she managed a tender smile.

'*Ay, mi Mario,*' she whispered, touching her lips lightly to his. 'Had but your father sent you to Court instead of the Godoy, you would be Prince of the Peace today – the greatest man in Spain.'

'Meaning what, *chiquita*?'

'Meaning that you exceed even His Highness, the great Godoy, in your unusual capabilities.'

'And how do you know?' He was immediately jealous. At this particular moment he had no desire to hear about the prowess of this other stallion.

She nibbled at his lower lip. 'Foolish boy! I talk of the Court of Maria Luisa. There at Court, those unfortunates who have not already experienced the Godoy have heard about him, for in truth the Queen talks about nothing but her Manuel.'

'So then, this grand Court of Spain which I have heard so much about —'

'— Is nothing but a cluster of high-born trollops, headed by the biggest trollop of them all, our Queen, Maria Luisa of Parma, who is seconded most ably by Her Grace of Alba. As for the men – can you blame the women if they have their Godoys, when their husbands are either drunken sots like mine or else lavish all their caresses on pretty Moorish boys?'

He turned his face away, but she drew it back firmly against her lips. 'Think you, then, that Her Grace of Almendares is any better than the rest? Surely you did not think tonight that you were bedded with any schoolgirl.'

'No, Cleora, your fire matched mine.' He laughed softly. 'You fought fire with fire.'

'And mine put yours out. What a pity.' She raised up on one elbow and placed fingers across his lips. 'Shhh – listen!'

He became aware of a soft scratching on the little door that connected his cabin with that of Ramon's. The scratching continued and he could hear Ramon's voice through the paneling, urgently demanding to be heard even though he was speaking softly.

'Your Excellency! Admit me at once! Quickly, if you value your life and hers.'

Mario grabbed the sheet from the floor and threw it over the Duchess, leaped across the room and flung open the door. Ramon stood with lowered eyes, that he might avoid looking at the woman on the bed.

'Quickly!' he warned. 'Have Her Grace come in here with her clothes. In a moment her husband will be here. Hurry!'

Cleora had heard him. With a bound she was out of bed and with one hand scooped up her gown and slippers from the floor. Another step carried her into Ramon's cabin. He closed the door behind her, grabbed a white nightgown that was on the foot of the bed, flung it over Mario's head, pushed him face down on the mattress and started to massage his back with long, even strokes. The door suddenly burst open without even a warning knock and Almendares lurched in the doorway, half collapsing on the threshold. The old man who had waited on them at table was trying to support him.

Ramon, without interrupting the rhythmic motion of his hands on Mario's back, looked up at the intruder and spoke quietly to Mario, whose face was buried in the pillow.

'You have a guest, Your Excellency. His Grace of Almendares has done you the honour of calling on you.'

Mario tried to adjust the voluminous folds of the nightshirt, turned over and sat up in bed. He greeted the Duke with as much dignity as any man could muster with a nightshirt swathed around his neck, bade him enter and be seated.

'Welcome, Your Grace. May I ask to what I owe the honour of this late visit?'

'My wife!' The old man grunted as he slumped into the chair.

'Her Grace? Has something befallen her? Can I help?'

Almendares shook his head from side to side so vigorously that his pendulous cheeks swayed.

'No, you Frontera bastard!' He balanced dangerously forward in the chair in an attempt to point a shaking finger at Mario. 'I came here to get her. Where is she?' The servant reached over and clutched the back of the Duke's coat to keep him from pitching forward on the floor.

'But she isn't here.' Mario's gesture took in the limited space of the cabin and he assumed a properly shocked and surprised expression. 'Why should you seek your wife in my cabin at this hour?'

'Because I know her for the slut she is. Because I know that when she sees any man, particularly a young man like you, she has only one thought in mind —'

'You misjudge both your wife and me, *Señor* Duke or Your Grace or whatever it is they call you. And furthermore, you are drunk.'

'Yes, drunk! Fuller than a Portuguese wineskin lying in the sun. Ha! Drunk? I'm always drunk! And why?'

Mario didn't particularly care why, but he felt that he must answer, if for no other reason than to give Cleora time to dress and leave Ramon's cabin. 'I'm not good at answering riddles.'

'Then I'll tell you why, my boy.' The Duke's voice became overly friendly and confidential. '*De veras*, I'll tell you. Because for the last ten years I've been chasing her away from first one man and then another.' He tried to stand up but fell back in the chair, and his voice changed into a cracked falsetto. 'I warn you, young Frontera, you'll find the bodies of all these fine young men scattered from Santander to Malaga – their firm young flesh rotting along the sides of country roads, polluting the peasants' wells, or gathering dust and corruption in the dungeons of my castles.'

Mario caught the slightest click of a door latch from the next cabin and received a quick signal from Ramon, who stood in the shadows. He arose from the bed and came over to where the Duke sat. Very gently he placed his arms under those of the old man and raised him up, supporting his weight, and turned him toward the door.

'She's not here, Your Grace, as you can see most plainly.

She has not been here. Believe me, sir, I am but too little accustomed to the ways of Spain to think that I could bed myself with a Duchess an hour after meeting her. I left Her Grace seeking the coolness of the night air on deck. Unfortunately my dinner did not set well on my stomach and I was forced to excuse myself from her company. That is why you found me as I was when you entered. My slave has healing in his hands; he was trying to alleviate my discomfort.'

The Duke leaned against Mario and tried to focus his eyes on him. Once more he became friendly with a maudlin intimacy. 'You're a good boy, Frontera. No, you're not Frontera, are you? I've forgotten what your name is, but you're a good boy. You're Cuban and not Spanish, that's why! Good boy!' He started for the door, with Mario's assistance, but suddenly he stopped, stiffened and threw Mario's arms down. He stood alone, weaving back and forth, then lunged for the floor and picked up the gold belt the Duchess had been wearing. 'And you're a goddamned liar, you. . . .'

Mario reached over quickly and took the belt from his hands. As he got it in his own hands, he squeezed tightly until he could feel the frail links of gold part company under the pressure of his fingers. He held out the broken pieces.

'Possibly you did not observe, *Señor* Duke, that the belt is in two parts. While on deck, your wife caught it on a nail and broke it. I told her my slave would mend it.' Out of the corner of his eye, he saw Ramon slip out the small door. 'But when I reached here I was so ill I had only one thought in mind – to find a convenient basin, or spew my vomit on the floor. The belt must have slipped from my fingers in my haste.'

The Duke shook his head and made a grab for the belt. He examined it closely but seemed still unsatisfied. The belt dropped from his hands to the floor and he buried his face on Mario's chest and started to weep. Between his drunken sobs, Mario caught the words, 'I love her, I love her.' He took a step, lifting the old man along with him. As they neared the door, he heard a knock. Ramon had silently re-entered the room by the other door and now went quickly to answer.

The Duchess of Almendares stood in the doorway, her gown hanging loosely from her shoulders.

'I did not think to find you supporting my husband,' she said to Mario, 'and why he should be here at all is a mystery to me. I was passing your door and saw a light under it, so I stopped to inquire if your slave had by chance mended my belt. My gown fits me ill without it.' She followed Mario's eyes to the floor where it lay, a thin thread of gold on the red Turkey carpet.

The Duke regarded her for a long moment.

'You broke your belt, Rosa?' His voice had a plaintive note of hopefulness.

'Yes, Fernando. I caught it on a nail up on deck and San Mateo offered to have his slave mend it for me.'

'And that is the truth, Rosita?'

'But naturally, Fernando. Otherwise how would the belt be here, or why should I be inquiring about it?' She turned to Mario. 'I hope your sudden illness is better. Perhaps it was just a touch of seasickness.'

'Take me back to my cabin.' The Duke lurched from Mario to his own servant. 'Help me back, Rosita, and I'll believe you because I want to. But how well I know that you are all lying to me, and that you and Frontera have been rolling on that bed!'

'Hush, Fernando.' She beckoned to the old servant to take him. 'Hush.'

'But I'll get him.' He waved a feeble finger at Mario. 'I'll get him as I got all the others you played with, Rosa – all the other strong, handsome boys that you've slept with. I got them all, one by one, and I'll get him too.' He stumbled out the door.

The Duchess followed him, turning to glance fleetingly over her shoulder at Mario. '*Es la verdad*. He tells the truth,' she murmured wistfully. 'They are all dead.'

The door closed and Mario sank down on the bed. He found that his hands were trembling.

'Many thanks, Ramoncito, for your quick wit.'

'*No hay de que*, Mario. But I think you have made another enemy. However, let us not worry about it. The Duke was drunk and perhaps he will have forgotten about it by morning.'

'Mayhap, Ramon, and yet in making an enemy I find I have also proved a friend.' Mario reached down and took Ramon's hand in his own. 'A real friend.'

Chapter Fourteen

THE NEXT week was a slow succession of monotonously happy days for Mario. He was experiencing for the first time the lonely isolation of grandeur. His cabin and those of the Almendares had no connexion with the rest of the ship. They were entirely apart – separated. He ate his meals alone in his cabin, with only the attentive Ramon for company. In between times he paced that part of the deck which was divided from the other passengers by a carved and gilded wooden balustrade.

On the rare occasions when the Duke and Duchess appeared on deck, they exchanged formal bows and inconsequential words. He both hoped and feared that Cleora might appear alone, but she sequestered herself in her cabin and was always accompanied on deck by her husband. Although she greeted him coolly with correct and meaningless little words, her eyes smouldered with fire when she looked at him. The Duke spoke to him absently, with studied politeness accompanied by a suspicious, questioning look in his red-rimmed eyes.

Mario would have welcomed some meeting with the other passengers who strolled the common deck below him but as he watched them he found them a dull and uninteresting lot. There was a giggling group of Cuban schoolgirls who were being shepherded to some convent in Spain by several horse-faced, white-coifed nuns. Some of the older girls might have been attractive had they been able to display their charms in anything but the clumsy long black dresses they wore. They did steal covert glances at him as he walked alone, and he was aware that they were discussing him, but they were far too young and virginal to attract him, even had they been able to elude the sombre dragons who continually hovered around them.

Mario was thoroughly bored with security and happiness and sleeping alone. This was the first time he had ever been faced with the necessity of amusing himself, and he did not have the slightest idea of how to go about it. Ramon sensed the mood he was in and opened one of the boxes that Frontera had sent on board. From it, he produced a number of books which

Mario tried to read. They were replete with the languishing words of love, gracefully twined into the honeyed garlands of Spanish poetry, but to Mario they were nothing but words and he found the printed page a poor substitute for warm flesh and willing lips.

Late one afternoon, he threw down the book he had been perusing, stood up, stretched his arms until they touched the low ceiling of the cabin. A sudden lurch of the ship caused him to clutch the bedpost for support. The floor of his cabin was no longer level, and a collection of loose objects started to roll across it. Slowly the floor righted itself, only to cant sharply to the other side. He balanced his way to the door and had some difficulty in making his way up on deck.

A violent blast of wind struck him in the face. A noisy gale, damp with sea spray, stung his face with salt. After the uneventful days of sun-drenched monotony, he felt a wild excitement in the turmoil of the grey-green seas, churning themselves into white foam. He felt like answering the scream of the wind in the rigging with some meaningless yell of wild abandon, and envied the quick movements of the sailors climbing aloft.

As the storm increased, the seas rose and the towering waves swept over the deck, battering the side of the ship and drenching him until, soaked to the skin, he sought the shelter of his cabin.

With his hands burning from desperately clutching at wet ropes, his face rimed with salt and his clothes dripping, he arrived below to find a nervous Ramon, kneeling in the corner, telling his beads with quick movements of his long fingers. At Mario's return, he looked up with relief, tucked the rosary in his pocket and started to remove Mario's wet clothing.

'Are you frightened, Ramon?' Mario noticed the livid colour on the dark skin.

'No, Mario.'

'Then why do you pray?'

'For you, Mario.'

'For me? But why?'

'Because you had been gone some time and I did not know where you were. I would have searched for you but I feared that you might return and I would not be here.'

Mario laughed and slapped him on the back. 'Ramoncito, you worry far too much about me but – yes, I do appreciate it. I've been all right.' He reached out and grabbed the foot of the bed as the ship gave a vicious dive. 'Holy Mother! One more of those and we'll all hit the bottom.'

'I even went to the Duke's cabin, looking for you,' Ramon continued.

'And how is His goddamned Grace?'

'Very ill, so the Duchess told me. I didn't see him, but she asked me to wait a minute while she sat down and wrote this for me to give you.' He produced a note, but before Mario could take it, Ramon warned him, 'Be careful, Mario; she is a dangerous woman.'

'Dangerous?' Mario's eyebrow lifted. 'Yes, dangerous but most delightful.' He read the few words that the note contained. 'Ah, the poor Duke! He is violently seasick and frightened out of his wits. He burns candles before three separate shrines while his lovely lady feeds him opium pills and arranges for a rendezvous with me at midnight.'

'Where, Don Mario?'

'Here, in my cabin.'

'*Madre de Dios!* I tell you it is ill-conceived. We did not fool the Duke the other night, although he had no way to prove we were lying. He is not convinced. He would like to believe his wife is innocent, but he knows well that she is not. The second time you will not convince him so easily.'

'But he is so stupid, Ramon.'

'No, Don Mario, he is not. Until he married her he was one of the ablest men in Spain. She has led him a merry chase, until he drowns himself in wine. Please believe me, Don Mario. If you value your life, leave her alone. Let me go now, let me tell her that you too are sick – even that you are vomiting all over the bed and in no fit condition to receive her. I beg of you.'

'Ramon, Ramon!' Another lurch threw them together. 'How right you are and how truly sensible. I would do well to follow your advice. But.... Know you that it is a week or more since Her Grace paid me that first call? And think you that even if the gates of hell were to open before me, I could resist another call from her? No, Ramon! In such things a man cannot be prudent. For such delights he would gladly risk his life and, after a week on board ship, I'll gladly risk mine for only a few moments with the lovely *Duquesa*. Did she say midnight?'

Ramon agreed, with a worried shake of his head.

'Then let's prepare for her. It is close to that hour now. First, let us discard these wet clothes. Then let us find something warm and dry, but something with a minimum of buttons.'

Ramon produced the India silk robe, and Mario put it on. Then Mario dismissed the slave and was glad to see Ramon's worried face disappear through the door of his own cabin.

The little room seemed too bright with so many swinging candles, so he extinguished all but one, then propped himself up in bed with the book of poetry. Now, with the prospect of Cleora's immediate arrival, the printed words of love and passion took on a new meaning – resolving themselves into the kind spoken by a man and a woman. They actually made sense now; he could understand them.

When her soft rap sounded and she lifted the latch at his whispered words of welcome, the door opened to catapult her into his arms. They found themselves in a welter of silk robe and taffeta gown on the floor, and as they tried to arise, another wave hit the ship and sent them sprawling on the carpet again. By now, they were so convulsed with langhter and the ship was pitching so violently, it was impossible for them to gain the bed, much less remain on it.

In the frantic melee of arms and legs, their lips met and his body pinioned hers to the floor, his weight holding her in one place long enough for him to speak to her.

'A wild night, Cleora *mia*.'

She hesitated a moment before answering. 'You mean the storm outside.'

'Not entirely. An even wilder storm rages within me,' he answered.

'Then I think the night will become even wilder.'

She was right. The wind and the waves that battered the ship were nothing to the untamed force that was released in Mario's cabin. All the pent-up longings of the last week that Mario had been trying to quench expended themselves, matched equally by the ardour with which she responded to them. It was as though the sea, the wind, the black hurrying clouds, and the driving storm had all become a part of their wild union.

As they lay upon the floor, it seemed as though they themselves controlled the movements of the ship, not the storm outside. Each wild downward pitch of the ship was derived from Mario's raging force. Each sudden rise of the ship was in response to Cleora's lifting of herself to meet his demands. The howl of the wind was nothing more than his lungs' quick intake of air, and the taut singing of the ropes as the wind played on them was only the soft, moaning noises from her throat.

The sea bore down upon the helpless ship, lifting it, tossing it, then dropping its relentless weight upon it. The sea raged with unquenchable fury, trying to crush the vessel in its brutal hands. Then, for a single second, it would forget its boisterous raging and become softly gentle, playing with the ship like some delicious bauble, caressing it with the tender touch of a gently slapping wave, only to engulf it the next moment in a turbulent whirlpool.

The ship resisted, struggled, fought against this all-enfolding embrace, but the sea increased its fury. The shriek of the gale mounted, causing the very skeleton of the ship to tremble and shudder as the sea gained full possession, swept over it and conquered it. One monstrous wave – a very mountain of a wave – broke over the ship, sweeping everything before it with an irresistible force.

The ship lurched way over on its side, paused, trembled for a moment, then slowly righted itself.

Mario rolled on the floor and Cleora clutched feebly for security to keep from sliding among the welter of clothes, bottles and furniture that pitched from one side to the other over the cabin floor.

'We must have hit something,' Mario gasped out. 'Quick, Cleora! Get to your cabin and put on warm clothes. The ship must be sinking!'

She managed to scramble along the floor, clutching her gown around her, and creep out the door on her hands and knees. Mario searched frantically through the litter, found a pair of trousers and pulled them on. Then crawled over to the opened door and fought his way crabwise along the corridor. He saw Cleora ahead of him and waited till he had assured himself that she had gained the door of her room.

A sharp gust of wind swept along the corridor, bringing with it the tang of salt and seaweed. Mario looked up and saw the captain slowly making his way down the hall, bracing himself against the wall with each step. When he reached Mario, he helped him to his feet, clamping Mario's hands on to the rail which ran along the companionway.

'Are you all right, Your Excellency?'

'Quite.'

'And the Duke and his lady?'

'I was just about to go to his cabin now. What has happened?'

'There is no immediate cause for alarm.' The captain was shouting to make himself heard against the wind that funnelled through the hall. 'We have lost one of our masts, but the ship is undamaged otherwise. We are only a short distance from the Azores and we can make Ponta Delgada safely.'

'I'll so inform the Duke.' Mario started to edge along the wall.

'No, return to your cabin and do not leave it again. All passengers are restricted to their cabins to insure their safety.' The captain opened the door of the Duke's cabin and stepped inside.

One streaking candle in its swinging glass shade had managed to survive. By its light, Mario crawled hand over hand along the guard rail. He halted for a moment, as the ship made a sudden headlong dive, waiting for it to right itself. Just as it started to climb on its upward course, the door at the end of the corridor opened again and the blast that came through it extinguished the one remaining candle.

In the dim blackness of the doorway, Mario saw the darker silhouette of a man. As he watched, the man slowly raised one arm high above his head and, in the second that followed, Mario felt a streak of fire flash through his left shoulder. His hand instinctively sought the source of the pain and encountered the smooth wooden handle of a knife protruding from his shoulder.

He managed to keep his grip on the rail, stumbled ahead two or three steps, then fell against the door of his cabin. It opened and Mario pitched unconscious on to the floor.

Ramon had been awaiting him. With difficulty he pulled Mario across the floor to the bed, then, slowly and most carefully, he extracted the knife, stanching the fountain of blood with a wadded corner of the sheet. Mario's eyelids flickered once; then he was quiet.

Chapter Fifteen

TWO DAYS later, just as the first pale streaks of dawn were bringing into jagged silhouette the dark, blue-green mountains of the Azores, the *Tres Castillos* limped slowly into the welcoming harbour of Ponta Delgada. The city rose in a froth of white, pink and pistache houses and climbed steeply from the edge of the water to wander up into the hills and mountains and finally lose itself in the all-pervading greenness.

Ramon stood silently a few paces removed from Their Graces of Almendares. Nobody on board had slept much the last two nights, least of all Ramon, who had sat watchfully by Mario's bed. Perhaps more through prayer than through skill, he had managed to stanch the flow of blood. Mario now lay below in a barely breathing coma, his face drained of all colour, his hands white and lifeless upon the sheets.

Ramon sensed, rather than saw, the Duke approach him alongside the rail. He kept his eyes on the distant city and the mountains behind it, and did not turn as the Duke stopped beside him.

'How is your master? He seems to be the only one of the passengers not on deck this morning. I trust he suffered no ill effects from the storm.'

'Not exactly from the storm, Your Grace.'

The Duke regarded him sullenly.

'Not from the storm? Then he is still indisposed? Perhaps a recurrence of the ailment he had a few nights ago. The boy must have a weak stomach.'

'No, hardly that, Your Grace.'

Almendares leaned over and spat in the water, then turned quickly to Ramon. 'Less impertinence, slave. Answer my questions properly. What did happen to the young fool?'

Ramon felt suddenly alone. With Mario unconscious below, he was, for the first time in his life, entirely without the protection of a master. Everything was now entirely up to him. He must make all the plans and take all the initiative. To offend the Duke now would have serious consequences. It could separate Ramon from Mario and leave Mario unprotected.

He bowed humbly to the Duke.

'There was no intention of impertinence, Your Grace. My master is ill. He stepped out on deck night before last during the height of the storm and became wet to the skin. He developed a fever which continued all day yesterday, although I am glad to say this morning he is somewhat better.'

The Duke seemed a bit confused. 'Fever? Is that all? Rumour is that he met with an accident.'

Ramon offered an ingratiating smile. 'No, Your Grace, merely a fever.'

'Then I repeat. Young Frontera is a weakling. First his belly aches and now he shivers with ague. Bah! When I was his age I could ride all day in the rain and ride all night in bed.' He turned and started back towards the Duchess, who had moved near enough to overhear the conversation. Halfway towards her, the Duke stopped, rubbed his unshaven chin, then turned again to face Ramon.

'The captain tells me that we shall be three days in port, waiting for a new mast to be refitted. Her Grace and I shall seek accommodations in some hotel on shore, rather than remain in these cramped quarters. We would be happy if Mateo would accompany us. My servant is somewhat of a physician and perhaps he could help him.'

Ramon looked beyond the Duke to see the Duchess shaking her head. It was an emphatic negative. At least she was on Mario's side. Her gesture cued Ramon's answer.

'If you will excuse me, I will go below and tell him of your invitation. He will, I am sure, appreciate your help, and I shall return and give you his decision.'

He bowed quickly and left. He had intended only to go on deck to appraise himself of their nearness to shore; he had not meant to leave Mario unprotected for so long. When he unlocked the door he was relieved to find Mario as he had left him. He pulled down the sheet to examine the red splotched bandage around Mario's chest. The blood around the edges had dried and, although the red centre was still damp, there was no evidence of recent bleeding.

Ramon sat down in the chair and watched the slow, rhythmic rise and fall of Mario's chest. He was faced with a problem – a most difficult one. He had no doubt but that the attempted assassination had been arranged by the Duke. Which one of the sailors had been hired to do it? Was there more than one in on the plot? When would he try again? Two things were certain: Mario was not safe on board ship, and certainly he would not be safe in any lodgings occupied by the Duke. For the present he and Mario were both prisoners in the little cabin. He must temporize. But how?

He locked the door of Mario's cabin from the inside and piled all of Mario's sea chests in front of it. Then he went through the door into his own cabin and the door which led to the corridor. He stepped out and locked it. Back on deck, he saw that Almendares and the Duchess were still beside the rail. He walked towards them, trying to hide his worry.

The Duchess saw him first and nudged her husband's arm. His smile towards Ramon had every evidence of being cordial.

'The lad is better?' He seemed genuinely concerned.

'Indeed he is, Your Grace. He was awake and asking for news and breakfast. I repeated your message to him and he is most grateful.'

Ramon looked down over the rail. A fleet of small rowboats had appeared, manned by strong, dark men with smiling faces. They were managing to push the big ship close up to the stone quay, warping it inch by inch to an accompaniment of straining muscles and much good-natured shouting. In a few moments they would be alongside.

He gestured towards the preparation of the gangplank. 'Since Your Grace is leaving so soon, would you be good enough to do my master a favour? When you have found lodgings, would you have your man look up a coach and send it for the Count?'

The Duke nodded in satisfaction, 'Indeed I shall. I do not know where we will be staying in the god-forsaken hole, but we'll find some place even if we have to turn the governor out of his palace. As soon as we do, I'll have my man come back with a coach.'

Ramon was voluble in his thanks and excused himself, returning below to watch over his master.

Part of the problem had been solved. Now, with the Duke out of the way and quite convinced that Mario would join him later, there was at least an hour in which Ramon could seek an answer to the rest of the problem.

The movement of the ship stopped. He paused by the bed on his way to look out the porthole and laid his hand on Mario's forehead. It was hot and dry with fever but his breathing was regular and some colour had managed to creep back into his face.

Whatever was to be done had to be done quickly. Ramon looked out of the porthole, wishing that he and Mario could quit the ship – go somewhere, anywhere – only not remain here or accept the Almendares' invitation. The little boats which had struggled so valiantly to dock the big *Tres Castillos* were now departing. Their work done, the men rowed leisurely towards the town, joking with one another, calling back and forth between the boats.

One of the boatmen noticed Ramon's face in the porthole and cried out to him, pointing to a basket of oranges which he held up. 'Fresh,' he cried. 'Cheap!'

Ramon waved his hand in return, motioning the man to come closer. A few sweeps of his oars brought him directly under the porthole, and he looked up and smiled again. Ramon examined him closely. He was a man of middle age, his black hair grizzled around the temples, with a face so frank and open, so honestly bright and cheerful, that Ramon immediately felt he could trust him. And with that realization of confidence, an idea was born.

'Tie your boat at the quay and come on board. Bring the oranges with you. But perhaps I can do far more business with you than merely buying a basket of fruit. Think you that you can locate this cabin?'

'*Si, senhor.*'

'Then come on board as quickly as you can. I will be waiting for you with the door of my cabin open.'

Ramon went into his own cabin and stood in the opened doorway to the corridor. He had not long to wait, for in another moment the man appeared with the basket of oranges in his hand. Once again Ramon examined him closely, and his second impression was even better than the first. Surely the man looked honest, a hard-working peasant type with patched and mended clothes that were immaculately clean.

'Your name?' Ramon did not waste time in formalities.

'Joao Almeiras. I have a farm up in the mountains behind the city, and I do some fishing too.'

'What I shall ask you to do, Dom Joao, is neither illegal nor dishonest. It has to do with saving the life of a very important person who is in great danger. Whatever you do will help in righting a wrong which has been done him. I'll pay you a hundred duros in Spanish gold. I don't know what that is in Portugal —'

'A hundred duros in gold? My god, it's a fortune. Even if what you want me to do were dishonest I should be tempted.'

'But it isn't. Now listen. My name is Ramon. I am a slave and belong to His Excellency the Count of San Mateo of Spain. He is in the next room. He has been badly injured and although he is already at the point of death, there are those who are still determined to kill him. I must protect him, yet I cannot leave him alone to go ashore and seek help. We are strangers here. So, *Senhor*, I am putting myself in your hands. Can we get him off this boat? Could you accommodate him in your house until he gets well?'

Joao reached out and grabbed Ramon's hand. 'For a hundred gold duros, *Senhor*, he can buy my house and have it for his own. My wife is an excellent nurse. She will care for him. A hundred gold duros! I'll be his slave for life.'

Ramon smiled. 'I already am one, but not only because he owns me. However, now the problem is to get him off the boat.'

'It is most simple,' Joao assured him. 'I will get a friend of mine who has a large wagon and a team of oxen. We'll fill the wagon with straw and I'll drive back to the pier. Then we'll carry your master across the gangplank.'

Ramon led him out the door, followed him and locked the door behind them. 'Stay here for a moment, Dom Joao. I shall return immediately. I have just thought of something else which will make our departure more than welcome.'

Joao waited in front of the door as the minutes dragged by. The more he thought about the matter, the stranger it seemed; but so far he had everything to gain and nothing to lose. A hundred gold duros would make him independent for life and if, added to that, he could save the life of the young man in there on the bed. . . .

Ramon came hastening back. 'It's all settled. This ship will be glad to see the last of us. Go now, Dom Joao, and get the wagon. I will pack what is needed; the rest can be stored with factors here. How can we carry His Excellency?'

'Two oars and two coats. We slip the oars through the sleeves of the coats. It makes a stretcher. Many's the poor devil drowned in fishing that has been carried to his home that way.'

Ramon waited until he saw the door of the companionway open and close, and then re-entered Mario's room. He hastily emptied two valises, went to the drawers of the wardrobe and took out two heavy leather bags which gave out a reassuring clink of gold as he placed them in one of the valises. He filled it up with Mario's clothes, then went into his own cabin and brought back some of his own. Finally he dumped the contents of another box – watches, fobs, rings and pins – in with the clothes.

He had not long to wait until Dom Joao appeared. This time he had his oars with him. The sleeves of two of Mario's coats were slipped over them and Mario was lifted on to them.

Slowly, one careful step after another, they carried Mario out on deck. The captain and the other officers were standing in a group by the gangplank but, as Ramon and Joao neared them, they walked quickly away. Ramon noticed that they were holding their handkerchiefs to their noses. As they passed the group, one of the men looked down at Mario on the improvised stretcher, noticed the pallor of his face and shook his head.

'He's so young. Poor fellow! And the plague is always fatal.'

Chapter Sixteen

MARIO OPENED his eyes wide and focused them on the low blotched ceiling overhead, then let his gaze wander slowly down over the plain white-plastered wall to the stout woman who was seated near him, busily knitting. She had iron-grey hair drawn tightly back into a knot on top of her head, and she appeared kind and motherly to Mario.

He had awakened with an intense awareness of being alive – but just where, he did not know. The low room with the vista of waving green branches through the tiny window was certainly not his cabin on board the *Tres Castillos*, and this wholesome woman whose flashing needles clicked back and forth in a tangle of grey wool was certainly not Ramon. He could remember a little now: the lightning flash of pain, the opening door of his cabin – but then nothing. Carefully, so as not to attract the attention of the strange woman, he slid his hand under the bedclothes and encountered the mummified wrappings that enclosed his chest and restricted his breathing.

For all her close attention to her knitting, the woman had seen the movement of his hand. She put down her needles, got up from her chair and tiptoed over to the bed. She looked down at him, and then saw him staring wide-eyed back at her. She turned towards the door as Mario reached out for her hand.

'Where am I, *Señora* – and who are you?'

'*Un momento.*' She disengaged her hand and felt his forehead. 'Ah, you are quit of the fever.' She smiled encouragingly at him then ran to the door and flung it open.

'Ramon, *Senhor* Ramon. Come! He is awake.'

'Mario, my Mario!' Ramon cried, entering the room and coming over to the bed. 'You are yourself at last. *Gracias a Dios!*'

'But where am I?'

'Quiet, my Mario. You are safe and well, and that is enough to think about for the present. Do not fret yourself by trying to understand too much too soon. See ... *Senhora* Almeiras comes now with something for you.'

She bustled in and set down on a low table the wooden tray she was carrying with the steaming bowl on it. She motioned to Ramon to lift Mario a little in the bed, scolded him for not doing it entirely to her liking, and then put one strong arm behind Mario and lifted him gently against her capacious bosom.

'The Holy Mother has granted our prayers, *Senhor* Ramon. Now, with my nursing, he will get well.'

Mario looked quizzically across at Ramon. 'Each time she speaks, I think I understand her, and yet I am not sure.'

'That is because she is speaking Portuguese. Many of the words are similar to Spanish.'

'Then we are in Portugal?'

'Not quite. We are in the Azores. There is much to tell you. But first drink the broth that the *Señora* has been making for you now these three days. Each day she has added another chicken to make it rich.'

Mario dutifully opened his mouth. The broth warmed his throat and stomach and gradually he felt his strength returning to him.

When he had finished the last spoonful he looked sternly at Ramon. 'And now it is time, Ramon, for you to explain how we got here and who these people are.'

'Please, Mario – be patient. Wait until Papa Almeiras comes. He is not far. And then all of us together will tell you the story.'

As Ramon spoke, the good woman gently transferred Mario back on to the pillow, which she propped into a more comfortable position, and then set back in her chair, smiling at both of them.

'We have been most fortunate, Mario,' Ramon continued, 'in finding this family. They are fine people. I sensed it immediately when I first saw Papa Almeiras waving his basket of oranges.'

'Oranges! What in the name of God have oranges to do with our being here? Make sense, Ramon, or, by God, I will have you flogged!'

But just as Ramon was about to answer, Papa Almeiras burst into the room, and suddenly he and Mama Almeiras were engaged in high-pitched conversation, of which Mario understood hardly a word except his own name. Then there was an introduction to Papa, who promptly sat down on the chair his wife had vacated for him. After this commotion subsided, Ramon leaned forward over the footboard of the bed and began his explanation. But it was a difficult process: no sooner would Ramon start a sentence than one or the other Almeiras would interrupt to corroborate his statement with enthusiastic smiles and gestures, and the torrent of foreign words would be set off again. Finally, however, a semblance of order was established, and Mario was slowly able to piece together a coherent narrative.

After having told the officers of the ship that Mario was coming down with the plague – thus making them only too willing to be rid of him – Ramon had hailed Papa Almeiras (which was where the basket of oranges came in), and together they had carried Mario off the ship on the improvised two-oared stretcher. Once they got Mario to the farmhouse they had felt safe: the fact that everyone thought Mario had the plague had kept all visitors – especially any whom the Duke might have sent to do him harm – away from the farmhouse. Only Ramon, Mama and Papa Almeiras, and their six stalwart sons, who took turns guarding the house, and their wives, knew the truth – that Mario had suffered a knife wound in his chest inflicted by a sailor on board the *Tres Castillos* in the pay of the vengeful Duke of Almendares. And the Duke, evidently convinced that Mario indeed had the plague and would die anyway, had decided it was not necessary to hasten what he thought was the inevitable. In fact, he and the Duchess were sailing away on the *Tres Castillos* today, and if Mario had been able to look out the window he would have seen, far down the mountain, the bellying sails of the ship as it moved out of the harbour.

Mario's convalescene was probably the happiest and most peaceful time of his whole life. He lost track of the passing hours, was aware only of Mama's scuttling back and forth between the kitchen and the bedroom, of Papa's beaming solicitude, of Ramon's ever-watchfulness. For two days there seemed to be a steady procession of Almeiras passing by his bed – six big, dark young men with flashing white smiles; six big, dark young women who appeared with all-enveloping black cloaks and huge hoods which they discarded to reveal gaily embroidered peasant dresses beneath them. At frequent intervals there was a stream of young Almeiras who were carried in arms, toddled along alone or tiptoed in pairs to gaze in silent, dark-eyed wonderment at the great patient.

The bowls of broth gave way to more satisfying meals – chickens roasted to a tender turn; morsels of fish cooked with a variety of sauces; wholesome dark bread, hot from the oven, with freshly churned butter; glasses of frothy milk and cups of hot, full-flavoured coffee – and always Mama Almeiras to urge one more morsel on him, just one more bit.

After a week of this, Mario was finally allowed to get up. The wound in his shoulder was nearly healed and bothered him only slightly. The big bandage had been discarded for a smaller one on which was smeared some pleasant-smelling green mess which Mama kept in a pot by the fire. Mario was almost well; he was eating like a horse and, most important, his mind was clear. The Almeiras boys had resolved themselves into distinct personages instead of brown faces with white smiles, and Mario was even beginning to understand a little Portuguese.

He sat under the tree one afternoon, watching the moving flecks of brilliant sunlight on the green grass. He had never known that life could hold such contentment. The Almeiras boys with their wives and children – how happy they were! They had their snug little houses, their land and the sea, and the produce they reaped from both. These were the boundaries of their existence – these and the sturdy sons and daughters they were raising to live in other little white houses, to till the land and fish the ocean. They had their small problems, yes, but they were also able to smooth away whatever the trouble might be, to wipe it out in their joy of life in the daytime, and in the dark intimacy of their beds at night. He envied them.

Ramon appeared in the doorway and Mario called him over, indicating a place on the bench beside him.

'Today marks the end of the Count of San Mateo, Ramon,' he said.

'I do not understand.'

'I've decided something. I do not want to go to Spain. I'm fed up with this life, and with everything in the past. Believe me, Ramon. I'm a different person now from what I was in Havana. I'm done with it all – with all the cheating and lying and whoring. Furthermore, I'm thoroughly convinced that life at the Court of Spain would be little different from life on the waterfront of Havana. There would be the same lying and cheating and whoring – if Her Grace of Almendares is any sample. Perhaps the sheets would be a little cleaner, the beds a little softer, and the girls' bodies a little whiter, but in the end it would all be the same.'

Ramon plucked a piece of grass and examined it. 'And so?'

'And so, I'm about to become the seventh son of Dom Joao Almeiras and buy myself a little white house with a plot of land, and marry myself a wife like those of the Almeiras brothers, and raise a brood of youngsters.'

'Most admirable, Your Excellency. And when the five hundred duros, minus the hundred we shall pay to Dom Joao, are gone, what will you do then? No, this life is not for you.'

'Then you had rather I go on to Spain and become a pincushion for the Duke's hired bravos, or those of my uncle? He is probably already waiting for the *Tres Castillos* to dock, to welcome me with a length of naked steel!'

Ramon shook his head. 'That I do not wish. But, Your Excellency, you have an obligation to perform. You accepted your father's proposal – and accepted it willingly. As a gentleman, you must fulfil your obligation.'

'Yes, but if I had been killed on the *Tres Castillos*? If the knife had been only a few inches lower?'

'But you were not killed, Your Excellency.'

Mario turned and faced him with impatient anger. 'I thought it was understood that between us I was to be "Mario," not some stupid title!'

'I am only trying to remind you, Mario, that you are also the Count of San Mateo, son of the Marques de la Frontera Baja. And as the Count, you are on your way to Spain, first to Cadiz, and then to take your place as your father's son at Court.'

Mario's thoughts travelled back to that last day in Havana, to the man whom he had met in the lobby of the hotel, the man who had embraced him before all of Havana and called him 'my son'. There was something more than that acceptance of him, regardless of what Frontera might have tried to imply. There was considerably more to it than merely using him as bait for an assassin's dagger. He recalled the elaborate plans his father had made, the days in prison, his purported execution, and the plentiful and minute preparations for his journey. But most of all he remembered the look on his father's face.

Yes, he was the son of Frontera Baja. Ramon was right. And he had an obligation to fulfil.

Chapter Seventeen

AS MARIO did not possess a single word of English, and as the officers on the ship were equally inadequate in Spanish, he was at a loss for much new company during the long voyage to Cadiz. Except for an occasional slow walk on deck, he spent most of his time in the first mate's cabin, which had been allotted to him. Talking with Ramon became his chief occupation. There was much that Ramon could teach him. Why not begin now, Mario thought. Certainly there was nothing else to do.

There followed a series of lessons in the cabin. Ramon was in turn the King of Spain, enthroned in the cabin's only armchair; a stern Frontera Baja; a simpering Queen Maria Luisa; and a coy and amorous Duchess of Almendares. Mario learned how to address them all, with exactly the correct inflection in 'Your Majesty' or 'Your Grace' for those who ranked above him and the correspondingly appropriate inflection for those who ranked below.

Ramon seemed to know everything. He had absorbed knowledge like a sponge while he had been valet to the Captain General of Cuba. From him Mario learned to talk without interlarding his speech with the argot of the Havana streets. He learned how to carry on a conversation that spoke much but said little, and to develop those niceties of words which would mark him as a man of the world. He learned the correct way to do many things he had never thought important – the right pressure that his lips should make on a hand he kissed, the polite way to pare a peach, the correct cravat to wear with court dress, and the most elegant manner of offering his arm to a lady.

But there was much for him to learn that Ramon could not teach him. He must learn to use the sword, for the sword was the weapon of a *caballero*. Then, even though he became familiar with a sword, he must learn to shoot a pistol, as more duels were now being fought with pistols than with rapiers. Then there was the matter of horsemanship. Every gentleman must know how to ride – even the Spanish word for gentleman was caballero, a rider of horses. Swords and pistols and horses! Three things he must learn as soon as possible, because they were all important to his position in life – and to his safety.

The bright days passed. Mario ate his meals with the officers of the ship and sat at the place of honour on the captain's right hand. But, except for bowing to each other, and the captain's '*Como esta?*' which Mario managed to answer by a 'Very-good-thank-you-sir,' there was almost no conversation. God help them! These English were a sober lot; they ate their meals in silence, with scarcely a smile or a word to each other. And yet Mario felt that they were strong men – men who did not wear their hearts on their sleeves, men of great hidden resources.

The miles fell behind as the *Pride of Ramsgate* cut the waves, curling them over into white foam until finally a dim coastline appeared on the horizon. Spain, the mother! Spain, who spawned Cuba and Mexico and Puerto Rico and Peru and all the amazing motley brood that clung to her skirts and carried her language from the Atlantic to the Pacific. This was Spain at last – even though it looked scarcely unique to Mario, until they sailed up the river and the great city of Cadiz burst upon them in all its regal whiteness – the oldest city in Europe it was said, older even than Rome. Cadiz of Andalusia, which had once been Cadiz of the Moors, and before that Gades of the Romans, and before that Godir of the Phoenicians.

The ship tied up at a stone quay not far from the centre of the city, almost within the shadow of the soaring towers of the cathedral. When they were docked and the gangplank lowered, Mario solemnly shook hands with the good captain and the other officers, and walked ashore, followed by Ramon. Mario stamped his foot on the cobbles and watched the dust rise. His journey was ended and this was Spain, and the dust which settled on his shoes was Spanish dust.

Surrounded by his luggage, he stood in the noisy crowd, an island of indecision. Except for the name of Baltazar Ruiz, he knew no person, nor had he the slightest idea of where to go. Ramon, with a quick look around and a word of warning not to desert the luggage, slipped away, only to reappear in a few minutes with a rented carriage. Its voluble driver, with much waving of hands, assured them that he knew exactly where the Moor, Don Baltazar, lived, and would drive them there. In between his forceful gestures, he mentioned a price, but

Ramon was dissatisfied and started to bicker with him. Mario cut the argument short by entering the carriage and telling the man to shut his mouth and help Ramon load the luggage.

They circled the little plaza in front of the cathedral and turned down through a series of narrow streets until they reached the broad avenue of the Alameda which followed along the bank of the river. The close-packed houses gave way to trees and greenery, to gardens and large mansions surrounded by high walls. They continued until they reached an old house, set back from the street, which stared blindly at them with a blank and windowless façade.

Where the other houses had been bright in white and pastel colours, this house stood alone and austere in its earthy brownish ochre, its forbidding aspect relieved only by the dark plumes of cypress trees towering above the red tiles of the roof. The heavy iron gate in the surrounding wall was closed and locked, but the coachman got down off the box and pulled a heavy brass chain which set off a doleful clanging. For a few moments nothing happened; then a boy appeared in the yawning darkness of the doorway. With steps so slow they scarcely disturbed the straight hanging folds of the robe he wore, he came down the gravelled driveway to the gate, unlocked it and stepped outside.

'This,' he informed them in passable Spanish, 'is the house of Moulay ibn Hussein, the representative of His Magnificence the Sultan of Morocco.'

'Known in the land of Their Most Catholic Majesties as Baltazar Ruiz.' The coachman pointed a black-rimmed finger at the boy. 'Exactly what we want, *muchacho*. We have a young gentleman here and this is where he wants to go.'

The boy came nearer and looked up into the carriage at Mario.

'Are you His Excellency, the Conde de San Mateo, whom we were to expect on the *Tres Castillos?* But no – you cannot be. We were informed that he was dead.'

'I am the Conde de San Mateo,' Mario answered. 'And as you can see, I am far from dead. Is Don Baltazar at home?'

'He is, *señor*. Enter.'

The driver started through the gates. When the carriage stopped, he got down off the box, opened the door of the carriage and put up his hand to help Mario out.

'You are San Mateo?' he asked.

'I am,' Mario answered.

The old driver laughed. 'I should have known it. San Mateo! Many's the night I've driven your father to keep a rendezvous in Cadiz. We are friends, old friends, Frontera Baja and I. Just ask him, ask him if he remembers Luis, and he'll tell you that we share many secrets together.'

Another figure appeared in the doorway. Mario saw that he was a tall man, slender and straight, with a face like carved yellow ivory. His black eyes peered out into the sunshine as if unaccustomed to the brightness of day. He walked slowly down the steps, with his gaze fastened on Mario, and then stretched out his hand.

'There will be no introduction necessary, Mario,' he said. 'I know you to be my friend Frontera's son, about whom he wrote me. The resemblance is unmistakable. Welcome to your new home, thrice welcome.' He turned to the coachman. 'And as for you, Luis, you misbegotten son of Shaitan, if I ever see your evil face around here arranging an assignation for Mario with some of your so-called clients, I'll take the whip to you.'

Luis laughed and brandished his coach whip. 'But listen to me, Don Baltazar. If young Mario wants to go out in Cadiz, what safer person could he find than myself?'

'Granted,' Baltazar said. 'But he won't be going. The young Mateo, although he does not know it yet, is about to enter my monastery, where he will find himself cut off from most of the world. Should he need your services, Luis, I'll send for you. Now, my servant will pay you and you will be gone.'

'I'm paid already, Don Baltazar.' Luis chuckled. 'I have already made a new client for myself, and if he's half the man his father was, before the week's past he'll snap his fingers at your monastery and come seeking old Luis and all the pretty little girls he knows.' He waved gaily to Mario and climbed up on the box, turned the horses and departed in a crunch of flying gravel.

Don Baltazar offered his arm to Mario and escorted him up the steps and into the house. Ramon and the boy followed. The tall wooden doors closed behind them, shutting out the sunshine and the sound of birds singing in the pointed cypresses which waved slowly in the soft breeze of Andalusia.

Chapter Eighteen

NONE OF the blinding light from the burning Spanish sun penetrated into the shadowy coolness of the long hall, and Mario had only a dim impression of polished tile floors and white walls with a series of low couches along the side as they followed Don Baltazar down the corridor.

They emerged at last into a sun-dappled patio with rows of dwarf orange trees set among the well-ordered greenery, apparently growing out of the marble slabs that floored the courtyard, and watered by small channels of water flowing from a central fountain. Don Baltazar, his long white robe billowing in the slight breeze, led the way. He stopped for a moment and pulled down a flowering branch of orange to smell the waxen blossoms, turned his head to smile an apology to Mario, and then led the way up a flight of marble steps and along a pillared portico. His slender hands fumbled in his wide sleeve and produced a key, which he handed to Mario with a ceremonious gesture.

'Your quarters, young Mario,' he said. 'It is my hope that you will find them comfortable. I shall leave you now, so you may repair the ravages of travel – and do, I beg of you, change into more comfortable clothing. Here in my house, we combat the summer heat by reserving our more formal clothing for the streets. When you have changed, if you will come below, we shall have an opportunity to discuss several matters pertaining to your stay here. Also, I shall present to you the members of my household. Please remember one thing: you are my guest, and this is your home while you are here.'

Mario found the proper words to thank him, as the old man touched his hand lightly to his forehead and backed away from the door. Mario handed the cumbersome key to Ramon, who inserted it in the ornate, old-fashioned lock and pushed open the door, swinging it noiselessly on its heavy hinges. Inside, they discovered an enormous room whose most prominent and decorative feature was a sunken, coffin-shaped pool of water in the centre. The lining of the pool, the floor, and the high wainscoting on the walls were all covered with an intricate design of varicoloured tiles. Those running around the wall seemed to depict some curious kind of writing which looked to Mario like a cursive script. But neither he nor Ramon could comprehend it, for it certainly had no relation to Spanish.

The ceiling was extraordinarily high and was made of some light-coloured, unpainted wood, intricately carved in a honeycomb formation that stepped itself up into the suggestion of a dome. In its centre was a small circular window, rich with jewelled glass which cast a pattern of reds, blues and greens on the still water of the pool directly beneath it.

Mario became aware of the strange odour which seemed to permeate the whole house. It was a combination of scents – a mixture of spiciness, suggesting cloves and cinnamon, the pungency of cedar, and a heavy musky smell like damp and decaying rose leaves. Although the odour was far from disagreeable, it gave the room an atmosphere of being closed, shuttered, and unaired, in spite of the opened windows which looked out on a garden.

The room was almost devoid of furniture. On one side, raised by a couple of steps and divided from the room by small twisted marble pillars, there was an alcove which contained a low, wide bed. Opposite it, across the pool, there were two low divans, covered with some glittery dark material, each with a low table of light, honey-coloured wood heavily inlaid with nacre and silver. That was all – the limpid pool, the bed, the two divans and the tables. But, in spite of its paucity of furniture, the room took on an air of subdued richness from the metallic covering on the divans, the large silken pillows which were strewn on them, and the dancing colours in the water.

A door beyond the pillared bed led into a smaller chamber, the walls of which were lined with massive wardrobes. A smaller couch in this room was presumably for Ramon. Evidently Don Baltazar had been advised that Mario would have a servant with him.

As they were completing their survey of the rooms, a knock at the door announced the arrival of Mario's chests. Ramon immediately began to search for one particular box, found the one he wanted, opened it, and lifted out a pair of white linen trousers and a shirt of thin white cambric. He shook them out and laid them carefully on the bed and then walked over to examine the pool.

'What do you make of it?' Mario pointed to the water. 'Is

it to keep fish in, an extra supply of drinking water, or a convenient place to drown one's wife?'

Ramon knelt and dipped his hand in the water. 'I suppose it could be used for all three, but I think it is a bath. See, here is a curious invention. This small round iron object seems to be a submerged charcoal stove which carries fire to heat the water. It's just the right temperature for bathing, far too warm to drink, much too hot for fish, and as you have no wife to drown —'

'I'll take a bath in it!' Mario began to shed his heavy coat and woollen trousers, which were damp with sweat. 'And you know, Ramon, this will be the first real bath I have had since that day in Vedado when you scrubbed me clean of the prison filth.' He sank down in the tub and gave himself over to the warm caress of the water, as Ramon returned to the other room and began the job of unpacking.

Mario leaned back against the tiles, watching the coloured lights play on the water. He shifted his hands, watching them change from ruby to sapphire to emerald. The water was comfortably warm and the room's dark quietness soothing after the confusion of disembarking. He felt his eyes closing, and let his thoughts drift into sweet reminiscences. Somewhere in Spain there was a duchess named Cleora. He heard again the sound of her voice, imagined her sharp teeth on the lobe of his ear, remembered the smooth olive of her skin and the night of tumult on the floor of his cabin. . . .

The click of a latch was almost inaudible, but in the sleepy quiet of the room it served to arouse him. He thought that a door had been carefully opened. He turned. No, the wide doors into the hall were still closed and so was the small door into Ramon's room. Yet he was certain that he was being watched. He felt unseen eyes upon him, staring at him, examining him, appraising him. Again he made a quick survey of the room. In the shadowy alcove above his bed there was a square of light and – yes, he was right! There was the outline of a face, shadowed and obscure. As he looked at it, the small door was hastily closed and the light disappeared. Again he heard the click of a latch.

The rim of the pool caused him to stumble as he bounded out, but he caught his balance and ran across the room, streaming water on the tiles. He jumped up the two steps to the bed and flung himself across it, grabbing at the small panel of wood above him. His searching hands found a handle, part of the intricately carved wall design, and he pulled on it, feeling an opposing force on the other side. But inch by inch he forced the small door open.

The face behind it was so delicately featured, so smooth, and so youthfully rounded that at first Mario did not know whether it was a young man or a girl. The eyes, frightened and embarrassed, looked at him from under long dark lashes. The nose was thin, its nostrils quivering with emotion – either fright or anger – and the mouth was full and red, parted now to draw in quick panting breaths. Above the forehead, Mario could see the white folds of a turban.

Furiously Mario reached through the opening, grabbed a handful of some soft white stuff and felt the warmth of flesh beneath it. He clung tightly to it as the other sought to wrench away.

'You goddamned sneaking little bastard! What do you mean by spying on me? I'll have no servants or slaves or whatever you are peeping at me. Do you hear?' He got a firmer grip on the thin cloth and heard it rip between his fingers. 'What are you – a man or girl?' He looked closer and saw the down of a moustache on the upper lip. 'A man! God help me, a man. Or are you a man? Perhaps you are just curious to know what a real man looks like. Come in here and I'll show you how a man is made, but don't go peeking through holes in the wall.' He gave a mighty shove, saw the youth on the other side unsuccessfully try to gain his balance, then fall backwards. Still shaking from his anger, Mario banged shut the cupboard-like door, saw a tiny wrought-iron bolt, and pushed it into place.

Ramon had heard the commotion and came out into the room. Mario pointed angrily at the little door. 'Nail it up!' he shouted. 'Nail the goddamn thing up. I'll not sleep here beside it and have my throat cut the first night I am here. Don't stand there looking at me! Find a hammer and nails – if there are any in this goddamn heathen house – and nail it up. Do you hear me, nail it up!'

'I will, Mario, I will. But first finish your bath and get dressed.'

'To hell with the bath! To hell with the clothes! If people in this house want to see me buck naked, I'll go down this way to Don Baltazar. I'll tell him what happened! I don't know who that bastard is, but he's some sort of a goddamn brown-skinned heathen. I'll. . . .'

'Mario, Mario, Mario!' Ramon's voice was soothing. 'Dress and let the heat of your anger disappear before you rush like a mad bull to Don Baltazar. Would you cause a scene in this house less than an hour after you entered it? Don Baltazar greeted you with courtesy and kindness. You must not blame him for the action of one of his servants. It was just some boy, probably curious as to the new guest, who wanted to look at you so that he might brag in the servants' hall that he was the first to see you. Come!'

By the time Ramon had dried him, combed his hair, and coaxed him into pants and shirt, Mario had calmed down.

'You're right, Ramon. Right as always. It would be wrong to blame Don Baltazar for something a servant did. In truth, now that I know it was a boy, I am not so angry. I had thought at first it was some wench, spying on my nakedness. But – ' his eyes circled the room – 'I am right when I say that this is a heathen house. Do you notice something lacking here – something which you have always seen in every bedroom you have ever been in? No matter how rich or how poor a person might be, no matter whether it was made of gold and ivory or some cheaply carved piece of wood, there was always — '

'A crucifix. Yes, Mario. But there is none here. You must remember Don Baltazar is a Moor, not a Christian. And now come, Mario, you must go below and talk with him. He said he would be waiting for you.'

'I'll not go alone.'

'But you must. I know that ever since Havana, we have been very close together, Don Mario. But now things have changed and we must change also. You are the master and I am the slave, and it is thus that our relationship must appear to others. It would be an affront to Don Baltazar if I were to accompany you.'

Mario had to admit that Ramon's words carried sense but, regardless of their truth, Mario disliked the thought of going down alone. He had been received with kindness, but he stood somewhat in awe of old Don Baltazar. Still, it had to be done. He squared his shoulders, lifted his chin and without further words opened the door – only to find himself sprawling on the tiles of the portico outside, his arms wrapped around a white-sheeted figure whose bare brown legs and buttocks stretched out on the floor under Mario and whose face was hidden by the folds of the white robe. Mario managed to get to his knees. His hand sought the throat of the other through the folds of cloth.

'*Dios mio!* Another one!' he shouted. 'First they peek through the cupboards and now they spy through the keyhole!' He raised himself to his feet, dragging the other up with him. The cloth slipped from the face and Mario saw it was only a boy, now gasping for air from the pressure of Mario's fingers on his throat. Suddenly the boy fell again to his knees and lowered his head to Mario's shoes. Mario drew his foot back as the boy started to kiss the toes of his boot, then reached down and yanked him back to a standing position. No, it was not the spy. This boy was younger, only in his early teens.

'I am Abdullah, your servant,' the lad managed to stutter in bad Spanish. 'But I am afraid I am a most improper one, as I failed to hear you open the door.' He looked down at the floor. 'Please, master, do not mention my clumsiness to Don Baltazar.'

Mario liked the boy's dark face and flashing black eyes. 'I'll not tell.' He nodded in secret agreement. 'But I already have a servant – one that I brought with me.'

'Then I shall be your servant's servant. While you are here in Don Baltazar's house, it is my duty to wait on you. This is my place.' He indicated the threshold. 'I shall always be here when you are in your room, and at night I shall sleep across the door, so that nobody may ever enter.' He reached in his sash and patted the handle of a silver dagger. 'I may not look very strong, but I am a master of this.' He pulled out the curved blade.

'And so was I when I was your age.' Mario grinned. 'Look where it has got me.'

Abdullah replaced the blade, adjusted his sash, pulled down his robe into straight folds, bowed low and said, 'Now, if Your Excellency will permit, I shall conduct you to Don Baltazar.'

Chapter Nineteen

THEY PASSED along the balcony and down the steps, then through the light and shadow of the patio, around the fountain and up a few steps to where the slender marble pillars of a small kiosk raised a bulbous dome of turquoise tiles on the far side of the courtyard. Don Baltazar was inside, seated on a pile of cushions. He welcomed Mario and indicated a place on a leather hassock opposite him where Mario might sit.

Mario found a low brass tray in front of him with a glass which Don Baltazar filled with a hot brown liquid. Except for the sprays of crushed mint in the glass it did not look particularly inviting but, as the older man started to sip from his glass, Mario raised his and tested it. At first it seemed too hot and far too sweet, but he liked its minty fragrance and after a few swallows he found that, in spite of its heat, it had a cooling effect. It was his first introduction to the refreshing mint tea of the Moors. The white cloud of steam that rose from his glass veiled his examination of the man in front of him.

It would be difficult to determine Don Baltazar's age. He might be somewhere in his seventies. His face was thin under the closely wound muslin turban and his high cheekbones stretched the pale ivory skin tightly across his face, leaving shadowy caverns from which his eyes peered, glowing like dark coals. The narrow, pointed beard on his chin was a chalky grey and the carefully clipped moustache revealed straight, almost colourless lips. The nose was thin, high-arched and extremely aquiline. So much so that there was a white line down the bridge, as if the skin were stretched too tautly across it. At first glance it seemed a cruel, predatory face – cruel with a selfish determination that would brook no opposition. But after Mario had studied it for some time through the diminishing steam from the glass, he decided that he had judged the man in error. What he had mistaken for cruelty was only a finely drawn intelligence. The eyes were not cruel. They were compassionate and generous.

Don Baltazar filled the glasses again, added fresh mint and let a slow smile spread over his face.

'Your illustrious father requested that I invite you to my home. Your father and I are friends. Although it is generally said in Spain that Frontera Baja has few friends, I am honoured to be one of them. I have known him for many years and, although I do not condone his faults, I admire him for his virtues. Therefore, through the friendship I have for your father, I am happy to welcome you. As I told you when you arrived – this is your home. And, if you would deign to consider a Moor as your second father, you are my son while you are here.'

Mario answered cautiously. 'Thank you,' he said, bowing his head in polite acknowledgment.

'Then, young Mario, let us get acquainted. First let me tell you that your father's letter from Havana has already informed me of much about you and your life there.'

'All?' Mario asked quickly.

Don Baltazar shook his head. 'That of course I do not know. However, for the time being, let us say "all".'

'So then you know —'

'That you have not always been known as San Mateo? Yes, I am aware of that. But your past is already forgotten, young Mario. Now, indulge me by letting me speak about myself for a moment. I am a difficult person to describe in that I am an anomaly – a Spanish Moor or perhaps a Moorish Spaniard. I have roots in both countries. I am a Moslem, and allowed to be one in Catholic Spain because I represent His Majesty, the Sultan of Morocco, in Cadiz. I bear a legal Spanish name as well as a Moorish one, having had a Spanish grandfather. However, the fact that I am a Moslem does not mean that I shall try to convert you to Islam or to make you a believer in our Prophet. Your father desires that you abide with me for a time because he has respect for my slight degree of learning. Such as I have I shall be glad to impart to you.'

'If you only knew how slight my knowledge is,' Mario found himself saying.

The old man nodded understandingly. 'So, in order to please your father, we shall try to transfer some of my learning to that fine head of yours. Suppose we devote an hour to study in the mornings. Then we shall review the morning's lesson in the afternoon. There are, however, other things you must learn that I cannot teach – fencing, riding and other sports in which I do not indulge. I have made special arrangements for your instruction in these.'

'It is most generous of you to give your time to me.'

Don Baltazar waved the protest aside. 'In return, young Mario, I have a few favours to ask of you.'

'They are already granted, *señor*.'

'Not too fast, my boy.' He held up his hand in warning. 'Perhaps you will find my restrictions rather onerous. For your own safety, I request that whenever you leave this house – and you are of course free to come and go as you please – that you advise me where you are going and when you expect to return. Also that you do not go out alone, but take with you either your own slave or the boy Abdullah. He is young, but he is a trustworthy slave.'

'May I ask if your solicitude for me is due —'

'To a certain member of your family about whom your father has warned me? Yes, Mario. While you are here, your safety becomes my responsibility. And now, there is an even more delicate matter about which I must speak to you.'

'Pray proceed, Don Baltazar.'

'You are not the only guest I have here. There are two others. One is my granddaughter, and the other is the young man she is about to marry. Before I present them to you, let me say that, in the world of Islam, women are not treated in the same manner as they are here in Spain. My granddaughter is a Moslem but she has not been brought up entirely along Moorish lines. She has been educated here in Spain, and has even attended a convent where the good nuns taught her many things. You see, even though a Moslem, I have a great respect, nay, even love for your Christian religion. I am sorry to say, however, a respect that is not shared by her betrothed, the young Prince Adan. He has insisted that my granddaughter keep in strict seclusion while you are here and adopt the veil whenever she leaves her quarters.'

Mario remained silent. There was really nothing he could say. Don Baltazar regarded him for a moment and then continued.

'This, then, has created a bit of a problem. The prince has even let it be known that he resents your visit, and I have had to guarantee your respect for her privacy. May I have your word on that?'

'Most certainly! It is a solemn promise.'

'Then I shall summon them here, and if Adan seems churlish and ill-mannered, please overlook it, as it is beyond my control.' He clapped his hands. There was a swish of white garments between the orange trees and Mario saw a servant running up the staircase on the opposite side of the patio from where his own rooms were. Don Baltazar leaned back on the cushions and lit a slender tube of paper which contained tobacco. It was the first cigarette Mario had ever seen. He was more accustomed to the thick, potent *cigarros* of Cuba.

At the sound of footsteps, he looked up to see the figure of a girl advancing under the orange trees. At first he could only see the pale rose draperies which fluttered around her as she walked, but as she drew nearer he saw that a veil covered her face, leaving only her eyes exposed. The veil was thin and could not conceal the beauty that it tried to hide, nor could anything dim the deep lustre of her eyes. She came slowly up the steps of the kiosk, sank on the cushions beside her grandfather and kissed him. Mario struggled to his feet, unwinding his long legs from the low hassock.

Don Baltazar brushed her cheek with his hand. 'Our expected guest, my dear, whose lateness does not diminish the warmth of our welcome. The reported reasons for his non-arrival were much exaggerated. Allow me, Zaydah, to present the young Mario, Conde de San Mateo, the son of my good friend Frontera Baja.' He lifted one of her hands and held it toward Mario. 'My granddaughter, Zaydah.'

Mario remembered Ramon's instructions about the kissing of hands. He touched hers with a mere brush of his lips, but in that fleeting moment, as his lips touched the warm silken flesh, he could feel the warmth of his own blood mounting to his face. He relinquished the hand immediately.

'Your servant,' he muttered, struggling to remember Ramon's instructions.

'Heavens no, Don Mario.' Her voice echoed the cool, clear music of the fountain. 'The place is already overrun with servants. Even one more would be a problem. Say instead "your friend" and I shall be much happier.'

Mario looked down on her. The veil was a mere pretext – it hid nothing. The long black lashes swept down over her cheeks, whose warm colour showed clearly through the sheer fabric. The smiling lips parted like the petals of a rose to speak the words of welcome.

'Your friend, then.' Mario found difficulty in forming the words.

Don Baltazar interrupted, 'And here comes the young falcon of the desert, Adan.'

Mario turned as he spoke and saw a young man, trailing a voluminous robe of white, his head bound in a turban of white muslin shot with gold, walk stiffly up the steps. He glanced once at Mario but, brief as the glance was, Mario recognized the face as the one he had seen peering through the secret panel into his room. But now, atop the tall, well built body, the face had lost all trace of the femininity Mario had noted in his previous view of the face alone. The frightened stare had been replaced by anger, which set the full lips in a stern line and gave power to the blazing eyes. That which had seemed rounded and soft, even girlish, was now sharply defined with a proud, overbearing masculinity.

The darting look he gave Mario held no hint of recognition. He turned his back on Mario and faced Don Baltazar, and Mario understood the brief inclination of the young Moor's head as a formal greeting to Don Baltazar and the girl.

The old Moor rose and Mario suddenly realized why he had sensed cruelty in Don Baltazar's features. No longer were they in repose. Instead there were deep lines between nostrils and mouth – cruel lines that etched authority in the face.

'Adan!' the force of his voice caused the young man to turn reluctantly to face Mario. 'This is our guest, the Conde de San Mateo. Mario, I want you to meet Prince Adan ibn Ibrahim, the son of His Highness, the Emir of Marrakech.'

Mario extended his hand, but the young Moor stood rigidly aloof. His hands remained hidden in the sleeves of his robe.

'Adan!' Baltazar's voice cracked like a whip. 'The law of hospitality is one of the strictest laws of the Prophet. You are in my household; therefore you share my obligation of hospitality, and you must obey that law.'

'I will not shake hands with an unbeliever. The law does not apply in that case.' Adan's voice matched Don Baltazar's in intensity.

'The law applies to all. Even the poorest Berber in his tent is compelled to share his last crumb with anyone who comes asking for hospitality. Creed makes no difference. And while you are here, I stand in place of your father. I order you to shake hands with Mario.'

Adan approached grudgingly. Mario noted the dark amber of his eyes and, again, the fuzz of hair on his upper lip. He saw the slender nostrils dilate and the red tip of the tongue moisten the lips. Even though the other looked at him in enmity, Mario had to admire his handsome features. And then, almost in contradiction to the hatred in his eyes, a hand came out from the folds of the sleeve to grasp Mario's in a cool, dispassionate clasp.

'Prince Adan greets the Conde de San Mateo.' He relinquished Mario's hand, turned abruptly, and walked down the steps of the kiosk.

'My apologies,' Don Baltazar began, but before he could finish, Mario had quickly excused himself and was down the steps. He overtook Adan, forced his way in front of him and blocked his path. Mario planted his feet firmly on the marble flags and again offered his hand. The other took it reluctantly, but as Mario spoke he managed to smile.

'The Conde de San Mateo greets Prince Adan,' Mario said, 'and in greeting him, he has a suggestion to make.'

'Such as?' Adan whipped the question back.

'That we seek some quiet place where we can be alone to discuss some important matters.'

'Such as?' Adan insolently repeated the two words again.

'As to why you spy on me, and why you refuse my hand.'

'I should explain my actions to you?'

'As we must live under the same roof, it might be better that we understood each other.'

'I agree. There is one way to a complete understanding.' Adan's hand rested on the hilt of a silver dagger, half concealed in his brilliant sash. 'With this.'

'If you prefer,' Mario answered. 'But to use that would be to dishonour Don Baltazar. I would suggest another weapon.' He clenched his fist and held it under Adan's chin.

For the first time Adan smiled. 'It is a fair offer, Your Excellency. I shall arrange a time and a place, but we shall not mention it to Don Baltazar.'

'No, we shall not mention it,' Mario agreed. '*Hasta luego*, Your Highness. Until then.'

'Until then, Your Excellency.'

Chapter Twenty

SOME MINOR disturbance filtered into the first deep, dreamless sleep of Mario's afternoon siesta and woke him. He did not want to get up but sudden perception that something had happened prevented him from going back to sleep. He shifted to his side, turned the pillow to seek a drier spot on it and discovered what it was that had intruded. Something was now on his pillow, a folded scrap of paper, glowing dimly white against the damp pillowcase.

The shuttered light inside the alcoved bed was too dim to allow him to see more than lines of writing. He stretched his legs over the side of the bed and stood up. In spite of the heat, his bare feet felt cool on the tiles as he walked across the window to raise the jalousie. The thin parchment was filled with lines of fine writing – a delicate cursive script which conveyed nothing to him.

Bearing the paper in his hand, he went to the inside door and called into the other room. Ramon shuffled out, his face heavy from sleep. He took the paper from Mario's hand, studied it, and then returned it to Mario.

'It's writing,' he said slowly, trying hard not to yawn. 'That much I can recognize. And as we are in a Moorish house, I presume it to be Arabic.'

'How did it get here?'

'That I do not know – except I am certain it was not here when you retired, else I would have seen it when I turned down your bed.'

Mario walked back to the bed and examined the little wooden door above it. No, the slender bolt was still in place. Puzzled, he walked over to the outer door and tried to push it open, but found that he could move it only a few inches. Two brown legs and the edge of a white cotton robe on the floor told him that Abdullah was true to his trust. The boy had been sleeping on a thin pad across the threshold, but the pressure of the door now awakened him. He jumped to his feet, his head bowed, one hand touching his forehead.

'Master, you wish something?'

Mario grabbed the boy by the shoulders and yanked him inside. 'Who entered this room while I was sleeping? Answer me! Who came in here?'

Abdullah's eyes rolled back in surprise. 'Nobody, master. I swear by the beard of the Prophet.'

'But this . . .' Mario extended the piece of paper. 'This was not in this room when I retired. When I awoke it was on my pillow. Certainly papers do not fly around this house and pass through thick walls or enter through solid doors or barred windows!'

Abdullah's shoulder lowered sufficiently to release him from Mario's grip. He walked across to the carved panel of wood above Mario's bed.

Mario followed him, shaking his head. 'Not that,' he said. 'It's bolted.'

'No matter.' Abdullah's warning finger enjoined silence. He slipped back the bolt and ran a probing hand down one side of the wood. The hand stopped on a certain carved arabesque, pressed, and the panel swung open a few inches. Abdullah pointed to a similar bolt on the inside of the door which controlled the one on the outside. He nodded smugly in his wisdom and beckoned Mario to come nearer. Mario peered through, and saw on the thick masonry wall another panel which evidently opened into the next room. Abdullah reached through, fumbled with the knob of another bolt, pushed it back and slowly pressed against the second panel. It opened silently. Through the aperture Mario saw another alcoved bed similar to his own – and, amid the rumpled sheets, a sleeping figure whom he recognized as Adan.

Quickly closing both panels, Abdullah took the paper Mario handed him.

'Can you read?' Mario asked.

'But certainly!' The boy stood scanning the writing.

'Well then,' Mario said impatiently, 'read it to me.'

'That I cannot do, Your Excellency. It contains remarks about you I would not like to repeat.'

'Read it. I'll not hold you accountable for what it says.'

Abdullah hesitated for a moment, looking up at Mario for further assurance. Then, at Mario's impatient nod, he began.

'From the noble-born Shereef Adan ibn Ibrahim, descendant of the Prophet, son of the Most High, the Emir of

Marrakech, to the infidel dog, Mario, cursed of all true believers —'

'Well, that's a good beginning,' Mario said, winking at Ramon.

'Although you offend my honour, son of a whoreson she-camel, and although honour should be settled with knives, I am aware of your sentiments in regard to the hospitality of our gracious host. Therefore, as you suggest, we shall settle this matter with our bare fists, and he who loses in fair combat shall depart from this house, as indeed it is not large enough to hold us both. I shall await you on the salt marshes this afternoon at sundown. Although circumstances necessitate that we must meet in physical contact, I shall try not to let the stench of your body sicken me, for one who is born of dung must stink of dung. You may bring your slave with you. I shall not kill you, but, as Allah wills, I shall punish you.'

'Is that all?' Mario asked.

'That is all.'

Mario dismissed the boy with a message to Adan that he would be on the salt marshes at the appointed time. Then he sought counsel from Ramon.

There could be but one conclusion. Mario must keep the appointment. Ramon was not too fearful of the outcome and, if Mario won, life in Don Baltazar's house without the presence of Adan would certainly be less complicated.

The shadows were already beginning to lengthen when Mario dispatched Abdullah to locate the old coachman who had brought him there that morning. He had felt a bond of fellowship with old Luis and wanted his friendly presence during the fight. Then, accompanied by Ramon, Mario sought out Don Baltazar to advise him that he would be out for an hour. Don Baltazar nodded silently, almost as if he had anticipated the announcement – and when Mario and Ramon arrived at the carriage they found Abdullah, looking very determined, seated beside old Luis. Evidently he had received instructions not to let Mario out of his sight.

Soon the narrow streets of Cadiz gave way to the barren outskirts of salt marshes, where since Roman times, people had been evaporating the sea water for its salt. The high-piled rows of salt cast purple shadows along the ground, and even the air had a saline tang to it. Luis drove them along a narrow cart path between the rows until Abdullah, turning from the driver's seat, pointed to two figures up ahead, scarcely distinguishable against the white salt. Even at that distance, however, Mario was able to recognize one of them as Adan, although the Moor was now dressed in European clothes. As the ancient carriage drew nearer, Mario saw that the other was one of the tall slaves who had helped bring the boxes up to his room.

Old Luis stopped the carriage, cramped the wheels wide, and Mario stepped down. As he did so, Adan advanced a step to meet him. But there was no greeting; his arm merely directed Mario down a narrow path to an empty space, well-hidden from the roadway by a towering pile of salt. When they got there, Adan beckoned to his slave, who hastened to him to help remove his coat and shirt.

Mario's actions repeated those of Adan, except that he accomplished his own disrobing, then handed his clothes to Ramon. When they had both stripped down to their breeches, they advanced barefoot towards each other in the centre of the space. Mario felt the fine dust of salt and sand between his toes. It was still warm from the afternoon sun and felt like soft powder.

Step by step the two came closer. Mario was surprised by the whiteness of Adan's skin. He had always thought of Moors as dark, but the man in front of him was as white as he was – only his neck and hands showed the bronze of the sun. He was tall and slender, but well-built, with whipcord muscles under his light skin, and Mario decided to discount the suggestion of effeminacy he had previously suspected. Stripped, the Moor looked every inch a man.

As they neared each other, Mario crouched, his left arm protecting his face, his right extended. Instinct alone taught him to take the pose, for he had had no training in hand-to-hand fighting. Before, he had always relied on surprise, but now his opponent was prepared. This was different indeed from creeping up behind some unsuspecting sailor in one of Havana's dark alleys.

They circled around each other cautiously, then suddenly Adan crouched like a cat and sprang at Mario, clutched at him and landed a glancing blow on his face. Mario freed himself, retreated a step and then swung, his fist landing with a heavy thud on the Moor's chest, knocking him backwards.

Adan stumbled from the blow, nearly lost his balance, then recovered and sprang at Mario a second time. Down they went, choking in the white dust, a tangle of arms and legs, and in the melee Adan gained the advantage.

He swung a crushing blow to Mario's face, splitting the skin so that blood ran down into the salt, staining it red. Mario gasped in pain, but the full weight of Adan's body, landing squarely on his chest, brought him quickly back to sensibility. He saw the Moor clasp his hands momentarily, and then a streak of fire ran across his chest in a long thin red line. Adan was astride him, knees locked tight around him.

'Coward that you are,' Mario muttered. 'We said no knives, and yet you have used one. By God, I'll take it and kill you with it!'

Suddenly he brought both fists together and catapulted them into Adan's face. Adan toppled backwards from the force of the blow, and Mario rolled over in the dust and climbed astride him.

'The knife!' His hand sought Adan's throat. 'Where have you hidden it?' As his fingers clutched deeper into the flesh, he saw the face below him turn purple and the eyes bulge out from the pressure on the throat. Slowly Adan lifted one hand, palm up, and waved it feebly before Mario. The gold band on his finger concealed a thin, curved spur of steel attached along its back, and although the blade was not long enough to kill a man, it was vicious enough to cut his skin to ribbons. Mario clenched Adan's hand in his own and forced it down inch by inch towards the young Moor's chest. He saw the thin blade enter the white skin and felt the warm blood spurt on his hand as he drew the blade across the flesh. The broad line of red on Adan's chest matched the bleeding wound on his own body.

' 'Tis a woman's weapon, you goddamed *marico*!' Mario growled, stripping the ring from Adan's finger. 'I can't kill you with it, but I can give you as good as you gave me.'

He looked down at the Moor, who was now strangely quiet. His eyes were dark and sullen, but the former blaze of hatred had died out of them. Suddenly Adan's free left arm swept upward and caught Mario around the neck, upsetting Mario's balance and bringing him down on top of the Moor's chest. But he quickly regained his posture and sat up again. His hand reached once more for Adan's throat.

'For the love of Allah,' Adan cried, 'or whatever God you believe in, stop! One moment, just one moment, I beg of you.'

'You ask mercy of me?' Mario spat in his face.

'Never!' Adan spat back but the saliva only dribbled on his own neck. 'You think I beg of you because I fear you? No; if you kill me it is Allah's will and not yours. But first let me speak.'

Mario sat back on Adan's stomach. 'I'll not kill you yet, Moor, but I'll make you wish you were dead. I'm going to rob you of something you hold even more precious than life.' He held the ringed blade before Adan's eyes. 'But before I turn you into a eunuch, speak. I would hear the words a coward mouths, for nobody but a coward would use a weapon like this.'

'Then hear me, Christian, and if you would kill me, kill me – but do not geld me. Hear me and know this one thing. Whatever you are or whatever you have been, at this moment we are brothers.'

'Brothers? Good God, what drivel! Do you think those words will save your precious jewels to breed more cowards?'

'They are true words, Mario. Look – your own eyes can tell you what is happening. See, the blood drips from the wound which I made in your chest. It falls on me and mingles with my own. When your blood enters mine we are the same blood, and can no longer be enemies. We are brothers, and, Mario, brothers cannot kill. Whether you wish it or not, it has already happened. Now, if you kill me, the curse of Cain will be upon you. No, we must change our thoughts, Mario. That which was hate must now become love.'

Dumbfounded, Mario looked at Adan and saw the ghost of a smile appear through the blood and spittle on his lips. He looked down at the Moor's chest and saw his own blood dripping into the other's wounds. Suddenly he was tired of fighting.

'I know not what the custom of your people is, Moor, but this much I will admit. We are both bleeding and our bloods have mingled. It means nothing to me, but if it is the custom among your people to respect it then I shall, for I see a certain logic to what you say.' He released his hold on Adan and stood up. Suddenly laughing, he reached his hand down to Adan and pulled him to his feet.

'You laugh, Mario, at our blood brotherhood?'

'No. I laugh to think what a brace of fools we have been, fighting each other for no good reason. Why should we hate each other? Come! If in your belief we are brothers, then let us be brothers. Here is my hand on it – a little bloody, to be sure, but who knows whose blood it is, yours or mine. And now tell me, Adan, why have we been such damn fools?'

Adan did not meet Mario's eyes. 'I provoked you purposely,' he said, 'and by that means I have accomplished what I set out to do – though hardly in the manner in which I had planned it. As brothers we must be honest with each other. I did not wish to kill you, Mario. I wanted you for my friend – yes, and even more than that, I wanted you for my brother.'

Mario shook his head in disbelief. 'You certainly went about it in a strange manner.'

'You see, Mario, I have never had a friend. As Prince of Marrakech, I have had many who professed friendship for me, but they were flatterers and I knew they could never be true friends. So when I heard that you were coming – a young man my own age – I hoped we might be friends.'

'And well we might have been without all this foolishness.'

'Wait, Mario. I would confess more. I was anxious to see what you were like. I could not wait. That is why I spied on you through the shutter that divides our rooms. I saw that you were everything I had always wanted to be myself – big, strong, and honest. There was no guile in you. But we have devilish minds, Mario, we Moors. We never come out and say what we are thinking. Instead we pursue our thoughts through some labyrinthine course that always leads from light to darkness. And so, I was jealous of you – jealous because you are more of a man than I. I feared that perhaps the Lady Zaydah would see more in you than in me, and if I returned to Morocco without her, my shame would be too much. Therefore I thought to bind you to me through the rite of blood, both that I might have your friendship, and that – as brothers – I would not fear you as a rival for Zaydah. So I brought you here this afternoon, and so I brought this knife. But' – he looked down at his dusty shoes – 'my plans went awry. I had hoped to gain ascendancy over you; then I would have nicked my own chest and that of yours and let my blood drip on you. But as it was, you were the victor.'

Mario looked down at the weapon in his hand. It was a curious mechanism, the blade curved like the spur of a fighting cock. He pressed it and its curve fitted exactly into the ring entirely concealing the blade. Then he hurled it high over the pile of salt.

'I do not fully understand you, Moor – or, since you use my name, Adan. But if you want my friendship so badly, you may have it, although it still seems to me you went about gaining it in a curious way. You almost lost more than you bargained for. However, let's forget about the whole thing.' He smiled at Adan. 'And now that you have succeeded in mingling our blood, let us find a way to stanch it so that we may both continue to live in the brotherly relationship you set so much store by.'

Chapter Twenty-one

DON BALTAZAR might have been curious in regard to the battered faces and the discoloured eyes of his two young guests, but if he was, he managed not to betray it. The fact that they were friendly, even intimate, did not seem to surprise him, and he let pass without comment their speaking to each other with the familiar *tu*. The next morning, however, he did allow a slight degree of curiosity to become apparent – a mere lifting of the eyebrows – when he saw Adan join Mario for the morning lesson. But he quickly welcomed both of them and started the day's lecture on geography.

Mario was surprised that the allotted hour passed so quickly. He would have been quite willing to have had Don Baltazar continue his discussion all day. Although Don Baltazar's favourite subject was the march of Islam, he did not confine his talk to the Moslem countries alone, but took in most of Europe as well. Mario found himself storing away many loosely connected but constantly interesting facts. There was the might of England, that little island off the Norman coast; the fast-ebbing grandeur of Spain; and the meteoric rise of France under that Corsican corporal, Napoleon Bonaparte. And much more, all weaving into a broad tapestry of geography and history, of the shifting boundaries of the many European states.

At length, after Don Baltazar had closed the book and ordered a slave to serve the hot minty tea, Adan requested permission for himself and Mario to be excused. The old man released them with a smile and an apology for having detained them longer than the allotted hour. Mario was in no hurry to leave, but he welcomed the chance to stretch his legs again; he was as yet unaccustomed to the traditional squatting position, tailor-fashion, and his knees felt cramped from it.

They walked across the courtyard, through a small door in the back to the outside garden, then down a path lined on both sides with growing cypresses.

Adan pulled back the sleeve of his white robe and gripped

Mario's arm. 'That wicked-looking cut under your eye, Mario, how came you by it?'

'I was outnumbered.' Mario grinned. 'As I was taking a short walk last night, I was set upon by eight ruffians, each with a knife drawn.'

'Only eight?' Adan expressed surprise. 'Ah, they little reckoned with your skill, my brother. They should have had double that number.'

'Indeed! But the first one who came at me had his mouth open, so I merely reached in my hand and pulled out his tongue. That finished him. Then I turned my attention to the other seven and dispatched them one by one. But with the last I was unfortunate. Before I killed him, I managed to get hit by a glancing blow. Here.' He pointed to his eye.

'*Ay, qué hombre!* But I also had a misfortune last night – though, alas, by no means as exciting an adventure as yours. Instead, I was sitting quietly at home in my own room when suddenly half the ceiling fell on me. It hit me here.' He indicated a purple swelling on his own face. 'I was tempted to call to you for help, but I found I was able to lift the ceiling back myself and nail it in place.'

Mario laughed loudly. 'All of which proves you're a far bigger liar than I am!'

They were close to another building which, judging by the odour of horses, Mario took to be a stable. In the paved courtyard in front, a Negro boy was holding a horse, patting its neck to calm it. The animal was restless; it reared its head, tossed its mane and waltzed in nervous, dainty steps on the cobbles. As Adan approached, it whinnied and started towards him, dragging the boy along with it. Adan held out his hand and the horse came up to him, nuzzled his palm, then stood quietly beside him.

'What a beautiful horse!' Mario cried. Although he had never ridden, long practice in watching the daily *paseo* in Havana had made him a judge of sorts. 'In fact,' he added, 'I believe it is the most beautiful horse I have ever seen.'

'Do you hear what he said about you, Zuleika?' Adan pressed his cheek against the horse's neck. 'He says you are beautiful, and indeed you are. Look, Mario! See her grace, the dainty steps she takes. Look at her face – the pointed ears, the intelligent eyes. Yes, she is indeed beautiful. But Zuleika is also a woman, and she is most capricious. She demands a master, and he must master her through love. That she will return; mistreat her and she will hate.'

Mario stepped back to look at the horse – her coat of rich cream, the lighter mane and tail, the glossy silkiness of her skin from the polished hooves to the tiny, tufted ears. He came closer, reached a tentative hand towards her. She allowed him to touch her, as a princess might allow a commoner to kiss her hand, but when he tried to stroke her as Adan had, she reared and would not again let him put his hand on her.

'I have a secret to tell Zuleika, and so I must speak to her in Arabic, as she does not understand Spanish,' Adan said. 'And now you may say she does not understand Arabic either, but I can assure you that she does, for she and I have long conversations and she knows everything I say.' He spoke several sentences to her and Zuleika became quiet, hanging her head and letting her ears droop.

'She is sad, my Zuleika,' Adan said. 'I have just told her that from now on she no longer belongs to me but to you.'

'To me? *Dios mio!* To me? But you must be crazy, Adan, even to think of parting with her. And I must tell you that I cannot ride. I've never been on a horse in my life.'

Now it was Adan's turn to be surprised. 'Not ride? How is that, my brother? But no matter, Zuleika is yours, even so. A small payment indeed for what those eight ruffians did to you.' He reached up and touched the bruise on Mario's cheek.

'Then how can I repay you for what that falling ceiling did to you?'

'By accepting Zuleika and being good to her. Soon I shall be leaving Cadiz. I return to my father's house in Marrakech to prepare for my wedding. Zaydah will follow me in a short time. I have already committed an offence against our customs by coming here, for no Moslem should ever see his bride before he marries her, even with her veil on. So I shall return to my father's house, satisfied that my first wife will be a fitting mother for my sons.'

'A mother for your sons?' The wrinkles that appeared on Mario's forehead betrayed his puzzlement. 'But how do you know if you love a woman before you see her?'

'Bah! I've had your so-called love crawling into my bed since the time I was too young to know what it was all about. Why, the first time, when I was but a lad and my father sent one of his favourite concubines to initiate me, I actually screamed in terror of her! But that is another story. The most I demand from my bride is her purity.'

'So now you trust me with your two most precious possessions – your bride and your horse.'

'The one I give you willingly, the other I place under your protection, for you are now my brother. As for your not riding, come, Mario, and I shall teach you. But not on Zuleika.' He turned to the boy. 'Fetch another horse and saddle this one.'

'How can I thank you?' Mario watched the groom lead Zuleika away. 'I realize this is no ordinary mare, and I also realize that this is no ordinary trust you put in me. What can I do, Adan, to repay you?'

'There are many things you could do for me, Mario, or that you could let me do for you, but until I know you better I shall not ask them. However, there is one thing you can do for me now. To you it may seem like a very little thing – almost inconsequential – but to me it would mean much.'

'Then ask and I'll do it.'

Adan held up his hand to deter Mario's willingness. 'Do not promise too rashly, my brother. To be sure, it is only a little thing, in that I ask you merely to repeat a few words – but those words have a great import to me.'

'Then tell me the words and let me say them.'

'Ah, but wait until you hear them. I do not forget that you are a Christian.'

Mario looked suddenly doubtful.

'You do believe?' Adan pressed the question.

Mario hesitated. 'I do not know, Adan. I do not know what I believe, and this is probably the first time in my life I ever really considered the matter.'

Adan's words followed quickly. 'Then, Mario, let me say this to you. Repeat these words after me and you will make me the happiest man in the world. I do not expect you to believe them now, for how can a man believe that which he does not understand? But, if Allah so wills, the time may come when you will understand them. Study your own religion and then study mine. In the end you may choose, but for now let us make our brotherhood complete.'

'My hand on it, then,' Mario said. 'If it means that much to you, I'll gladly do it.'

Adan motioned to him to follow and preceded him down a

small path that led to a spouting fountain in a cluster of trees. There was no sound but the splash of water in the basin and the singing of nightingales in the cypresses. Above, the sky was a bowl of blue and the hot Andalusian sun shone fiercely down on them. Adan stopped on the gravelled path that ran around the dripping basin.

'Mario de San Mateo, will you repeat these words after me?'

'As you say, my brother.'

'Then this.' He turned and faced the sun. 'There is no God but Allah, and Mohammed is His Prophet.'

Mario's eyes fastened on those of Adan. 'There is no God but Allah and Mohammed is His Prophet,' he repeated.

Adan came closer. His face was now transfigured with a holiness which sat strangely on his sensuous features. 'You have now entered the ranks of Islam, my brother, and the hour of prayer is already upon us. See, up at the house, Don Baltazar comes out on his balcony and faces in the direction of Holy Mecca. Let us then pray too. Spread your coat on the ground, Mario, as I spread my *djellabah*. Kneel as I do, and, although you will not understand my prayers or my actions, I shall pray for us both. When you arise, then you will be my brother indeed, and my father will be your father, and my God your God.'

Mario took off his coat, spread it on the ground, and knelt awkwardly beside Adan. He little comprehended the step he had taken or how it would someday influence his life. The stones of the gravelled path hurt his knees through the thin fabric of the coat and, although he thought Adan's acrobatic genuflections rather comic, he made his obeisance towards Mecca, feeling somewhat ridiculous himself with his rear end stuck up in the air.

As he listened wide-eyed to Adan's torrent of unintelligible words, movement in the nearby wall of cypresses suddenly caught his eye. Before the green branch moved back into position, he saw a face, lighted with eyes of fanatical hatred, staring at him. He recognized it as one of the Spanish grooms of the stables. The branch once again became a part of the thick wall of greenery, but through the screen Mario heard the noise of running footsteps. He would have arisen and followed, but he feared a disrespect to Adan – and that he did not want to show. Well, so be it.

As they rose, Adan cast off his serious demeanour like a cloak. Once again he was gay and carefree as he led the way back to the stables, all the while explaining the intricacies of the Arab saddle – the shortness of the stirrups and the difficulty of riding Moorish style. 'But,' he said, 'as in all things, although it may at first seem absurd to you, the Moorish way is always the best. And why not? It has endured these many hundreds of years. Come, Mario, and in a few days I will have you riding Zuleika. Know you what we call our Arab horses?'

'No.' Mario shook his head.

'Drinkers of the wind. And the little mare will teach you why. Come, Mario.'

Chapter Twenty-two

ADAN WAS a patient teacher and certainly Mario was an apt pupil, being very eager to become a horseman. After a few discouraging starts in which Zuleika nipped him with force and intention, Mario gradually was able to make friends with her. But it was a slow process. At first she would not let him near her without baring her teeth. But, after being coaxed by Adan, she permitted Mario to stand close to her and talk, and then, after a few days, even suffered him to touch her head. Each day found her condescending a little more towards the strange young blond with the unfamiliar speech – for Zuleika, being an Arabian princess, understood only Arabic. At length she evidently decided that the sound of Mario's Spanish was soothing and pleasant, and it was not too long before her tasselled ears twitched with expectation when she heard his voice, and the soft muzzle would seek his hand. He had won her.

But interesting as learning to handle and ride Zuleika was to Mario, there were other things just as necessary for him, and one of the most important was fencing. Don Baltazar found a French fencing master who had stopped being a soldier of fortune long enough to set up headquarters in Cadiz, and who welcomed Mario as a student. When Adan found that the Frenchman had previously taught the sons of the Bey of Tunis, he too decided to become a student.

With the rapier he and Mario were on equal ground, for neither had ever used a sword before. Adan was adept with the curved Moorish knife and Mario had had plenty of practice with the short, straight Cuban dagger, but a sword was a new experience for both of them. What with geography and history in the morning, riding and fencing in the afternoon, and excursions into the city with old Luis, the coachman, for their guide, their days and nights were well-filled. In fact, their time was so completely taken up with each other that it puzzled Mario to the extent that one day he mentioned it to Adan.

'I can't understand it.' Mario looked quizzically at the

Moor. 'How it is that you are affianced to the granddaughter of Don Baltazar, that you came all the way from Morocco to see her, that you decided to marry her, and yet you never pay her any court while you are here? Now, if I were affianced to so charming a young lady and lived in the same house with her —'

'I have a very good idea of what you would do.' Adan bent the point of his rapier with one hand and then tested the blade in the air. 'But, *hermanito mio*, you and I are quite different. You have been brought up as a Christian and until your recent conversion' – he glanced up from under his long lashes, but as he perceived no change in Mario's expression, he repeated the words – 'and until your recent conversion to Islam, you were quite ignorant of our Moorish customs. Will it surprise you to know that I shall not see the girl again until I unveil her on our wedding night? Nor, my brother, shall you.'

'But do you not think of her often and realize that only walls separate you from her? But perhaps that is why you seek the little gypsy girls of old Luis with me – so that you will not think too much about her.'

'It is you who seek the gypsy girls, Mario. Not I! I go along merely to be with you. We have always gone at your suggestion, never at mine.'

Mario admitted that he was right. Adan had always gone, not unwillingly, but without any great enthusiasm, and although he had listened with interest to Mario's boastful braggings about his prowess in gypsy beds, he had never recounted any experiences of his own. For all Mario knew, he might have listened to the girl play a guitar and done nothing else. Adan's whole attitude in the matter was one of indifference; but perhaps that was the way things were done in his country.

'You mean you'd marry a girl,' Mario pursued, 'without even seeing her? *Ay, hombre!* What a chance you take. Without her veil she might be ugly as a hag.'

'The fact that one wife might be ugly does not matter particularly to a Moor. According to the law of the Prophet we are allowed four wives, and, if these are not sufficient, we can have any number of concubines besides.'

Mario's lips parted in a wide grin. 'And that's the law for Islam?'

'Most certainly.'

He whistled. 'And you tell me that after having said those words to you the other day, I am now a Moslem?'

'You professed our faith.'

'And I may have four wives and any number of concubines?'

'Of course.'

Mario touched him playfully with the tip of his sword. 'Then, my brother, let me thank you. I'm happy to be a Moslem.'

Adan's mood changed suddenly. The smile departed from his face; he laid the rapier with which he had been practising down on the ground and came over to stand directly in front of Mario. 'You said you were happy to be a Moslem, but when you said it you were laughing. Do not make a joke out of this, my brother. Our faith is not to be taken lightly.'

Mario returned his look with equal seriousness. 'My regrets,' he said simply and sincerely. 'I spoke without thinking, and I fear I was making a joke out of the matter. For this I am sorry. How can you expect me to be happy about a matter – or sad about it, or even interested in it – when I know nothing about it? I know even less about Islam than I do about what passes for Christianity – and aside from the names of a few saints, I know almost nothing about that.'

'About Islam, I shall teach you. Let me make you more familiar with it. And I shall ask Don Baltazar to teach you, too. Together you and I shall read the Quoran, and we shall talk about it, for, as many times as I have read it, there is much for me to learn too.'

Mario lifted up the fingers of one hand and ticked them off with the other. 'One,' he said as he touched his little finger, 'Mario learns the arts and sciences, and two' – he touched the next finger – 'Mario learns to ride, and three, Mario learns to fence, and four, Mario learns to kiss a duchess' hand and walk into a drawing room, and five, Mario learns to become a Moslem. Think you, Adan, that this poor brain of mine can stand it all?'

'I do. Ask your slave Ramon to fetch my book from my room. To learn about Allah one must first become acquainted with our Prophet, and to learn about Him, one must know the Quoran. But wait, I'll go myself. Your slave is an infidel and his touch would defile my book. Wait here for me; I shall return.'

Mario sat down on a bench beside the shadowed stable wall. A few moments later Ramon appeared from the direction of the house carrying a letter, which he handed to Mario. The paper was crisp and heavy, and the red seals on the back burned brightly with the impression of an elaborate crest.

'Who is it from?' Mario asked.

'I do not know. It was left by a messenger, and Don Baltazar asked me to deliver it to you.'

Mario's fingers broke the seals and he unfolded the heavy paper. There were only a few lines, but they made Mario grow pale under his tan. He read them slowly, aloud.

'A welcome to Spain, my nephew! My curiosity about the young San Mateo who, my friend Almendares informed me, was slain in Ponta Delgada, provoked me to investigate this most unfortunate incident. Alas, I have been informed that Almendares was clumsy in his methods and that you are now, through the good graces of Godoy, recognized as my legitimate nephew throughout all Spain. My congratulations, Mario, and I shall look forward to the pleasure of calling on you before my brother returns from Cuba. Naturally, I am most anxious to meet you and have you become acquainted with. . . .

> Your fond uncle,
> Eliseo.'

'What does this letter mean, Ramon?'

The lines deepened in Ramon's forehead. 'I do not know, Don Mario, but I suspect it should not be taken lightly.'

'I am getting rather tired of being a pincushion for other people to stick knives into,' Mario said angrily. 'First my father pricks me with his sword at Aña's house. Then Almendares' *bandidos* let the air into me; and just recently Adan slits my belly. I no sooner heal from one scar than I get another. Now it seems my uncle comes to kill me.'

'And who would think of killing you, Mario?' Adan had arrived, his thin yellow slippers making no sound on the rounded cobbles.

Mario handed him the letter to read.

'I do not read your Frankish writing,' Adan said. 'But do not worry, my brother. He who would kill you must first kill me, and while I may not be the best swordsman in Spain, I do have this.' He pulled the curved dagger from its silver sheath.

'And you have this, Don Mario.' Ramon reached under his shirt and drew out the same knife which Mario had last seen spinning on the floor in Ana's house.

He took it from Ramon, moved over on the bench and made room for Adan to sit down. As Ramon got up to leave, Mario motioned for him to stay.

'Adan will bear with me if I permit you to remain, Ramon.' He looked at Adan for confirmation and accepted his nod of assent. 'I think we had better tell my new-found brother something about my life. Surely I should have no secrets from him, and he will divulge naught that I tell him. He can then understand why my uncle's arrival might concern me.'

'You fear this uncle?' Adan asked.

'Wait till you hear my story.'

'But before you tell me, Mario, let me tell you this. I had thought to leave for Morocco soon, but if one comes who might desire to harm you, then I shall stay. And now, I shall be a good listener. Begin!'

The shadows of the cypresses had crept halfway across the courtyard before Mario finished. He told everything, omitting no details, no matter how uncomplimentary, and when he was finished he was glad. He could be himself once more – at least in front of Adan and Ramon – and it was pleasant, momentarily, to drop the role of San Mateo. Even though he could never return to being El Rubio, he could be Mario.

Chapter Twenty-three

THE FRIENDSHIP between Adan and Mario developed quickly, and there were so many interesting things to do that the hours sped by and the days soon multiplied into weeks. No further word having been received from Eliseo, the matter of his arrival was quite forgotten. A pleasant daily routine was established which both Mario and Adan followed. The first one to awaken opened the panel between their rooms and called to the other. Often they were up and dressed and off for a ride in the cool of early morning before either Ramon or Adan's slaves knew that they had departed.

Both Mario and Adan made rapid progress with the rapier. At first Adan had disdained the thin, flexible weapon, sneering at it as too dainty and ineffectual when compared with the curved scimitars he had been accustomed to in Marrakech. But as their lessons progressed he realized that, delicate as the rapier might seem, in the hands of an experienced swordsman it was a far more deadly weapon than the Moorish blade.

There was more to their days, however, than riding and fencing. There were long sessions with Don Baltazar, and together the three of them explored far distant kingdoms and lost centuries. Mario learned of the Greeks and the Romans and of the far-off civilizations of Egypt, Persia and Babylon. He learned of the birth of the Christ and the fall of Rome and the deadly oblivion that came as the black cloud of ignorance settled over Europe after the fall of Roman power. Then he learned how the candle of knowledge was lighted some six hundred years after Jesus by the Prophet Mohammed, and how the knowledge of the ages was preserved by the students of Islam, while it was dissipated by the barbarians of Europe.

He followed the little band of fanatics from Arabia as they spread the message of one God and his Prophet Mohammed over half the known world. He entered Spain at the head of the Moorish Army, saw the culture of Islam sweep over the Iberian peninsula, gloried in the delicate beauty of the Alhambra, the pillared mosque of Cordova and the Moorish castles that dotted Andalusia. He saw Isabella of Castile united to Ferdinand of Aragon, and Columbus carry the red-and-gold banner of Spain to distant lands across the sea. Sorrowfully he watched the star of the Mahgreb sink in Spain, as Boabdil left his palace of the Alhambra.

With the departure of the Moors and the discovery of the new world, Spain was in her ascendancy. Gold-filled galleons with billowing sails brought the riches of Mexico, Peru and the Indies to this very city of Cadiz. The Spanish waxed proud and presumptuous with their Holy Inquisition, which became more deadly and more feared than any Moorish sword had ever been. The Moors had fought with honour, but the crawling informers of the Inquisition killed their own brothers with lies and treachery.

Men watched in silent horror to see their neighbours, their friends, and their families disappear – sacrificed on the altars of narrow-minded bigotry and the lust for gold and power. Even now, the Inquisition was still a force in Spain; but it was losing its power, thanks, Don Baltazar said, to the open-mindedness of Manuel Godoy, Prince of the Peace and Prime Minister of Spain.

But things were not going too well with this royal favourite who twisted the painted harridan, Maria Luisa of Parma, Queen of Spain, around his fat little finger. He had become involved in too many unsuccessful diplomatic manoeuvres with France, and today his position was tottering – temporarily buttressed, however, by the doting affection of a silly queen and a stupid king. . . . Yes, Mario was learning many things, and the days were passing quickly.

He saw little of Don Baltazar's granddaughter – only an occasional passing of gossamer draperies on the gallery across the patio; but he saw as much of her as Adan did, and he marvelled at the fact that the Moor could live under the same roof as his betrothed and display so little desire to be with her. Apparently Adan did not care. But Mario could not refrain from speaking of her one afternoon as they lounged in Adan's room.

'I heard her singing last night. It could have been a nightingale, she sang so sweetly.' Mario gazed drowsily across at Adan.

'The Lady Zaydah?' Adan smiled. 'She sings sweetly indeed, and I am convinced that she herself is as sweet and as delicious as her song. Soon now I shall see for myself.'

'Does that mean you are leaving Spain?' Mario found himself dreading the answer. The lofty rooms of Don Baltazar's house would seem lonely indeed without Adan's constant smile.

'Yes, my brother. I must go in a few days. I had meant to speak to you about it, but I find it difficult to think of parting from you. Your friendship means much to me, and the longer I remain in Spain, the more precious it becomes. Were Spain still ours and did it not belong to these cursed *N'zranis*, I would be content to stay here always.'

'And Zaydah? Does she accompany you?'

'Indeed, no. She does not accompany me as my concubine. She will follow me in about a week.'

'Why don't you get married here and take her home yourself?' Mario's voice betrayed his impatience at the other's indifference.

Adan shrugged his shoulder on the pillow. 'She marries me as a Moslem maiden should – in my home, surrounded by my family. We celebrate our nuptial night together in the palace of my fathers, and when I throw out the napkin my father must be able to see the virgin stain on it. Were there no stain, I should divorce her immediately.'

'Even if you loved her?'

Adan raised himself on one elbow and looked across at Mario. 'You harp continuously on love, Mario. Love, love, love! I marry to beget sons. Love does not enter into it. But my sons must be pure; therefore I would not take a woman for my first wife who had lain with another. She must prove her virginity.'

Mario thought the remark over carefully. 'Then you intend to have other wives besides Zaydah?'

'Of course, *hermano estupido*! Are you so poor a Moslem, after all I have taught you, that you do not remember the Prophet allows us four wives? Through my marriages I shall ally myself with wealth and power. Don Baltazar is a wealthy man, so I marry his granddaughter. My other marriages will be for politics or more wealth. But Zaydah will be my first wife and the first of my *hareem*. That is a position of honour and, even though my *hareem* be filled with three other wives and more concubines than the days of the year, it is the first wife who rules all. Thus I honour Zaydah.'

Mario accepted the answer. He stretched out amid the pillows and let his eyes close. Sleep welcomed him, but before he succumbed, he stirred himself, opened his eyes and mumbled, 'You I shall miss, Adan.'

'And I you, Mario.' Adan sat upright, shook his long hair from his eyes and crossed over to Mario's divan. He seated himself on the side and reached for Mario's hand. 'Come, brother Mario. Leave this Spain behind you and accompany me to Marrakech.' He leaned forward the better to plead his case. 'In my father's palace you can become a great *sheik*, for you will not only be my brother but my father's son. I promise you honour and riches and, if you want them, the most beautiful girls in Morocco – Frankish slaves, blue-eyed Berbers, Negresses with skins of black silk.'

'You tempt me by exciting me, Adan.'

'And what have you to lose? By your own admission you came here to meet death at the hands of your uncle. Of what use is the paltry Spanish title of count compared to that of Prince of Marrakech? Come with me, brother.'

Mario sat up and took the proffered hand. 'I thank you, Adan – and that I say in all sincerity. I would like to come with you, for I think the land of Morocco might offer me more than Spain – and someday I promise you I will come. But now I owe something to my father who has sent me here.'

'But your uncle. . . .'

'Should I fear him? Would you have me run from Spain out of cowardice? No, Adan! When I come to you, it will be because I have quitted myself honourably here. But while you are gone, I shall remember those few words I repeated for you and the Arabic prayers you taught me. I cannot tell you truthfully that I believe in them as yet, for they are new to me, but I shall not forget them. And now let us sleep, for I cannot hold my eyes open longer.'

'Let us sleep, my brother.'

How long he slept he did not know, but he awakened immediately, suddenly aware of another presence besides Adan's in the room. His half-opened eyes did not betray his wakefulness, but he made a quick survey of all that he could see without moving his head. He could see nobody. Turning, as if in his sleep, he faced the wall. The shuttered opening between Adan's room and his was open, and through that opening he saw a face. It was the face of a girl, more beautiful than any he had ever seen before.

Slowly she leaned forward, looking down at the two men, and as her head came through the aperture her hair fell over the casement. It was long and dark and lustrous, but the highlights that it caught only complemented the dancing lights in her dark eyes. Her skin had a dewy, tea-rose freshness; her lips were full, moist and red, and as she regarded them, the lips parted in a beautiful half smile.

Mario did not dare move, even to reach for the sheet to cover his nakedness, for fear of startling her or waking Adan. Instead, he opened his eyes wide and looked up at her. Their glances met and she started back in momentary confusion, then shook her head ever so lightly and smiled, putting her finger against her lips. 'He sleeps?' she whispered, pointing to the form of Adan on the wide divan beside Mario.

An almost imperceptible movement of Mario's head assured her that he did.

'You will say nothing?' Again she whispered the almost inaudible words.

'*Nada*,' Mario assured her.

'He is handsome, my lord Adan.' She swept Adan's body with her eyes. 'But not as handsome as you, my lord Conde. It is you that Zaydah loves.'

The carved door closed slowly and Mario heard the click of the latch.

He lay there for a moment, wondering if he had dreamed; but no, no dream could ever be as perfect as the vision he had just seen. Without waking Adan, he eased himself up from the divan and flung open the shutters. It revealed his own room, empty. But on the floor there was a veil, stretched across the azure tiles – a veil of white tissue shot with gold, which moved ever so slightly in the faint breeze. Mario reached for his clothes and dressed hastily, taking care to make no noise. He opened the door of Adan's room quietly and went down the gallery to his own door.

Once inside, he picked up the veil and held it to his face. Its silken softness lay smooth, warm and perfumed against his cheek. He sniffed the mingled odours of musk and patchouli and, as he closed his eyes, he seemed to rest his cheek against soft, rose-coloured flesh, perfumed with the same clinging odour.

The scarf he would keep for himself. He looked around for a place to hide it, then tucked it into one of his boots in the wardrobe. He was about to leave the room when the shutter opened.

'I awoke and missed you.' Adan's sleepy eyes peered through the opening.

'And I awoke and did not have the heart to waken you,' Mario answered, 'you were sleeping so soundly.'

'But I had dreams.' Adan rolled his eyes back in ecstatic contemplation. 'Dreams that exceeded all the pleasures of paradise.'

'Did you awaken to see any fantastic *houris*?' Mario's anxiety almost betrayed him.

'Alas, no.'

'But I awoke with a need of them,' Mario said, becoming enthusiastic. 'Come, Adan. Let us send Ramon to summon old Luis. We shall go and listen to the flamenco singers tonight. The little gypsy girl who dances in the Café of the White Dove has a way of soothing one's thoughts.'

Adan agreed listlessly. 'As you wish. But for me, with so little time left to be with you, I should not mind staying here.'

'No, Adan. Tonight I am not in the mood to discuss abstractions. Your promise of Frankish slaves and blue-eyed Berber maidens, as well as four future wives, has led my thoughts in another direction and created a desire I must now satisfy. Let us dress and go.'

Adan nodded assent. 'Your wish is mine. Send Ramon for old Luis, and lend me one of your Spanish suits. I have become tired of those I own, and perhaps, dressed in your clothes, I shall be able to emulate your desires.'

At the mention of his name, Ramon came into the room and Mario directed him to choose a suit and take it to Adan. Ramon opened the doors of the wardrobe and called to Mario to come over and choose one. When Mario was safely screened behind the opened door, Ramon pointed to the wisp of white veil protruding from Mario's boot. 'You are about to make another enemy, Mario,' he whispered. 'I could not help but see what happened. Take care to give Adan no cause for jealousy.'

Mario shook his head. 'But she is not for me, Ramon. She is lovely, and under other circumstances I would indeed be tempted. But she is betrothed to my best friend, even my brother, and I would never place the horns on his head to satisfy my own desires. Besides, when he marries her and throws out the napkin, it must bear the mark of her virginity. Of that I cannot rob him, nor' – he was silent a moment – 'can I rob her. I think, Ramon, nay, I fear that with only one glimpse of her, I love her far too much to harm her.'

'Remember those words, Mario, and let them guide you during the week that he is gone and she is left behind.' Ramon selected two suits and laid one on Mario's bed. He carried the other to the door, but before he opened it he turned to Mario and shook his head sadly. 'The weeks have passed far too quietly, Don Mario. Keeping you out of mischief has been too easy lately. Now I am afraid. . . .'

'Don't worry, Ramoncito. After seeing the little gypsy tonight, I shall be a good boy tomorrow.'

Chapter Twenty-four

THE GYPSY girls at the Café of the White Dove did not see either Adan or Mario again during the days that intervened before Adan's departure. Mario sensed that Adan did not want to go, and decided he could well postpone his visits and devote his time to Adan alone.

Strange how this friendship which had been conceived in blood and then sealed by that blood had become so vital to both of them. There were times when Mario felt that Adan had entirely forgotten about Zaydah – and Mario had tried to forget her too. But he couldn't, and his desire for her made it all the more difficult to understand Adan's indifference. Surely if he, Mario, had been leaving so lovely a creature, even for a short time, he would have been desolated; but Adan seemed almost matter-of-fact about his departure from both Don Baltazar and his granddaughter. He was, however, overcome with sadness at the thought of separation from Mario.

On Adan's last night they were sitting alone in the patio with no other sound than the musical splashing of the fountain. Don Baltazar had long since excused himself, having sensed their desire to be alone. Their conversation had died out. Somehow they had said everything that needed to be said. There were no plans to discuss for the morrow or the day after or the day after that. At length, Adan stirred himself, stood up, stretched his arms high above his head and let the sleeves of the white *djellabah* fall down from his wrists.

'It's hot here.' He shook his head. 'The walls of the courtyard keep out the breeze. In my room it will be much cooler, as the breeze will be coming in the windows. Come, Mario, let us go there and we can shed these stifling clothes and seek comfort by the open window.' He reached down, took Mario's hand and pulled him up.

They walked slowly across the marble tiles, up the narrow steps and along the corridor to Adan's room. A broad band of pale moonlight cast a white shadow on the tiled floor; otherwise the room was in darkness. When Mario reached for his tinder box, Adan put out a restraining hand. 'Even a single flame would make the night seem warmer. The moon is full and when it rises above the cypress trees, we shall have plenty of light. Come, my brother.' He reached for Mario's hand in the darkness and drew him to a low divan in front of the window. 'Let us spend some time here in comfort, for only Allah knows when we shall see each other again.'

Mario stripped off the sweaty, clinging shirt, slipped out of his trousers, and threw the damp clothes on the floor. He sank down on the divan beside Adan. In the pale light he could see the other's profile, etched in bronze against the sky. The straight line from brow to nose gave way to the shortness of the upper lip, and the fullness of the mouth curved into the roundness of the chin. Mario watched him until he turned and he could see Adan's eyes – two darker spots in the darkness of his face, each with a single highlight from the moon.

'I shall miss you, Mario.' Adan was the first to break the silence. 'Our friendship has been a good one, and now I shall be lonely, for there will be many miles between you in Cadiz and me in Marrakech.'

'But you will have company?' Mario made the statement a question.

'Who but a lot of stupid Moorish boys who live only for their horses, their hawks and their swords!'

'I was not speaking of companions, I was speaking of Zaydah. Think, Adan, in a little more than a week she will be your wife. Of what need will you have for other companionship? With Zaydah beside you, you'll even forget the name of Mario. I'll be just something out of the past. You'll be far too busy to think of me or miss me.'

The moon slipped over the pointed tops of the sombre cypresses, bathing the room in a silver light. The deep bronze of Adan's face caught the light and became brighter.

'So you say, Mario, but not say I. Yes, I am to be married. Yes, I shall be busy with the many days of festivity that make up my marriage. Yes, I shall bed myself with my wife. . . .'

'Whom you love?'

Adan was silent. Finally he smiled. 'Again you speak of love, Mario. I cannot understand this strange idea of love which you *N'zranis* have. You put your women on a pedestal, worship them as something precious, and keep murmuring about love. You idolize it as did the Persian poets. Bah! The Persians were a weak and insipid race. Love! Think you that the feeling a man has for a woman is love?'

'But of course!'

'And have you known this love, my brother?'

Had he? Mario pondered the question silently. What had he known of love? Were the sticky caresses of the girls in Ana's house love? Was the stormy passion of the Duchess love? Was the studied coquetry that the gypsy girl had lavished on him the other night love? He found himself answering *no* to each of his questions, but through them all he saw the haunting face of Zaydah. He spoke and his words came slowly, each weighted with sincerity.

'I shall answer your question truthfully. No, I have never known the kind of love I speak of, but somewhere down in my heart I know it exists. It must; it is what I live for. I have saved a place for it, and when it comes it will be so beautiful that it will consume my whole body like fire. No, Adan, I have never loved. But by the same token that I know this, I also know that I shall love, and I am eager for that day to come.'

Adan laughed, reached over and lifted one of Mario's hands, examined it closely, noted the strength of the fingers, the broadness of the hand and the vitality that it possessed even as it lay inert in his palm. He let it drop to the cushions of the divan. 'That hand of yours, Mario,' he said softly, 'would fight for me. Were I in danger it would protect me. It would be beside me in battle, clenching a sword to guard my life. If I fell it would lift me up. If I were wounded it would nurse me. Could the frail hand of a woman do that for me? No!'

'But her hand could rest on yours in light caress. It could send little shivers of ecstasy down your spine. It could creep softly along your skin, searching over your body, and transport you to another world.'

'Agreed! For a moment, perhaps it could. But after that moment I would quit it, and then I would seek another which would do the same thing. Think you that the brief hours I shall spend with the women of my *hareem* can ever compensate me for the strength of your hand beside me in battle? No, Mario. We of Islam have our women. We keep them locked away from the world for whatever purpose we may see fit to use them. They are to be the mothers of our sons, and if they do not provide us with sons, we seek others who will. Our women are our property; they belong to us like our horses, our palaces, our jewels. But, Mario, the hours we spend with them are not the important hours of our life. Think, Mario! Since the day you arrived, you and I have been together constantly. We have lived and breathed as one person. We have become so close that at times our very thoughts have intermingled and become one. Companionship like that I could never hope to find in a woman.'

'Nor would you want to. A woman is to be loved.'

'And there you are wrong. A woman is to satisfy a man's appetite. If we are hungry, we eat. If we thirst, we drink. If our thoughts become warm with desire, we seek a woman. And we shall always find one. When I return to Marrakech, I shall start my *hareem* with Zaydah. Then I shall add three more wives, and the sheiks and shereefs of Morocco and Algeria and Tunisia will send me presents of other women whom I shall add to my *hareem*. To each of these I shall be the only man they ever know, so, in the end, it becomes a chore to satisfy them all.'

'You'll be nothing more than a royal stud – well-pedigreed for the breeding of descendants of the Prophet.'

Again Adan laughed. 'You're very nearly right. Of course we shall strangle most of the daughters, but we'll raise the sons, and I hope there will be more than a hundred of them. What I am trying to tell you is that all your cant about loving one woman is ridiculous. My idea of love is something different.'

'Such as?'

'Something much rarer than the women of my *hareem* can ever offer – the companionship I have had with you and would like to have with you, were you to go to Marrakech with me. There we would catch the first streaks of dawn as our horses sped across the desert. We would ride high up into the snows of the Atlas, and, even though you rode ahead of me, I would know that you were waiting for me around the next turn. We would fight for each other, and I would protect you as you would guard me. If need be, I would die for you, as I know you would for me.

'Together we would release our hawks into the clear sky and watch them drop swiftly on their prey. Together we would tread the *souks* of Fez and Sale and Meknes, seeking in their shadowed shops some precious jewel which I would present to you, or some silver-hilted blade from Damascus that you would give to me. This, then, Mario, is my idea of a true affection – not the clinging embrace of soft arms on a silken divan, not the passion that is released in one hysterical gasp, but the lifetime of companionship that I could have with a person such as you.' He turned his back to Mario, leaned his elbows on the broad window ledge and gazed out into the night.

Adan's words had touched Mario. His own affection for the young Moor was strong, but he had no idea that Adan's feeling for him had reached such a depth. It disturbed him, for he knew he could not return it in its entirety. He knew that Adan was pleading with him to accompany him to Africa, and that he could not do. But most of all, it disturbed him when he thought of Zaydah.

Adan did not turn around, so Mario addressed his back. 'Then you do not love Zaydah?' He tried to keep the exultant edge of hope out of his words.

'Not in the way you define love, my brother. She is beautiful. She brings me a large dowry. She is gracious and well-bred and of excellent family. All these are things I desire from the mother of my sons. She and I will unite the blood of the Prophet, for she too is a descendant of our Lord. I shall honour her and place her at the head of my household, and until I tire of her and take another, she shall be the sole occupant of my bed.'

Mario turned quickly. He heard the faintest of noises on the other side of the room. He was on his feet in an instant and silently crossed to the little door that communicated with his own room. As he neared it, he could see it move in the darkness. Mario reached out and tugged at it but, by the pressure on the other side, he knew that someone was holding it. He turned and walked back to the window and laid his hand gently on Adan's shoulder.

'Do not be too sad at our parting, my brother. I promise you I shall come to Morocco, and together we shall taste the cool air of the desert dawn and roam the *souks* of Fez and Meknes.'

Adan turned around. The moon shone brightly on the dampness of his eyelids. 'Swear it, Mario!'

'If Allah wills, Adan.'

'That is surety enough for me. I am so happy – let us make this a night we shall never forget. I want to fill it with such poignant memories that I shall remember it always.'

'And why not? We shall spend it sitting here, watching the moon. We shall talk, Adan, of many things, but mostly of the future, because I shall surely join you in Marrakech. But first, let me go to my room a moment. I want to choose something that belongs to me, that I may give it to you so you can remember this night and Mario.'

'Thank you, Mario. I shall cherish the gift, but you have already given me much by giving me tonight. I had feared you might propose another trip to the Café of the White Dove.'

Mario laughed and slapped him on the back. 'Not on your last night, *chico hombre*.'

Adan rose to accompany him, but Mario pushed him back on the divan. 'Let my gift to you be a surprise when I put it into your hand.'

He was across the floor to the outside door before Adan had a chance to get up again. He ran the few steps to his own room, lifted the latch and entered. Just inside, in the darkness, he stepped into soft arms that met around his neck. Zaydah's lips were pressed closely against his. He felt the dampness of tears against his cheeks. For moments that seemed like eternity he held her in his arms, so close he could feel the fluttering of her heart. Then she loosed his arms gently and pushed him away. A thin ribbon of light came through the door as she opened it. Then the door closed and there was nothing left but the cloying scent of her perfume in the warm darkness – and the beating of his heart.

Chapter Twenty-five

MARIO AND ADAN sat throughout the long night, talking at times and then lapsing into long silences. The pink streaks of dawn were lighting the eastern sky, turning the whiteness of Cadiz a pale rose, when finally Mario retired to his own room.

When he awakened, he could tell by the slatted reflections of the sun on the tiles that it was already past noon. His half-opened eyes roved the room, saw that the little shutter which connected his room with Adan's was wide open and that a piece of paper fluttered there, impaled on a silver pin.

With an effort, he lifted his hand for it. The thin cursive lines of calligraphy that marched across the white parchment were beautifully drawn, but were still unintelligible to him. For the second time he sought Abdullah's assistance as an interpreter.

'Is it from Adan?' Mario asked impatiently.

'Yes, Your Excellency,' the boy replied. 'He left here early this morning, soon after you retired.'

'Without bidding me goodbye!'

'He explains that here in this note.'

'Then read it to me.'

'My brother,' the boy began, choosing his words slowly, 'I looked in at you through our little private door, but found you sleeping so soundly it hardly seemed right to awaken you, just to repeat the sad words of farewell. Our parting will be only for a little while. I say *a little while*, for I hope that you will keep your promise to me and arrive at your home in Marrakech soon. That shall be as Allah wills. However, the human mind is always lifted up with hope, and I am sure that Allah, having once let me taste the joys of perfect friendship, will not deprive me of them now. In the meantime, I commend to your watchful vigilance the honour of my wife-to-be. I salute you, my brother. Adan.'

Mario dismissed the boy and walked across the room. Slowly and with regret, he closed the little door. Much had transpired through its narrow confines since he had come to the house of Don Baltazar, and it was going to be lonely without Adan. Indeed, life to Mario was becoming a series of too many and too quick changes, too many sudden adjustments, too many friends made and lost too soon.

Mario remembered the night before, but the memory of Adan was now crowded out by another. He could still feel the pressure of warm lips against his own as he had opened the door of his room. Would this perhaps end like his relationship with Cleora? Would he again find himself slit from belly to gullet by some other knife? Must his life always be complicated by women? He was about to make himself a solemn promise to the contrary, when there was a rap at the door.

Ramon opened it. One of the household servants stood outside. He spoke quickly to Ramon and then, with a deep bow to Mario, turned and left.

'There are two people below,' Ramon said slowly, 'who wish to see you – your uncle, Eliseo, the Conde de Camporeal; and Her Grace, the Duchess of Almendares.'

Mario looked at Ramon and shook his head in despair. 'Things are happening altogether too suddenly around here. Adan leaves, bequeathing me the care of his bride. . . .'

'Which is going to complicate matters,' Ramon said.

'Not half as much as this unexpected arrival of my uncle. I suppose I am to be offered up as a scapegoat to protect the life of my father. But, even worse, he is accompanied by the wife of the man who had my belly slit a short time ago.'

Mario sighed and passed his hand over his chin. 'I'll not take the time to shave, Ramon. I'm far too anxious to know the reason for this visit. Come, dress me and I'll go below. Cleora has seen me unshaven before and, as for my uncle, it will make no difference to him. Let's just hope he'll refrain from killing me in Don Baltazar's house.'

He slipped into the clothes which Ramon held for him, then turned around for Ramon's brief approval and rushed out of the room. He took the steps two at a time, walked briskly across the courtyard under the chequered shadows of the orange trees, and into the darkness of the big salon. In the dim light he paused, waiting for his eyes to accustom themselves to the gloom. A shadowy form arose from one of the divans and came across the room to greet him. Mario heard the click of heels on the tiles, saw the silhouette of a tall man who walked with the springing step of youthful vitality, felt his hand clasped in a powerful grip, and looked up to see a face towering above his own. In spite of the dim light he could see it was a handsome face, with lips that parted in a smile to show a row of even white teeth.

'Mario!' The voice was low and rich. 'Mario – my nephew?' He shook his head as if to deny the question. 'But of course!' He nodded in confirmation. 'Although my brother has not written me about you, I heard the news. Welcome to our family, Mario, and, in truth, if you are your father's son and my nephew, you must be as much of a rascal as either one of us – perhaps more so. But welcome nonetheless.' His hand relinquished that of Mario's, and his arm encircled Mario's back in the Latin embrace.

Mario suffered the pressure of the arm for a moment, then stepped back. He could see the man plainly now – the dark olive skin, the black eyes, the curling crisp black hair and the broad shoulders under the red-and-gold uniform.

'Then you are Camporeal?' he asked, appraising the man.

'Of course. And your father's brother. But call me Eliseo – and don't call me Uncle Eliseo, either. I'll be the laughing stock of the Court if you make me a *tio*. All the girls will be mocking me with "*Tio* Eliseo". But wait, boy, we are most negligent. There is another here who waits to greet you. Cleora, *mi querida*.' He stretched out his hand towards the divan. 'Your prodigy has arrived. Even though you mourned him as dead in Ponta Delgada, here he is, very much alive, and, I am sure, overjoyed to see you.'

As she came towards him, Mario saw the eagerness of her half-parted lips and the welcome of her open arms. But he stood still, bowed formally and lifted one of her hands to his lips.

'We meet again, Your Grace.'

'Mario, darling!' She came closer to him. 'If you could but know the nights I've spent mourning for you. If you could understand how the memory of your kisses has tortured me. I've never forgiven Almendares. Never!'

'Nor have I.' Mario laughed. 'I've something to remember him by. Here.' He pointed to his shoulder.

Her hand ran lightly across his body, touching it with a fleeting caress. 'But you are here and that is all that really matters now.'

'And you are here, Cleora, and does that mean —'

'That once again you stand in danger of Almendares' thugs?' Camporeal finished the question for him.

'Or yours?' Mario looked at his uncle.

'Now what would give you such an idea?' Camporeal's laugh sounded genuine. 'You have nothing to fear from me or from Cleora – or her husband either. We come asking a favour from you, Mario.'

'From me?'

'Yes, from you. We come waving branches of olive and palm. We are prepared to go down on our knees to you, because you are the only one in all Spain who can do what we desire. It matters not what our personal feelings may be towards you. No matter how much Cleora may be fired with a passion to have you for herself alone, and no matter how many evil things you may have heard about me, we have something far more important to talk about than Cleora's desire and my villainy. We're here to ask you to save us, and in so doing, to save your father and yourself in the bargain.'

'But I don't understand.' Mario looked from one to the other.

'You would hardly be expected to. I'll put it simply and quickly. Manuel Godoy has left the court.'

'And left it in disgrace!' the Duchess added.

'But what has that to do with me? The Prince of the Peace leaves the court. So how can that affect San Mateo, sitting quietly in the house of Don Baltazar in Cadiz?'

'Very greatly,' his uncle answered. 'It seems that Cleora has known you – well, for want of a better word, let us say intimately. She has also had some stolen moments in times past with the Prince of the Peace – enough to make a valid comparison – and she assures me that you are not only a worthy substitute for him, but that you even exceed him in certain capabilities which have made him famous.'

'All of which means nothing to me.'

'Ah but, my boy, it will.' Camporeal became more serious. 'Listen to me. For years Manuel Godoy, the Prince of the Peace, has controlled Spain. For years he has kept the King and Queen exactly where he wants them – right under his broad thumb. And know you this, my boy. In Spain today there are only two classes, the *ins* and the *outs*. Since my brother introduced Godoy to Maria Luisa, we have all been on the inside, thanks to our good but stupid Manuel. The house of Frontera Baja and the house of Almendares have ruled Spain through Godoy. Poor Godoy has had only one thing to recommend him, but that was more than sufficient to satisfy Maria Luisa. Now that he has been forced out by our enemies, Ferdinand, Prince of Asturias, and the Alba tribe will be in power. The Frontera Bajas and the Almendares will be the *outs*. That we cannot allow. Therefore it is imperative that we seek a substitute for Godoy. We must replace him with someone who has our fortunes at heart. We must forget our personal differences and cast our lots together. Cleora tells me, and she swears she is a competent judge, that you are the one to replace Godoy in the Queen's affection.'

'Are you so sure I am the one?' Mario noticed the smile on the Duchess' face as he asked the question.

She came closer to him. Her hand reached up and stroked his cheek, her body curved against his. 'Do you not remember my telling you, Mario, the very first night I met you, that, had your father but sent you to Court instead of Godoy, you would have been prime minister of Spain instead of him?' Her hand seemed to favour the roughness of his beard.

Mario nodded.

'And now you shall be. Maria Luisa already has a hint of what is in store for her, and she is impatient to meet you. She and the King will arrive at the Alcazar Palace in Seville tomorrow, and we return there immediately to greet Their Majesties, and to whet the Queen's appetite a little more. You will arrive tomorrow.'

'And after I appear?' Mario found it impossible to return her smile.

'We shall introduce you to Her Majesty. Then we shall leave you with her, and it will be up to you, Mario darling, to keep us all in her good graces. Through your influence over her, our positions at Court will be secure. Neither Ferdinand nor the Albas can produce as perfect a substitute for Manuel as we can in you. I know.' She stood on tiptoe and brushed his lips with her own, as Camporeal laughed and slapped Mario on the back.

'But aren't we taking too much for granted?' Mario demanded. 'Suppose the Queen does not like me – or suppose I do not like the Queen?'

'As for Her Majesty's not liking you' – Camporeal laughed

even louder – 'there'll be no difficulty about that – assuming what Cleora says is true.' He looked at her for confirmation.

'There can be no doubt of that,' she assured him.

'And as for your not liking Her Majesty. . . .' Camporeal's voice lost its laughter and became threatening. 'I can only say one thing. It is not a question of whether or not you will like her. Your likes or dislikes do not enter into the matter. You *must* like her.'

'But if I refuse?' Mario persisted.

'Ah, but you won't refuse.'

'And why not?'

'Because of this.' Camporeal unbuttoned his scarlet tunic and withdrew a paper which he unfolded.

'What is that?'

'Merely a few words, written on paper by the Inquisitor General,' Camporeal said softly.

'What would the Inquisition want of me?'

Camporeal shrugged his shoulders. 'Merely a few questions. Perhaps something about your kneeling in prayer in the direction of Mecca, the Holy City of Islam.'

Mario turned pale. The colour drained from his face as he regarded Camporeal. The Inquisition was a name only to be whispered in Spain.

'But come.' Camporeal replaced the paper in his tunic. 'We'll say no more about it. Tomorrow you shall appear in Seville. Drive directly to the Alcazar. Cleora suggests that you wear a certain blue coat and tight white trousers which she much admires. She will present you to Maria Luisa, who by that time will be all too anxious to meet you. Then, my dear nephew, the rest is up to you. Our fortune depends on you, and I might add' – he dropped his voice to a confidential whisper – 'your fortune, too, and even more important to you – your life. Do you quite understand?'

'Apparently I must.'

'Most apparently. We leave now, my nephew, to sing your praises in Seville. Tomorrow you leave. The road from Cadiz to Seville passes through Jerez de la Frontera. Not far distant from the town, on the other side, you will see the castle of Frontera. Regard it well, as it is one of the most imposing in all Spain, and may one day be your home. But, in passing, keep this in mind. Under its sunny towers are several most unusual dungeons. In them today are some who have felt at one time or another they could outwit the two Frontera Bajas – your father and me. Just remember, as you pass by on your way to Seville, that the sunny towers above are much pleasanter than the damp dungeons below.'

Chapter Twenty-six

THE COURT of Spain was seething with uncertainties – and when the court was off balance, it followed that all Spain was in a turmoil. Only yesterday the Prince of the Peace was supreme. He had successfully weathered the attacks of the Church, which had sent a papal nuncio from Rome to excommunicate him, and had even placated Maria Luisa when she had heard rumours of his secret marriage to the Maja Pepita – Josefa Tudo. In both rounds he had emerged victorious. In the case of the Church, Inquisitor General Cardinal Lorenzana had hesitated to prosecute so exalted a personage; and in the case of Maria Luisa, Manuel had only to threaten her with the complete loss of his favour, whereupon he was entirely forgiven and Pepita became one of her ladies-in-waiting.

So far so good! But there were powerful forces working against Manuel Godoy – forces headed by the Infante Ferdinand, Prince of Asturias and heir to the throne. And the flame of this hatred was fanned by the Albas, who saw in Ferdinand's ascendancy to power – if and when old Don Carlos died – a chance to renew their influence in Spain. Furthermore, France, once friendly to Godoy, was now turning against him, together with the English element under the powerful Duke of Osuna. Only the mad infatuation of the Queen and the foolish friendship of the King held Godoy in power, and the end seemed near.

Suddenly on March 28, 1798, his enemies struck. It was a minor affair – merely a matter of whether the standing army should be increased or reduced – something which he would ordinarily have survived. But there were too many forces aligned against him, all working severally and secretly for his downfall. Godoy demanded that the army be increased, but one of his ministers, Saavedra, later assumed to be in the pay of the French, opposed him. From such a minor disagreement the entire Cabinet split and Don Carlos, with his usual stupidity, not knowing which way to turn, and probably acting on a latent jealousy, sided with the opposition.

It was the tiny spark which set fire to Godoy's pasteboard

palace. He had no alternative but to resign. He did, handing his portfolio to the King, who now, with tears in his eyes, regretted what he had done. But it was too late to remedy matters. Arrayed against Godoy were the Infante Ferdinand, the House of Alba, the Church of Rome, the Ambassador of France, the Ambassador of England, and a host of other enemies, big and little, whom he had created for himself, or who simply noted the opposing forces and chose the winning side.

And poor Manuel Godoy, Duke of Alcudia, Prince of the Peace, favourite friend of the King and cherished bedfellow of the Queen, was no longer the power that ruled Spain. With him, in his fall down the palace back stairs, would go the House of Almendares, the House of Frontera Baja, and all the others who had basked in the effulgence which had once lighted Manuel's path. Handsome Manuel. Stupid Manuel.

Some of this Mario had heard about. Other aspects of the situation Ramon explained to him when he went back to his room, after Camporeal and Cleora had left. And now he, Mario, with the background of the Havana waterfront, had been hand-picked to be the next stallion in the royal stables. He, Mario, not long out of the slums of Havana, was chosen to keep the Frontera Baja fortunes intact. With a wreath of vine leaves in his hair, he was to be offered up as a priapic sacrifice on the altar of a haggard queen, masquerading as Venus. He was to feel the touch of Maria Luisa's tired hands, to receive the kisses of her weary lips, and to be something more even than the King of Spain. And apparently there was no way out.

No way out? None but a single avenue of escape – Adan! Adan and Morocco were just across the narrow stretch of water which separated Europe from Africa and Christianity from Islam.

He stopped his restless pacing and spun suddenly in the middle of the room, his decision made.

'Ramon,' he called.

The door of Ramon's room opened. 'Yes, Mario.'

'I'll be damned if I'll do it! I've been pushed around enough, and this is all I can take. I'll not go to Seville! I'll be no male whore for Maria Luisa or anyone else. It's time I started living my own life – not as El Rubio and not as San Mateo, but as myself!'

'And what do you propose to do, my master?' Ramon looked at him anxiously.

'I intend to leave Spain and all the crafty intrigue and all the below-stairs filth that has accumulated in it. What has Spain to offer me?'

'At least you are here tonight instead of swinging on a gallows in Havana, and tomorrow night you will be in Seville. And, who knows, perhaps the day after tomorrow you will be in Madrid, ruling Spain.'

'But I don't want to rule Spain. All I ask is a chance to live my own life.'

'As the Conde de San Mateo, confidant of the King and —'

'And – let's face it, Ramon – lover of the Queen.'

'Would that be so difficult for you, Mario?'

'Damn it, yes! Suddenly it seems the most difficult thing in all the world. For the first time in my life I have caught a glimpse of what real love might be. And this time it is the woman herself I want, not just her body. Indeed, loving her seems to be sufficient, without possessing her.'

'Her Grace, the Duchess?' Ramon glanced at Mario from the corner of his eye.

'Good God, no! Not Cleora.'

'But not —'

'Zaydah? Yes! And although I can never hope to have her, belonging as she does to the one person in the world I can call my friend, yet I love her.'

Ramon sank down on a chair. It was probably the first time he had ever sat while his master was standing. He shook his head in bewilderment.

'But do not worry, my good Ramon,' Mario continued, 'I have no evil intentions against Zaydah. That she is to become Adan's bride makes her sacred to me. But the fact that I do love her casts a different light on other things. Loving her as I do, I cannot seek the arms of the Queen. Can't you understand that?'

Ramon nodded in dazed agreement.

'But I can follow Zaydah to Morocco. I can be near her even though I never see her and, in being near her, I can be with Adan. I can quit myself of Spain forever. True, I'm no Moor, but Adan said that the words I repeated after him made me a Moşlem. Then let me seek the Moors and find sanctuary with them. I'll shed San Mateo as easily as I have shed El Rubio. Both names are accursed. Come, we have no time to lose!' Mario started his impatient pacing again.

Ramon rose slowly. 'And what now, Don Mario?'

'Go to the waterfront. Inquire from the boats if there is one leaving tonight that will take me to Africa. What is the name of that port where Adan was to land?'

Ramon thought for a moment. 'Casablanca, I believe.'

'Then ask for a boat that is going to Casablanca. If none is going, hire one.' He handed Ramon the keys to the money chest. 'In some way we must leave Cadiz before morning, else I shall be starting on my way to Seville. Go, Ramon! In the meantime I shall explain matters to Don Baltazar.'

Ramon came over to where Mario had paused in his pacing and laid his hand gently on Mario's shoulders. 'Think you, Don Mario, that this is the best solution?'

'It's the only solution! If I were to stay in Spain and win the Queen's favour which, God forbid, I do not want, what would my life be then – tied to her royal apron strings? Mario, do this, and Mario, do that and Mario, Mario, Mario! Then the time would come when I would fall from favour like Godoy, and where would I be? Think you that my uncle would smile upon me then?'

Ramon shook his head.

'Then, Ramon, this is the best way and the only way. In Morocco I shall at least have freedom, and that is more than I have enjoyed since I have been San Mateo. So no more argument, Ramon; just go. And when you return we shall make further plans.'

They walked swiftly the length of the corridor, down the steps and across the patio. Mario hesitated in front of Don Baltazar's room, waiting for the big front door to open for Ramon. For an instant he saw Ramon's figure, black against the square of brilliant light; then the big door closed.

Mario found Don Baltazar in his room, seated on a divan, a small writing tablet on his lap.

'Welcome, my son.' The old man held out a thin hand. 'Twice welcome now; my other son, the fiery Adan, has already left me. Soon my Zaydah will be leaving and I shall have none left but you.'

Mario shook his head sadly. 'Ah, but I must also leave you – today, tonight, at the very earliest opportunity.'

Don Baltazar laid down the pen with which he was writing,

wiped it carefully with a bit of soft leather, replaced it in the richly filigreed gold case, slowly put the stopper in the ink bottle, shuffled his papers and then looked up at Mario.

'My hospitality is no longer pleasant to you?'

'Far from that, Don Baltazar. The days I have spent here have been among the happiest of my life, but I had callers this morning.'

'Yes, I know. Her Grace of Almendares and your father's brother, Camporeal.'

'He has no love for me, and yet this morning he came in peace. I am to leave for Seville tomorrow.'

The large dark eyes in the parchment-white face looked up at Mario. 'Your father sent you to me. Until I hear from him that you are to go, nobody has the right to take you away.'

'But, Don Baltazar, if I do not leave for Seville tomorrow, I face prison. I can be sure of that. My uncle does not equivocate. It's either Seville tomorrow or the Inquisition.'

'But I do not understand, my boy.'

Mario explained, and when he came to the part where he was to supplant Godoy in the Queen's affections, Don Baltazar's kindly eyes blazed. But he did not speak until Mario had finished.

'I fear I cannot help you, my son. As a Moor and a Moslem, I have only sufferance here in Spain. The Spaniards hate me, but they do not dare to harm me. As the representative of the Shereefian Empire I am outside their jurisdiction, but the Court of the Inquisition would be happy to stretch me on the rack at the first opportunity. As a Moslem I am afraid I have no influence to exert for you in this matter.'

'But you can help me.' Mario's long legs doubled under him as he sank down on the tiles beside the divan. 'I do not intend to go to Seville.'

'But no? You prefer prison instead? Let me warn you that the dungeons of Spain – either the cells of the Inquisitor General or the dark holes of the Frontera Baja castle – are far from pleasant, and you will land in one or the other if you do not go to Seville.'

'But you forget. I have a friend.' Mario spoke the words proudly. 'Adan wishes me to come to Morocco. It seems that the day our blood mingled we became brothers – and also, it seems that some words I repeated after him made me a Moslem, if not a Moor.'

Don Baltazar turned and looked quickly at Mario. His hands clenched the folds of his robe.

'What were those words, young Mario?'

Mario saw the Moor's apparent distress and hesitated.

'Come, Mario, tell me!' Don Baltazar's request was urgent.

'There is no. . . . There is no God but Allah and Mohammed is His prophet.'

'Do you believe them?'

'I do not know, Don Baltazar. When I see what Christians have done in the name of the gentle Jesus, when I see the inhumanity that man uses against man here in Spain, and hear of the horrible tortures of the Inquisition, what can I believe? True, I have heard that Moslems can be cruel too. But can they be more cruel than Christians, who preach a doctrine of love? I doubt it. But this much I do know: I want to know more about your Lord Mohammed. I know little enough of the Lord Jesus and his saints – except that nobody follows Him today. Therefore let me learn more of Mohammed, and perhaps in learning about him I shall better understand Jesus.'

Don Baltazar laid his thin hand gently on Mario's shoulder. 'You are not the first that has come to this house a Christian and left it a Moslem. Others before you, sickened by the persecutions of the Inquisition, at the risk of their lives have turned to the Prophet of Islam. I believe you, Mario; I have faith in your sincerity. If you wish to go to Africa to join Adan, I shall help you. We must make preparations.'

'I have already begun,' Mario said. 'Just now, before coming here, I sent Ramon to the waterfront to make inquiries about a boat leaving for Africa tonight. I told him to hire one if possible. He will return soon with information.'

Don Baltazar turned quickly and faced Mario. The cool benignity that had marked his features changed. He shook his head, his eyes blazed, and Mario saw his teeth bite his lip.

'Fool that you are, my Mario! Methinks you have signed your death warrant! This house has been guarded by soldiers since your visitors of this morning. Ramon will get no farther than the gates, and, if he does, then it is even worse, for he will be followed and his every word noted. I doubt if you will ever see him again, but, if you do, he will not be the same man that left here this morning. The torture chamber of Cadiz knows how to force the truth from a man. Why didn't you wait, instead of rushing off so impetuously? My men have free passage. No soldier of Spain can touch them. I have a boat at the pier – a swift felucca which can make the passage from here to Casablanca. We shall try to arrange it in spite of what you have done.'

'I should have spoken to you first,' Mario admitted.

'You did what you thought best. *In'sha'allah*. It is as Allah wills.'

'You mean —'

'I mean that nothing ever happens by our own will or our own thoughts. Allah is great. Allah is the all-seeing, the all-knowing, the all-powerful. Everything that happens is the will of Allah.'

'Then' – Mario bowed his head – 'it is as Allah wills.'

Chapter Twenty-seven

CONTRARY TO Don Baltazar's forebodings, Ramon did return, late that afternoon, but not without distressing news. He had spent most of his time in waterfront cafés trying to pick up some information about ships that might be leaving for North Africa. He had finally been informed of one, and had located the vessel and talked with the master. During their conversation Ramon had noticed a sailor standing nearby whom he had seen in the café. He saw the man leave, and then almost immediately a company of soldiers had appeared.

The corporal in charge had questioned Ramon as to who the passenger might be, but Ramon had apparently allayed their suspicions by telling them it was the granddaughter of Don Baltazar. They seemed satisfied, for they had heard of her betrothal and her coming departure. They appeared well-informed about all the details of Don Baltazar's household, including Adan's departure. But Ramon had satisfied them, and they had released him and told him to go back home.

Don Baltazar listened to him with a grim look, and then advised Mario to go to his room and collect what few belongings he would take with him in a single small Moorish bag. He warned Mario to be in readiness to move quickly; Ramon too, because Don Baltazar thought it best that Ramon should accompany him.

Mario's confidence returned with Don Baltazar's efficient planning. Without trying to express his thanks, which he knew would be impossible, Mario went up to his room. Ramon followed him, carrying the small bag Don Baltazar had supplied. Abdullah opened the door and pointed to the bed. There, spread out in orderly folds, Mario saw two complete outfits of Moorish garments – snowy white *djellabahs*, two lengths of thin white muslin for turbans, two long, embroidered Moroccan shirts, voluminous undertrousers of a thin white material and two pairs of yellow *babouches* – heelless slippers with pointed toes.

Ramon disappeared into the small room but returned almost immediately. He piled several small bags of gold coins alongside the clothing on the bed and then disappeared again. When he returned the second time, he carried a small chest full of watches, fobs, rings, chains and other articles of jewellery. He emptied these, along with the gold coins, into the Moroccan bag, padding them with one of Mario's shirts so they would make no noise when carried. There was room left only for Mario's razors and a few toilet articles.

When Ramon had finished, he turned to the two identical outfits of clothes on the bed.

'A bath first, Ramon.' Mario wanted to feel the cool smoothness of the Moorish garments against a clean skin. 'And while I bathe, go below and have the cooks prepare a supper for the two of us.'

The water in the tub was cool and refreshing and the scent of bergamot leaves made Mario drowsy. For the first time in many months he was completely relaxed and happy. He had infinite trust in the ability of Don Baltazar to get him out of Spain. He was now satisfied with the way the dice had fallen, and anxious to put the Court of Spain, Cleora, and Camporeal, yes, even Frontera Baja behind him. He envisioned a new life, uncluttered with courtly double talk, free from the sword that had always been suspended over him as San Mateo – not to mention the hangman's noose that had threatened him as El Rubio.

He laid his head back against the cool marble coping of the tub and closed his eyes. He was content – so content that he did not hear the door open, silently and slowly, inch by inch. He was not aware of another's presence in the room until he caught the same warm perfume that he had smelled the night before, and looked up to see her beautiful face bending over his.

'Mario.' Zaydah put her fingers to her lips and whispered, 'Do not speak aloud. Your whispers must be enough for me, as mine are for you.' She knelt down on the tiles. 'Do not ask me what I am doing here or why I have borrowed the role of a maid so as to come to your bath.'

Mario smiled up at her. 'My body is not entirely unknown to you. I seem to remember that last night —'

She waved his words aside with an impatient hand. 'That does not matter. Look at me, Mario. Look at me without my veil and tell me that the kiss you gave me last night had more meaning than those you and Adan squandered on the gypsy girls you sought.'

Mario did look at her, but her face was so very close to his own that he had to push her gently away so he might see its pale ivory oval, the dark lustrous pools of her eyes with the deep fringe of lashes, and the warm, red curve of her mouth. He had never seen her entire face before, but he had constructed an image of her beauty. How false that image was! How vain his feeble imaginings! Never in all his dreams had he pictured her as beautiful as she was at this moment.

She moved closer and stretched out her arms, gathering his damp head to her and pressing it close to her warm body. 'Oh, Mario *mio*, we have only minutes instead of hours – for I have heard that you leave for Morocco tonight – but in these precious minutes I must tell you how much, how very much I love you. Do you realize what that admission means to me? But when my whole being yearns for you, no silly code of conventions can keep me from telling you. So I thrust myself upon you, not knowing whether my love for you is returned or not, but knowing only this one thing – that from the day you came here, life has held nothing else for me but you, Mario.'

'But your grandfather! Where is he?' Mario turned his face so that he might look up at her.

'He is down at the docks. There is nobody in the house but the servants, and I have seen to it that they are all occupied. Your Ramon will not return for an hour; the cooks will keep him busy in the kitchen. And Abdullah is at the door to warn me if Don Baltazar returns. So now, my love, for these paltry stolen moments that we have alone, let us live in them and in each other. We may never have them again. Oh, Mario, tell me that you love me, that I can believe in the kiss you gave me last night!'

He sank his head deeper into her arms, feeling the rigid points of her breasts press through the thin gauze of her dress against his cheek. He pulled her face down close to his own, and his mouth sought hers in another kiss. It lasted through centuries and extended into eternity. Cradled in her arms, he felt the water in the bath engulf him. With her lips pressed against his own, he swam in a delirium of sensation, hardly knowing what was happening until suddenly it was over and he was descending to the depths. Her lips released him and her arms loosed their hold.

He sought the breath to speak. 'Last night, Zaydah, was the

beginning, and now this is the ending. It was well, Zaydah, that you caused my passion to spend itself so quickly; otherwise my head could not have ruled my actions. Believe me, Zaydah, this must be the end.'

'You repudiate my love for you?' She pushed his head away from her and sat back on her heels. 'Why did you let me so abase myself? Why did you give me that proof of your love which you released so freely, and then spurn my love in your next breath?'

He reached over the marble edge for the towel Ramon had laid out for him, stood up and tied it around his waist, then stepped out of the bath. Gently he reached down, took her hands, and drew her up to him.

'I'll tell you now, my Zaydah, that I do love you. Never forget that. How much I love you I shall never know, for I have never really known what the word meant. Even now – when all desire has left me – I still love you and still want you, and that, believe me, has never happened to me before. But, Zaydah, that is all I can do or say. If you were free, and I were free, it would be very different. Oh, if some power could change us into two poor peasants, meeting together on a moonlight night, free to declare our love for each other! But we are not peasants and we are not poor and, above all, we are not free.'

'But you are a man and I am a woman.' Her arms encircled his dampness.

'Yes, I am a man who is about to flee from Spain rather than rot in some dungeon. I am a man who fled from Cuba with the shadow of the gallows over me. I am a man who fled from the Azores with this.' He pointed to the scar on his shoulder. 'And now I am fleeing again, this time from the wrath of my uncle and the displeasure of the Queen. Where think you I go for sanctuary?'

'To Adan,' she answered, her lips pressed against his chest.

'Yes, to Adan. There is no other place I can go. Tonight when I quit Spain I shall put it all behind me and seek sanctuary with your Adan. Think you that I could despoil him of you, and then go to him as a suppliant? What would I say to him – "Adan, I have come to you, but, before coming, I took something very precious away from you"?'

She raised her head and looked up at him. 'You heard

Adan's words last night, as I did,' she answered. 'He does not love me. I shall be but one of many in his *hareem*.'

'He has chosen you to be the mother of his sons.'

'And I could be the mother of your sons. Oh, Mario, what sons they would be! Let us leave now, at this moment. We can ride towards Portugal and find shelter there.'

'With Camporeal's men, the Queen's Dragoons, Don Baltazar's Moors and Almendares' brigands all behind us?'

'But we could at least die together,' she pleaded.

'Much as I love you, Zaydah, I love life even more. No! We must forget this folly. We must both believe it has never happened. Tonight I go to Adan. In a week or so you will follow. Then we shall be there together, you and I, in the red city of Marrakech. At night when you look out of your windows and up at the snow-capped mountains behind the city, know this: that I too am there looking at those same mountains, wanting you, craving the touch of your hands and the taste of your lips. Let us know that we shall be together, even though separated by the walls of Adan's *hareem*. Let us know that a love like ours can exist in spite of those walls —'

Mario cut his words short, pushed her from him and walked quickly across the room. She followed him with little running steps. He opened the door and looked down the long gallery. There were moving lights in the patio below; torches flickered among the orange leaves. He brushed his lips against hers and pushed her gently through the door. Her veils caught the light of the torches as she ran along the corridor and down the steps to the courtyard.

Mario reached for the *djellabah* on the bed and slipped it over his head. His feet sought the yellow slippers as he wound the length of muslin around his head. The door burst open and Ramon entered.

'We're caught!' He almost screamed the words. 'The soldiers are below, but they are not the soldiers of the Queen nor the men of Camporeal.'

'Then who are they?'

'They wear the uniform of the Inquisitor General,' Ramon cried. 'They have Don Baltazar with them, and they are coming for you. I hear their steps on the tiles in the gallery. *Dios mio*, Mario, they are here!' He stepped back as a man entered the room – a man dressed in black and silver, with a black mask over his face.

'You are Mario, Count of San Mateo?' The lips under the mask formed the question.

'No,' Mario answered. 'I am Prince Adan, son of the Emir of Marrakech, affianced to the granddaughter of Don Baltazar.'

'You lie, Mario of San Mateo. The young Prince left Cadiz this morning. We keep strict watch of all the infidels who enter and leave Spain. We know who you are, and that you plan to quit Spain tonight. Most important of all, we know that you have become a Moslem.'

'Then at least you should respect me as a man.'

'Bah! Simply because you do not seek the bed of Maria Luisa? That matters little to us. We are interested in only one thing. Some months ago, according to our information, you repeated certain words of allegiance to another faith. But, San Mateo, the Church is a Holy Mother. She does not let her children stray. She is always anxious to reclaim those children who wander away from her – and tonight she reclaims you.' He turned towards the door and beckoned. Two other men entered and pulled up the long sleeves of Mario's *djellabah*. With a thin cord they bound his arms behind him and pushed him roughly to the door. Ramon started to follow him, but the masked man shoved him back.

'We do not want you, slave.'

Ramon's eyes met Mario's. Then he turned to the man in front of him. 'And I too,' he shouted, 'I too declare that there is no God but Allah and Mohammed is His prophet.'

'You've just signed your own death warrant, black.' The man's rapier flashed from its scabbard.

'Stop!' Mario's voice had a ring of authority. 'The man is my property. If you represent the Church, you cannot kill. Even the Inquisitor General offers any man a trial.'

The sword slipped back into its scabbard. 'Then start moving, both of you.' They walked along the corridor, down the steps, across the patio, and under the orange trees where the fountain tinkled, and then they saw Don Baltazar surrounded by another group of masked men.

He reached his hand out towards Mario.

'*In'shah'allah*, my son.'

Mario looked back at him. '*In'shah'allah*,' he replied.

Then he turned to Ramon, beside him. 'Why did you do it, Ramon?'

'Because I did not want you to be alone, Mario.'

Chapter Twenty-eight

THE RIDE in the interior of the shrouded coach was a series of confused impressions to Mario. He could hear the rattle of the horses' shoes on the cobbles and the screech of the iron-shod wheels as they turned a corner. Ramon braced against him to keep himself from falling.

How long they travelled he did not know, though it was certainly for several hours. The cobbles had long since given way to the soft dirt of country roads. At times the coach moved slowly, as though it were going uphill, and at other times Mario heard the whine of the brake against the wheels as they went downhill. Finally the coach stopped. There was a hum of voices outside, muffled commands were shouted, a key rasped in the lock on the door and it was opened cautiously.

A dim and watery early morning light crept into the coach, and beyond the open door Mario caught glimpses of grey masonry walls. Rough hands pulled them from the coach and they were led down a narrow arched passageway to a crude latrine, where, under the unblinking eyes that watched them from behind black masks, they gained momentary relief and comfort from the long journey.

Once more they were pushed down the passageway, but instead of returning to the coach they were herded into a long, low room where the shadows of night still hung from the smoky rafters. There were a rough table, chairs, and more masked soldiers in black. There were also wooden trenchers on the tables, filled with a hot porridge that gave off a wholesome steamy scent. They both ate silently and, although the food was nearly tasteless, it was warm and comforting, and Mario began to feel somewhat refreshed.

As soon as they had finished they were again conducted back to the coach, and again the door was slammed shut and locked. Gradually the blackness inside changed to a dusty light and, dim as it was, Mario was able to see Ramon's face. In whispers, so as not to be overheard, they discussed their situation. But whether their arrest was due to the Queen, Camporeal, the Duke, friends of Godoy, or the Inquisitor

General, they could not determine. The black masks of the soldiers, however, and their livery of black and silver, together with their refusal to speak, all pointed to the Inquisition. This was cold comfort, but it at least meant that they would have the formality of a trial – even if they had, in accordance with Inquisition custom, already been adjudged guilty. They knew what arrest by the Church meant – torture, and after that, death; the Church was merciless to heretics.

But, precarious as their position was, the brief stop with the chance to stretch their legs, the warm porridge, and the glimpse of the outside world had heartened them. They were together, alive, and so far unharmed, and there was a small chance of survival.

Regardless of the gravity of their present situation, Mario felt relieved on one count. Everything had happened so quickly, from the moment he had held Zaydah in his arms, that he had had no chance to do anything he should now blame himself for. Had the soldiers delayed only an hour, he might have yielded to the temptation. Zaydah had pressed close to him, and her kisses had already begun rekindling the fire in his veins.

The soldiers had timed their arrival well. At least he had not broken faith with Adan – even if he could hardly take the credit for that himself. But he had seen Zaydah's face and felt her lips against his own. No matter what happened to him now, he would never forget that one brief moment of ecstasy when he had pillowed his head against her breast and tasted eternity. Nothing could ever erase that memory.

Gradually the brightness disappeared from the cracks around the door and, after some time, the cracks themselves seemed to disappear, bringing the realization that they had been travelling all day. There had been several halts, which Ramon guessed from the noise outside had been to change horses, but when the coach stopped again there was absolute quiet. They had at last reached the end of their journey.

Once more they heard the key in the lock and saw the door open. This time the flickering light of a torch illuminated the inside of the coach. An arm, uniformed in dull black with silver lacings, beckoned them out. They stepped to the ground and then were blindfolded with thick black cloths and led down a sort of paved corridor, the sound of their footsteps echoing back to them. They heard a door creak on its hinges, and then a few more steps and they were halted by a sharp command.

No light penetrated the blindfolds, but they could hear movement around them. There was a rustle of heavy silk, a laboured breathing, whispered commands which they could not distinguish. Then, without warning, the cloth was whipped from Mario's eyes, and he stood blinking in the bright light. As his eyes became accustomed to the brilliance, he realized that they were in a large room with a lofty ceiling supported by arched pillars of stone. There were a multitude of candles in tall iron candlesticks standing on the floor and hanging from the ceiling in wrought-iron chandeliers.

Facing Mario, some distance down the room, was a long table, and he could see a number of shadowy people standing behind it. More prominent than these was the man seated at the table. He, too, wore black and his face was hidden by a length of black cloth, pendant from a conical black cap. Holes in the cloth showed a pair of eyes high-lighted with pinpoints of light from the candelabra on either end of the table. The man sat motionless; even the parchment-coloured hands with their exquisitely long fingers, lying on the table, did not move.

'Step forward, Moor.' The voice from behind the mask was low, with an overtone of cruelty in it.

Mario looked behind him quickly to see who might be addressed, half fearing that poor Don Baltazar had been arrested.

'I mean you.' The long fingers pointed at Mario. 'And the poor deluded Negro with you. Come closer, both of you.'

Mario did not move, and reached out a restraining hand to keep Ramon back.

'I am no Moor.' He planted his feet wide apart and placed his hands on his hips. His voice rang out strong and clear, without a tremor. 'I am Mario, Count of San Mateo, the son of the Marques of Frontera Baja.'

A gesture of the thin hand on the table brushed the answer aside. The eyes between the two holes in the mask glinted as the man leaned slowly forward. The pendant cloth puffed out slightly from his breath as he spoke.

'A few hours ago you were only too willing to be a Moor.'

'Because I was trying to escape from Spain. Now there is no reason for me to make such a claim.'

'No?' The single syllable slapped back at him. 'So you have become a Christian again, in spite of your Moorish rags?'

'I am now the same as I was a few hours ago, nothing more and nothing less.' Mario did not quit his position. 'I have been other things before I was San Mateo, but now I am San Mateo.'

'Then why were you, the son of a grandee of Spain, trying to quit the country? What reason had you for leaving?'

'Do you not know?' Mario flung the question back to him.

'I ask the questions here, not you. I alone give the orders. I told you to step forward.' The voice was impatient.

'And if I refuse?'

The questioner leaned back in his chair and Mario felt rather than saw the smile of sarcasm on his lips.

'It might be easier if you did not refuse. Come! Come nearer. I would speak with you, and I refuse to scream the length of the room.'

Mario clutched Ramon's arm and together they walked to the edge of the table. Only the polished boards separated him from the man in black.

The thin fingers drummed on the table a moment, then one hand raised and pointed to Mario.

'Now answer my question. Why were you fleeing from Spain?'

'Not wanting to be a kept man for Her Majesty's pleasure was one reason. Wanting to keep my head on my shoulders was another. And further, I am sick of Spain and its rotten intrigue, its plotting and counterplotting. I do not know where I stand from one moment to the next. First I am told that my uncle, Camporeal, is my enemy and wants to kill me. Then he comes to me, bribing me with friendship—'

'So Camporeal came to you and made you a proposition – and you refused?'

'No, I did not refuse. I agreed to come to the Alcazar today. But instead I changed my mind and decided to leave Spain.'

Mario's inquisitor turned, beckoned for a masked soldier to come to him, wrote a few words hurriedly on a scrap of paper, and waved him away. He turned to Mario again.

'It hardly seems natural that you would prefer to live in an infidel country with unbelievers, rather than follow the suggestion of your uncle. You were offered a high position in

Spain, yet you refused it. You preferred a life with infidels—'

'To being slobbered over by an old whore, even if she is the Queen of Spain!'

The hand rose slowly, palm outward, in a gesture of warning. 'Be careful, young man. In addition to your other crimes, you can also be guilty of *lèse majesté*.'

Mario laughed. 'If calling the Queen of Spain a whore is a crime, then indeed I am guilty. Along with a million others.'

The man stood up, reached his hands across the table and grabbed the front of Mario's *djellabah*. With more strength than Mario would have credited to the delicate hands, the robe was torn from neckline to hem.

'Regardless of what Her Majesty is or does,' he screamed, 'she is still Her Most Catholic Majesty of Spain! Strip yourself of those accursed robes – we'll have no sign of the heathen Moor here! Cast them aside, I say.'

The *djellabah* fell from Mario's shoulders and he stood naked before his accuser.

'And now,' the voice continued on its pitch of hysteria, 'the important question. Are you or are you not an infidel?'

'I do not know.'

'Then – are you a Christian?'

Mario shook his head in doubt. 'That I do not know either.'

'Then pray tell us,' the voice shouted in exasperation, 'what *do* you believe?'

Mario placed both hands on the table and leaned forward until his face was inches away from the mask with the burning eyes behind it.

'You ask me what I believe, and once more I tell you I do not know. How can I know? Since the day I was born I have been pushed, first by one hand and then another. I have been hounded through the streets of Havana because I stole to keep my mother and myself from starving. Hers was the only love I ever knew, except for the caresses of some sweaty whore.'

The conical cap tipped slightly to one side and the voice behind it jeered, 'A most pitiful story indeed. But now you are no longer a Cuban pimp, you are —'

'A Spanish nobleman? Yes! Suddenly I was lifted out of the gutters of Havana and given clean clothes to wear. But still everyone's hand has been against me. And you ask if I am a Christian. If being a Christian means being kind – being filled with love for one's fellow creatures – then I have known too little of that in my life among Christians. If you and others like you profess to being followers of Christ, then indeed I have no desire to be one of you, for the God I worship cannot be one of hate, distrust, suspicion and lies. And that is all I have found in Spain or in Cuba, except for the months I have been in the house of Don Baltazar.'

'The Moorish infidel!'

'Yes!' Mario was shouting now. 'But infidel or not, he was good to me. He is an honourable man. And the young Prince Adan who was his guest was my friend.'

'Only a friend?' The sarcasm in the voice was thinly veiled. 'Ah, we know these Moors so well. Perhaps your delight in this so-called friendship was what decided you against granting your favours to the Queen. Did your young Moor make you less than a man? You were with him much, both waking and sleeping. Now you wish to follow him to Morocco. It would appear that you cannot bear to be separated, that you are more than just friends.'

It took a moment for the implication of the words to sink in. Then Mario found himself shouting in anger. 'Yes! Adan is more than a friend. We are brothers, and we love each other as brothers do – and not as you imply with your filthy words. I love him as a brother and I respect him as a brother – and that's more than I can say for any damned Spaniard. Therefore, if I were to choose a religion to pattern myself after, it would be his and not yours.' He shifted his weight suddenly and his right arm shot up, grasping the hanging black cloth, and ripped it from the man's face. Mario retreated a step in stunned surprise. His inquisitor with the gleaming eyes was none other than his uncle. These were the same eyes he had seen in Don Baltazar's house, the eyes of Camporeal!

The full lips parted in a smile to show an even row of white teeth. 'So. . . . We shall talk face to face, my dear nephew. Perhaps it is better. You seem surprised to see me here, *verdad?*'

'Nothing surprises me here in Spain,' Mario found the words to answer.

'The Inquisition has its lay brothers as well as the clergy, and the good Cardinal Lorenzana was willing to make me his deputy in your case. So you tried to slip from my hands when I had only good to offer you. Very well! Be that as it may. But now, Mario of San Mateo, you are in the hands of the Inquisitor General – and you won't skip through his hands so easily.' Camporeal beckoned behind him, and a robed figure stepped out from the shadows. 'Give this man some clothes to cover his nakedness and then conduct him and the Negro to a cell.'

The man reappeared in a moment with a pair of rough trousers and a worn shirt, which he handed to Mario. Other robed figures came from behind the table, surrounded Mario and Ramon and started to lead them away. They had only gone a few steps when Camporeal halted them with a word. He walked from behind the table, crossed the tiles and stood directly in front of Mario. As he regarded him, the ghost of a smile flitted across his face.

'Alas, poor Maria Luisa! She will never know all that she has missed. *Ay, qué lástima!* She would be desolated were she to know what I have seen. If she were here now, you would be prime minister of Spain within the hour. But what she does not know, she cannot miss. Doubtless we can find a worthy substitute.'

'It should not be too difficult.' Mario forced an answering smile to his own lips.

'On the other hand, it may be well-nigh impossible. However, I must not forget one thing. You are my nephew – the very son of my adored brother. Therefore I must show some avuncular interest in you. You may keep the black fool with you while I think of some suitable punishment for you both.' His finger reached out and traced the scarlet thread of Adan's scar on Mario's chest. 'The mark of your blood brotherhood, eh, Mario? You see, we know much about you. But I think we could perhaps do an even better job than your Moorish prince.'

He turned and walked back to the table, as the black-robed men led Mario and Ramon from the room.

Chapter Twenty-nine

THEY LOST track of the number of days they spent in the cell of the Inquisitor General. At first, Ramon had begun to make a mark for every day, but the day came when he could not remember whether or not he had made a mark for the day before. But they agreed that it must be nearly three weeks since they had been brought from Cadiz to Seville – which was where they had decided they were.

Contrary to what they had anticipated, their cell was not some damp underground dungeon, but was instead located on the upper story of what seemed to be a large ecclesiastical building – possibly a monastery. They heard bells at frequent intervals, and the faraway tones of an organ. Although a blank wall of stone faced their cell window, there was still a little slit of sky that could be seen around one corner of the wall, and against the sky there was the outline of a tall tower. Ramon believed it to be the famous Giralda tower – a Moorish remnant which had been incorporated as part of the Cathedral of Seville. And if this was Seville, it followed that they were under the jurisdiction of the Inquisitor General, Cardinal Lorenzana.

Mario was grateful that Ramon had been allowed to remain with him. Had he been alone he would not have heard the sound of a human voice. None of their jailers ever spoke, and the only sign of animation was the flash of bright black eyes that peered from behind the holes in their masks. Three meals a day arrived promptly; it was plain food but wholesome, and, except on fast days, there was plenty of it.

Their cell was comfortably large, much larger than the dark hole Mario had been confined in during his stay in the *carcel* in Havana. It was light, dry and clean. The walls were starkly whitewashed, without the embellishment of the lewd words and pornographic scratchings of the Havana cell. Two rough cots, not uncomfortable, were covered with clean straw mattresses and coarse blankets. A deal table, two rush-bottomed chairs, and two wooden bowls completed the furnishings – except for the large black crucifix which filled nearly all of one wall. On it hung an attentuated pain-wracked figure which dripped painted drops of blood. It was difficult to reconcile these hideous, twisted features with the gentle Jesus.

More and more, Mario's eyes strayed to this emaciated figure of pain. He was both repelled and fascinated by it. The features of the face were so contorted by suffering and grief that there was nothing left of love, or gentleness, or even of humanity. The long, narrow eyes were closed, but it seemed to Mario that at times they opened mutely to plead with him to wrench out the cruel nails that impaled the lifeless hands and feet to the black timbers of the cross.

Often, while he and Ramon were talking, Mario would get up walk across the room, and stand in front of the figure. It seemed to cry out in its horrible pain, and at times Mario felt that the wooden limbs writhed in their agony. Its torture obsessed him, and he had an insane desire to wrench it from the cross and give it rest and peace, in the hope that some other expression than suffering might possess the carved and painted face.

They talked, the two of them – master and slave – and of one thing they were both certain: whatever lay ahead of them would be far from pleasant. Death would be the easiest punishment, if it could only come quickly, without torture. They had more of the stigma of unbelief than most; both of them were avowed infidels; their heresy was not merely suspect, it had been declared openly.

'Why did you do it, Ramon?' Mario said at one point, looking up at Ramon, who was pacing the room.

'Do what?'

'Proclaim yourself an infidel, when all the time you knew as well as I did that you are not.' Mario pointed to the black crucifix on the plastered wall. 'You know you believe in Him. You pray to Him and to His mother. Then why did you deny Him?'

Ramon stopped his pacing and stood before the crucifix. He studied it closely and then gave a slight shudder. The pink tip of his tongue came between his white teeth. He lowered his eyelids, swallowed heavily, and then his fingers drew the sign of the cross in the air. He turned slowly and regarded Mario, but his eyes seemed to look through him to something beyond the walls of their cell.

'I did it, Mario, because I thought by serving you I could serve Him even better. He was willing to sacrifice Himself for the world. Surely I could do as much for you.'

'But *Dios mio*. . . .'

'By what god do you swear now, Mario?'

'Ask me not, Ramon. I still do not know. But surely I cannot accept such devotion from you. I've done nothing to deserve it. I've always taken from you rather than given.'

Ramon crossed the room slowly and sat down at the table opposite Mario.

'Perhaps you have given me more than you realize, Mario. But let's not talk about that now. We're in this together. How we got here is still a question in my mind. Evidently the Inquisition knew that you had more than a passing interest in Islam. They seem to have followed your every movement at the house of Don Baltazar. It is said they have spies everywhere, and now I believe it.'

Mario nodded his head slowly in agreement. 'But why did they delay so long in arresting me?'

'I think your words to Adan were only a pretext to bring you here. Without knowing it, you became the centre of a dangerous political intrigue. Camporeal thought that you might serve him, and when you were unwilling to play along with him, he took this as an easy way of getting rid of you.'

'He could have killed me on the spot.'

'Not Camporeal! That would be too easy and too simple. He's the cat that likes to play with the mouse before he kills it.'

'Granted, Ramon. But now you are here too. You have sacrificed your freedom, perhaps even your life, for me.'

'No, Mario, not for you alone, but for Him.' Ramon pointed to the figure on the cross. 'You see, my faith in Him was all that kept me going in the past. A slave's life is not an easy one. I had to have something to love, either God or man, and until you came into my life, Mario, I had only God. And loving God is an affection one does not easily forget.' His head sank in his hands and he remained motionless.

Mario finally broke the silence. 'You once said my words to Adan were stupid words. You cannot say that. What have I to thank Him for?' He clenched his fist and shook it at the crucifix. 'Nothing! Nothing, nothing, nothing!' Mario stood up suddenly and pushed back his chair. He ran across the room to the cross. 'See that face of pain! See that blood! He couldn't help Himself; how can He help me? But I can stop His suffering, Ramon. I can put an end to it. I've looked at that tortured face as long as I can stand it!'

Mario was sobbing. He reached up and wrenched the figure from the cross. The dry, brittle wood parted in his hands and he dashed the broken image to the floor, stamped on it with frenzied feet until only a mass of dusty chips remained on the tiles. 'Now' – he returned to where Ramon was sitting and pointed to the wall where the black cross hung empty and naked – 'He will bother me no more, and you need not say you have sacrificed yourself to Him. To me, yes! That I can understand, and can thank you for. But not to Him!'

Ramon reached up one hand and placed it on Mario's arm. 'Quiet,' he said softly. 'You have aroused the guards. I hear them on the stairs.'

The bolt grated slowly and the door swung out. Camporeal walked slowly into the room, his long black robes making an even blacker shadow on the floor. With downcast head, he looked at the chips on the floor, then raised his eyes to the black cross still on the wall. Reverently he knelt, swept the chips together, and placed them tenderly in a fold of his robe. Only then did he look at Mario.

'It matters no longer, Mario of San Mateo, why or how you happen to be here. This one thing that you have done is enough. You stand convicted even without a trial. Your punishment will follow quickly. I hope you are prepared.'

'I am ready for anything.' Mario tried to keep the quaver from his voice.

'Anything? Have you any idea of what the cellars of this building hold?'

'I have only one life. When you finish that, it marks an end to my suffering.'

'Ah yes, but I do not intend to let you off so easily. Your father was right when he told you I desired your death, but now, I think, in view of what you have just done, it might be better that you live. In the eyes of the Church you are already dead, so nothing we do can possibly harm you. You are unfortunate, my nephew, because you cannot even make your peace with God. That consolation has been denied you.'

Mario felt a new courage. He walked over to his uncle and looked steadily at the hard, black eyes in the sallow face.

'*In'sha'allah*,' he said slowly. 'I only recently learned those words, and if you do not know what they are I shall tell you. They are Arabic and they mean, 'As Allah wills'."

Chapter Thirty

THE HEAVY door had scarcely closed behind Camporeal when it once again banged open and several masked jailers entered the room. In a moment both Mario's and Ramon's hands were pulled behind their backs and tied with thin cords that ate painfully into their wrists. They scarcely sensed the descent of the spiral stone steps that led them down, down, down until they emerged into a hall below. Squat pillars of rough-hewn stone supported the low stone vaulting of the roof, and a thick, resinous smoke from the burning torches wreathed the pillars with undulating grey streamers.

Looming out of the shadows they could see the ominous outlines of strange machines standing on the floor and propped against the walls. These were the machines that broke a man's soul as they tore his body. These were the wheels that turned slowly but inexorably until every bone was broken; the racks that stretched a man's body until his bones separated at their joints and there was nothing left but a skin full of loose bones. There were coffins, cunningly fashioned and lined with sharpened spikes that closed and locked the still-breathing victim inside.

Ramon shuddered and Mario followed his heavy-lidded stare to where a fire blazed beneath a small cauldron of bubbling molten lead. Beyond that, another fire contained within its embers the white-hot glowing tips of pincers. Wherever they looked in this sinister room a new form of terror greeted them.

Mario did not lack for physical courage, but here he was helpless, and in this helplessness he felt fear – the same overwhelming fear that had caused him to clutch the bars in the jail back in Havana. He looked at Ramon and received encouragement from the other's calm gaze. Strangely enough, there was no fear in Ramon's eyes. He looked steadily at Mario and, although his lips moved, his voice came in hoarse whispers.

'I do not fear what may happen to me as much as I do what they will do to you. I can stand it, Mario, because I shall be doing it for a purpose. Only have courage, Mario, and death will be a sweet release.'

His words were cut short as a door opened, letting in a brilliant light from the room beyond. Camporeal entered, calling on his way to one of the masked figures, who brought a chair and placed it directly in front of Mario. Camporeal seated himself with elaborate care, straightened the folds of his long black robe, and regarded his nephew.

'As you know,' he barked, 'we have no sympathy with heretics. We might, if pressed, be able to find some small morsel of sympathy for an infidel – one who had been born in ignorance and knew no better – but for you, Mario, no. You have deliberately cast yourself away from our great Mother, the Church – and in addition you have committed such a heinous act of sacrilege that we can find no sympathy. Therefore, we must try to fit the punishment to the crime. These' – he waved his hand at the instruments on the walls and along the floor – 'are scarcely adequate. They might cause you some moments of exquisite pain, but then your suffering would end in death.'

'So let it come soon. Kill me,' Mario said, stretching the cords around his wrists, 'as I would kill you were my hands unbound.'

'Be not over-anxious,' Camporeal's hand raised a handkerchief of delicate linen and lace to his nose. 'Ay, but you stink, my nephew. Step back! Your unwashed strench offends me.' He waved the perfumed handkerchief in front of his face. 'Now where were we? Oh yes, you were desiring death. Don't worry, it will come in good time, as it does to all men. We could open your veins and pour in molten lead. Or' – he pointed to the pincers glowing hot in the brazier – 'we could strip the muscles from your bones with those. Then there is the rack, the wheel, and yonder coffin called the Spanish Maiden. But all of them wrack a body so that death is almost inevitable. We have decided to use none of them. I deem them too crude for one of my own family. They lack a certain refinement.' He leaned forward in his chair and his voice became heavily confidential. 'We shall cause you no pain, either of you.' He regarded Ramon, who stood at Mario's side with head bowed. 'You too, black,' he asked, 'you have also transferred your faith?'

Ramon did not answer.

'Methinks you are not so devout a follower of Islam as my nephew. Possibly that's because you have no Moslem brother whom you love. Nevertheless, you did profess the Islamic creed, and for that you will be punished along with my nephew.'

Camporeal looked at Mario and Ramon for a moment, then summoned the black-masked men to him. 'Seize them both and to the racks with them!'

As soon as he had spoken, strong hands grabbed Mario, stripped the clothes from him, and carried him across the room to a wooden frame that stood up from the floor like the posts of a crude bed. The tight bonds were cut from his hands, but almost instantly both his hands and feet were strapped to the wooden supports. He turned his head quickly and saw that Ramon was being tied to a similar contraption. Mario let his head fall back. There was nothing to support the weight of his body, and it sagged painfully between the posts, the dead weight pulling at his wrists and ankles.

'Straighten them out!' Camporeal's words made the men jump to the wheels at the head and foot of the framework. 'Now turn!'

Mario felt his body stiffen as the wheels turned. He could hear the metal ratchet click into the notch as each turn was made, and he could feel his arms and legs stretching until his body was taut and straight between the frames. Camporeal came over and felt of his arms. He ran his hands lightly along the tense muscles of Mario's legs. 'Enough,' he said. 'One more turn and you'll pull his bones apart, and we do not want that to happen. Now, straighten out the black and start to work.'

His hand reached down, clutched Mario's hair, and jerked his head up. 'In some ways, my nephew, you are most fortunate. Allowing for the temporary discomfort that you are undergoing, you shall feel no further pain. Merely a few pricks of the needle. See?' He reached to a nearby table and held up a handful of long steel needles. 'They will not hurt you much, especially when an expert' – he inclined his head to a man who was already busy at the table beside Mario – 'works on you.'

The man leaned over Mario. He seemed to be mixing some sort of powdery liquid in a little bowl, stirring it with a wooden spoon. Then another bowl, and still another. He placed them in a row on the table and shuffled away, only to return with a large piece of white paper which he fitted neatly over Mario's chest and belly. It reached from his neck to his groin. Cloth tapes held the paper securely against his skin.

His head was stretched so far back he could not see what was on the paper, but he could see the man who had been working over him take a tiny hammer, dip one of the needles in a bowl and place the point of it through the paper against Mario's chest. He felt a tiny prick as the needle penetrated his skin. It was not painful, scarcely uncomfortable. The initial prick was quickly followed by another, still another, and another. The man worked with astonishing rapidity, changing needles quickly, forcing the points in with delicate blows of the tiny hammer.

The stretching tension on Mario's wrists and ankles became unbearable. His whole body was taut to the point of breaking, but still the man worked over him – a quick dip of the needle, a puncture, another dip, another puncture. Mario forced strength into his neck muscles to turn his head partially, and he could see that another man was standing over Ramon, repeating the same process. With an effort that cost him his last bit of strength, he raised his head and looked at Camporeal, who was standing over him. Then he let his head sink back, and as it fell, he lost consciousness and was swallowed up in a sea of blackness that had neither beginning nor end.

Gradually he was aware of light. As he forced his eyes open, he found that his hands and feet were no longer bound. He could feel the welcome support of the stone paving under his back. Slowly, he was able to raise himself to a sitting position. As he sat up, he looked down on his chest and saw a blur of colours on his skin. He closed his eyes, shook his head, then opened his eyes again. The lines of colour were still there.

'What have they done to me?' he gasped.

'The same as they did to me,' Ramon answered from beside him. 'Look at me, and you will see yourself as if you were looking in a mirror.'

Mario's eyes focused more clearly, and he regarded Ramon. At first it was difficult to see the coloured lines on the man's dark skin, but gradually they took form, and Mario saw the outlines of a cross, extending down from the throat to the thick matted hair of the groin, and across the chest from one nipple to the other. In the centre was the same pain-wracked figure which he had torn from the cross in the upper room, only this time it was engraved on Ramon's flesh. Mario looked down at his own chest. Again he saw the same figure, the same cross, only on his white skin the lines of blue and black and red showed up more clearly.

His eyes sought Ramon's, but Ramon did not speak. He was looking beyond Mario to Camporeal, who sat casually in a chair, one leg thrown across the carved wooden arm.

'Think you that you will ever forget the church you renounced?' His question was directed to both of them, but it was at Mario that he looked. 'No, I think not. You will have a constant reminder as long as you live. The only way you can efface it is to carve open your own belly, and I doubt if you have the courage to do that.'

Mario regarded him sullenly as Camporeal got to his feet, but he said nothing.

'And now,' Camporeal continued, 'now that you have a lasting reminder of that which you spurned, we are going to see you take full advantage of it and the protection it will give you.' He rose and came over to where Mario was standing, and ran his fingers lightly over the swollen outlines of the cross. 'A beautiful job, Don José.' He smiled at the masked man in the background. 'A really beautiful job. Quite a work of art. I most admire the curves of the crucifix. Italian, I would say, rather than Spanish. Did you by chance copy the one in the Queen's chapel in the Escorial?'

The man nodded his head in assent.

'Then you are to be congratulated, Mario, and you too, black, for the original was designed by Cellini. Little did that admirable artist think that his design would some day be reproduced on warm, living flesh. Indeed, Mario, you should feel most complimented.'

The smile faded from Camporeal's face. 'And now,' he said, 'our time is running short. You and I are soon to part, Mario. I doubt very much if we shall ever see each other again – and, believe me, for this I am rather sad. If things had been different, we might have been very close to each other, Mario of San Mateo. Perhaps, it would have been simpler to have let you die on the rack, but I would rather you suffered a little to compensate my dear brother for all the trouble he took in finding you – and also to give you time to contemplate the decoration on your chest.' He sighed and shook his head. 'And so we part, Mario. You to a weird sort of living hell.' He stopped and looked expectantly at Mario. 'Do you not wish to ask me where you are going?'

'Would you answer me if I did?'

Camporeal rubbed his hands together and smiled. Still with his handkerchief in front of his nose, he stepped closer and let his finger trace the outlines of the cross on Mario's skin. When he removed it, there was a thin film of blood on his finger. He wiped it on his handkerchief and smiled.

'Our blood of Frontera Baja is not as blue as I might have expected. Oh yes! As to where you are going. I shall tell you, but first let me tell you this. Catholic Spain is not entirely at enmity with her neighbour to the south, Islamic Morocco. Oh no! The Sultan Suleiman in his palace at Fez always appreciates a gift from Spain and, in return, he occasionally does some small favours for us, when requested. So what better gift could we send him than two Christian slaves? And they are Christian slaves beyond cavil, for they bear the mark of their faith indelibly tattooed on their chests.

'You will have your wish, Mario. You go to Morocco – not as you might have wanted, to your dear friend and brother, his young highness, the Shereef of Marrakech, but instead to the Sultan Suleiman at Fez. The Sultan needs workmen to build the walls of his city, erect his mosques, and beautify his palace. Already a swift courier has preceded you to His Shereefian Majesty – along with, I might add, a considerable sum of money.

'We have informed the world of Islam that, no matter how much you may deny the cross you bear, they have only to look at you to see your passionate devotion to it. Moreover, the Sultan has been requested not to spare you in the way of labour, and so I am sure that you will be kept busy. I cannot say *adios* to you, my nephew, for *adios* means to God, and you have no God. Therefore I can only bid you farewell.' His hand dropped to his side and he looked long into the eyes that stared back at him. 'Forever,' he added.

Chapter Thirty-one

MARIO AND Ramon never returned to the cell on the upper floor. Instead, they were pushed across a paved courtyard littered with straw, then down a few steps, through another narrow passage and out at last through an iron gate, beyond the walls of their prison.

Once again they saw a coach awaiting them – the same one that had carried them from Cadiz to Seville – and once again they were pushed in through the door, which was immediately closed and locked. With the turn of the key, they knew they were on their way.

Morning came, or at least daylight entered the cracks around the door, but it brought them neither food nor drink. Again they watched the sunlight shift from one side of the coach to the other. Some time during what they judged might be midafternoon, they stopped. The door was unlocked and opened enough for a jug of water, a loaf of bread, and a piece of cheese to be pushed in, then slammed shut again and locked. As they ate, they watched the light grow dim and the cracks disappeared in blackness.

Much later they heard a shout from the coachman, followed by the sound of running feet as the coach lumbered to a stop. The key turned in the lock and a voice commanded them to come out. They could hear the noise of the sea, and the night air was so chilly that they shivered in their thin cotton garments as they stepped to the ground. The black-robed figures had disappeared, but masked soldiers in the black-and-silver uniforms of the Inquisition had taken their places.

One, who seemed to be in command, knelt on the ground and scraped together a pile of twigs and dried grass. A spark from his flint ignited the tinder and he blew on it until it burst into flame. In a second the pile was blazing, and the soldier walked back to the coach, climbed upon the high seat and took down a heavy blanket, which he unfolded. Two of the soldiers spread it open and held it in front of the fire, then slowly lowered and lifted it again.

Ramon nudged Mario and nodded with his head in the direction of the water. Through the blackness a light appeared, bobbing up and down on the waves. Then this too was momentarily extinguished, only to appear again. Once more the soldiers shielded the fire, then lifted the blanket. Again the bobbing light answered. This was evidently the signal the men had been waiting for. They led Mario and Ramon down through the rocks and out on to the narrow strip of sand.

They did not have long to wait. Slowly the darkness on the water parted to reveal the prow of a small boat, the white waves on each side glowing with phosphorescence. As the boat approached nearer, Mario could see the white outlines of men in it. He heard the crunch of the prow on the sand, saw the men leap into the shallow water and walk up the beach. The white shapes turned into *djellabahs* and the dark blotches that were faces became the brown visages of Moors.

The man who preceded the others was taller and more elaborately dressed. He walked up to one of the soldiers and greeted him in fluent Spanish. The soldier gestured towards Mario and Ramon, and then beckoned the Moor farther down the beach, so that Mario was unable to hear the rest of their conversation. When the brief conference was over, the soldier and the Moor returned. A small chest was lifted from the sand and handed to him. The Moor opened it, nodded his head in satisfaction, and Mario caught the glint of gold coins and heard them clink together as they fell from the Moor's hand back into the chest.

The scudding clouds which had hidden the moon parted and the light illuminated a silver path which dappled the water out to a larger ship, anchored a short distance off shore. It rested low in the water, darkly ominous with its single triangular sail. Mario could see no light aboard, merely the rakish silhouette of the ship against the sparkling sea and the angry moon.

The soldier led the Moor over to where Ramon and Mario were standing.

'These are the men, Sidi Mokar – the ones we have been talking about. They are a gift from His Excellency, the Count of Camporeal, to his good friend the Sultan of Morocco.'

The Moor came closer to Mario and Ramon – so close that Mario could see the dancing light of the moon in the dark eyes that regarded him from under the white turban. He put his hands on Mario's shoulders, slid them slowly down his body, turned him around, regarded him carefully, and then examined Ramon.

'They are young and strong,' he said, nodding his head with satisfaction. 'They should make good workmen.'

'Yes, both of them are young and strong, and the Count feels they will accomplish much for his friend the Sultan. He urges you to see that they are well-employed. It is not good for slaves to have idle time on their hands, particularly these two. They are dangerous men, Sidi Mokar.'

'Hah!' The Moor laughed and spat in the sand. 'Think you, *Señor*, that we do not have ways of pulling their fangs? No Christian slave is ever dangerous in Morocco. If they prove too troublesome we castrate them. If they survive, they have little spirit left, and are fit only to wait on the ladies of the *hareem*. That you consider them dangerous does not concern us.'

He pulled a long, curved dagger from its silver sheath, and held it up before Mario, laughing. 'I might even do it now, if you will hold him.' The moon caught the blade and silvered it with light, but Sidi Mokar only laughed again and slid it back in its scabbard. 'No, they'd probably bleed to death. Come! It is not well for us to linger here in Spain, even when we are protected by the soldiers of Camporeal. Move, dogs of infidels!' He pushed Mario and Ramon ahead of him and started to walk towards the boat.

The soldier ran alongside of him and clutched at the sleeve of his *djellabah*. 'Just one thing more, Sidi Mokar.' He raised his voice so that Mario would surely hear. 'Perhaps these men will try to tell you some fantastic story of their conversion to Islam. But it will be a lie – *una mentira, nada mas!* If they try to tell you that they are no longer Christians and are being sent from Spain because they have abjured Christianity, do not believe them. Look!' He grabbed at Mario's shirt and opened it wider. 'Look at what you see!'

Sidi Mokar stopped and turned Mario so that the moonlight fell squarely on his naked chest. He glared at the puffed and swollen lines of the crucifix and the figure that seemed to be painted with blood on Mario's belly. His clenched fist rose in the air and descended on Mario's face, knocking him backwards into the sand. 'A Christian fanatic who wears his God on his body!' Sidi Mokar's voice rose. 'All Morocco will see how the dog parades his misbelief. Even though he plead to accept Allah, he never can – not with that hideous picture on him.' He looked down at Mario. 'Come, dog, we go!'

Mario started to rise from the sand. Up until now he had suffered without protest, almost without comprehension. Now, as his hands touched the dry sand and he started to help himself up, he suddenly realized that his passive suffering was at an end. He must make one final stand, feeble though it might be, to regain his own self-respect. If he died in the attempt so be it. All the accumulated hatred bottled up since he left Cadiz suddenly effervesced to life.

He delayed his rising until his bare feet had found a firmer stance in the sand. He flexed his arms for greater leverage and, with a mighty effort, lunged forward against the Moor, bearing the man down with his weight. For a moment Mario was atop him and felt the Moor's muscular body writhing under him. He lifted his arm and brought his fist down straight in the Moor's face. There was a stab of pain in his own hand as he heard the dull thud of his fist on the other's face. Blood spurted from the Moor's nose and Mario felt the warm stickiness trickle across his fingers.

But before he could exult in his one short moment of victory, heavy hands pulled him back, forced him to his feet and held his arms behind him. Slowly the Moor arose, his white *djellabah* showing a widening crimson stain as the blood spurted over it. He wiped his face with the sleeves of his robe, spat blood from his mouth, and came closer to Mario.

'How you will wish that you had died, dog! How you will pray to whatever god you pray to that he will bless you with death. You are the first cursed *N'zrani* that has ever defiled my body with your filthy hands. I bleed, Christian, and as I bleed, count you the drops that I shed. Count them well, because for every drop that flows from me, your veins will spurt blood like a fountain – and even then you will not die, no matter how much you wish it.'

Mario did not hang his head. He traded hatred for hatred with the Moor.

'Think you, Moor,' he said evenly, 'that you can do anything worse to me than my own people have done? As He was crucified, so have they crucified me – and if Spain has not already killed me, Morocco can do little to hurt me. Where there is no feeling left, Moor, there can be no torture. So take me, Moor! No matter what path you lead me on, I shall follow willingly – just so long as that path leads away from Spain.'

Mokar held up his hand as the soldiers started to release Mario. His face came so close to Mario's that he could feel the warmth of the man's breath on his cheeks and see the drops of blood as they coursed down his chin. A flicker of admiration supplanted the hatred in the Moor's eyes.

'You will make a bad slave,' he said grudgingly. 'A man always makes a poor slave. It's only those who whine for mercy and cringe at the whip that end up as good slaves. You are not one of those. You are a man, yea, more than a man, I believe, for only the devil himself would dare to strike me. Perhaps you are Shaitan, the devil, with your Christian god painted on your chest. Come then, Shaitan.' He signalled the soldiers to free Mario. 'Walk ahead of me, devil that you are. And don't try to escape; my men can outrun you.'

'Escape?' Mario turned to look over his shoulder. 'Where to?'

'Ah yes,' Mokar smiled. 'Spain sells you to Morocco and gives us twice your value in gold to take you away. Where would you escape to?'

Mario felt Ramon's presence beside him as they walked down the sand and into the cool waves out to the boat. They tumbled in over the side and the Moors bent to their oars. A cloud covered the moon, blotting out Spain and the turbulent months he had spent there.

Chapter Thirty-two

THE BROAD muscular backs of the Moors bent the oars in long sweeps, carrying the little boat quickly through the water to where the *felucca*, with its triangular lateen sail, swayed drunkenly with the ground swell. Rough hands pushed Mario up the rope ladder. Ramon followed him, and then they were left standing on the deck while Mokar and the boat crew came on board.

Shouts in Arabic sent the sailors climbing up the mast and the helmsman aft to unlash the wheel. The sail bellied out, and the boat started to move slowly away from the black cliffs that marked the shore of Spain.

Once they were under way, the sailors lighted lanterns on the deck. A heap of silk cushions was brought out, awaiting Sidi Mokar, who presently appeared at the top of the ladder that led up from below. He came over, eased himself down on the cushions, and regarded Mario. Mokar's smile was scornful as he passed his hand over his face, now clean of the clotted blood.

His servant, a fair boy somewhere in his late teens, whose lithe figure was only partially concealed by a thin white *kaftan*, appeared and placed a brass tray on a low tripod in front of Mokar. The boy filled a glass with a hot liquid which gave off the strong odour of mint. Mario guessed that it must be the same syrupy tea that he and Adan had so often shared together. Mokar tasted of it, nodded his head in approval, and spoke a few rapid words, the tone of which indicated praise to the boy. The latter looked at Mokar and smiled his gratitude.

When the third glass of tea had been finished, Mokar beckoned for Mario and Ramon to come closer. Now, with the light of the lantern shining on him, Mario could see the Moor's face more clearly than in the pale moonlight on the beach. He was a young man, possibly no older than Mario himself, and Mario was surprised to find himself thinking that he would have liked the man for a friend rather than an enemy.

Although Mokar's face was dark in colour, Mario could see that where the folds of his white *djellabah* parted on his chest, his skin was white and, when he lifted his hand to set the glass back on the tray, the wide sleeves fell back and disclosed arms that were white above the bronzed hands. The high cheekbones, the narrow face, the hawk-like nose and the wide nostrils all receded into the background, overpowered by the heavily lashed eyes that moved slowly over Mario and then, with less interest, regarded Ramon. Mokar examined them silently, placed the glass back on the tray, and then, as if inspired by some unusual thought, turned to his serving boy.

'Here, Juanele,' he said in Spanish, 'you see two more infidel dogs, bound for the slave quarters of His Sublime Greatness. See how powerless their god is, Juanele, even though they wear him on their bodies as a talisman. Do you know what lies ahead for them, Juanele?'

The boy forced his eyes from the crucifix on Mario's chest. 'I have an idea, Sidi Mokar.'

'And what is that idea, Juanele?'

'I have an idea that they will soon be engaged in building the new walls of the Sultan's palace at Fez.'

'And you are quite right. Tell me more of what you think they may be doing.'

'Undoubtedly they will arise before the first streaks of dawn, when the *muezzin* mounts the minaret of the mosque. They will fight with the other slaves for a meagre handful of breakfast from the common trough. Then they will be marched out to the walls, where they will work till after sunset. No matter how hot the sun or how cold the rains of winter, they will work there day after day until one day they will drop from hunger and exhaustion.'

'And then?' Mokar prompted him.

'And then the slave master's whip will put an end to their sufferings.'

'And is that all?'

The boy stole a look at Mario as though he was reluctant to proceed, but Mokar rapped sharply with the glass. Juanele lowered his voice almost to a whisper. 'Then, Sidi Mokar, if they are fortunate enough to have died, their bodies will be rolled into the mud and pounded into the walls. And, if by chance they are not dead, the mud will strangle them and the walls will be built around them.'

Mokar smiled indulgently at the boy. 'A most excellent invention! It strengthens the walls, because the bones of men do not rot. And you, Juanele – would you like to work on the walls of the palace, instead of being my slave?'

'Oh no, Sidi Mokar! Being your slave makes me happy. I enjoy serving you. Do I not prepare your meals to your taste? Do I not make your tea exactly as you like it?'

The Moor nodded gravely, each nod agreeing with the boy's protestations. He waited as the boy knelt before him, poured another glass of tea from the brass teapot, and handed it to him. As he took it, his hand lingered for a brief moment on Juanele's fingers and his eyes lost the sharp fire of anger. Then he drank the tea slowly and handed the glass back to Juanele.

'Now go and fetch the smith from below. Tell him to bring the heaviest leg irons and the locks.'

Juanele skipped down the ladder, and Mokar raised his eyes to Mario.

'You will be punished, *N'zrani* dog, for striking me tonight. But before I punish you, allow me one moment of weakness. I am almost glad you had the courage to strike me. It shows that you are not one of these mewling Christians that have strength only to make the sign of the cross and turn the other cheek. Would that you were a Moslem. Morocco has need of men like you.'

Mario advanced a step, fell on one knee and stared at Mokar. His words came haltingly, 'There is no God but Allah. . . .'

'Do you mock my moment of weakness, *N'zrani*? Think you that I shall allow you to profane the name of Allah when you carry that infidel caricature on your body for all the world to see? Back, dog! We'll hear no more protestations of faith from you. Do you think the picture Juanele painted of the walls of the Sultan's palace too fanciful for you? Do you think you can avoid that by mumbling a few words which you do not mean? Never! Not with that picture on your body, which is an insult to all true believers – as well as to the Quoran, which forbids the delineation of man or beast.' He sank back on the pillows and Mario realized the hopelessness of the situation. He slowly rose to his feet again.

There was the sound of iron striking against iron as an old man came up on deck. He placed his hand on his forehead, bowed low before Mokar and dropped the heavy chains to the deck. At a signal from Mokar he fitted the shackles around Mario's ankles, joined the links together with a huge iron padlock, snapped it and handed the keys to Mokar. A second pair were quickly fitted over Ramon's legs. The old man stood up, bowed again, and departed. As he went, the boy Juanele arrived back on deck. Mokar stretched out his arm to the boy's proffered hand and hoisted himself up.

'Let them stay on deck.' He waved casually towards Mario and Ramon. 'No need to dirty any of our cabins with them. They'll not jump overboard with those heavy irons on, but if they should decide to, let them sink. Come, boy!' He placed his arm around Juanele's shoulders as they headed for the ladder. But before they descended, he stopped and pointed to a bucket attached to a rope.

'Fetch salt water to my cabin,' he said. 'I got up so quickly it started my nose to bleeding again. When you get the water, soak napkins in it and apply them. It will stanch the blood.' Then he turned and barked impatiently at Mario and Ramon. 'You'll find the boards of the deck far softer than the beds you'll have in Fez. Sleep! There are not many more nights of sleep ahead of you.' He turned his back on them and yelled at the boy. 'Juanele, by the mercy of Allah, be quick!'

He stood poised at the head of the ladder, a square of reddened cambric held before his nose, and watched the boy fling the bucket over the side. Juanele had fastened the noose on the end of the rope over his wrist. As the bucket fell into the water and filled, the force of it pulled his arm over the low railing. He clutched at the rope with his other hand, trying to lessen the pull, but as he reached out to get a better purchase on the rope, his foot slipped on the wet deck. For a second he struggled to regain his balance, but the force of the bucket dragging in the water was too powerful. It seemed to Mario that it took minutes for the boy to go over the side, he went so smoothly, so effortlessly, but it had all happened in a second. He was gone, and a splash in the water muffled his agonized scream.

Mokar rushed to the rail where Juanele had plunged over. His outstretched hands spread wide in horror as he scanned the water. Mario expected him to jump, but he remained motionless, screaming the boy's name over and over again untill his voice broke in a shrill falsetto. He turned around and stared helplessly at Mario. Hobbled by the iron shackles, Mario ran across the deck, the heavy chain thumping on the deck boards.

Without thinking of the consequences, he shook Mokar

rudely, until he came out of his stupor, and pointed to the padlock. The Moor fumbled in his robe, pulled out the key and handed it with trembling hands to Mario. Fortunately the lock was well-oiled and the key turned easily. Mario shook his feet free from the irons, ran to the rail, and leaped over. Far away in the moonlight he could make out a patch of white, bobbing on the water. The far-off days of his boyhood, when he had dived for copper coins thrown from the decks of transient ships in Havana harbour, now came back to him. His arms flailed through the water with speed and certainty. He lost the floating patch of cloth, then saw it again. Stronger strokes brought him nearer, and he saw the boy's head. Just as he was about to reach out and grab Juanele's hair, the youth disappeared under the surface.

Mario dived down into the enveloping blackness, his hands seeking in the darkness for that which he could not see. Something with a pale, phosphorescent whiteness shone dimly before him. Although his lungs were bursting, he plunged deeper, found his hand against the cool solidity of flesh and grabbed, finding purchase in the sinews of a wrist. His feet kicked him and his burden up through the water, but he could not seem to make the surface. With one last burst of strength, he flailed his feet together and then felt the blessed relief of air against his face. With a deep gulp, he filled his lungs, pulled Juanele's head above water, and cradled it in the curve of one arm as he struck out with the other.

The ship was far ahead of them, but he could see that the triangular shape of the sail had fallen and that the ship had stopped. Now it was merely a question of endurance – the strength of his muscles against the strength of the sea. As he reached the crest of a wave, he saw lights on board and he could hear shouts. The boy was coughing. That meant he was alive. Mario spoke to him.

'Can you understand me?'

There was a faintly murmured '*Si.*'

'Then I shall turn. Grab me under the arms. Can you hold on?'

He did not hear the answer but he felt the pressure of hands in his armpits. 'Looser!' he cried. 'Do not be afraid. We'll make it if you let me swim.'

At last they were near enough to see a small boat being lowered from the side of the ship. Sailors clambered down the ladder and the boat started towards them. When it came alongside, strong arms reached out and pulled them in. Mario lay gasping on the bottom, with the boy beside him. When they touched the side of the ship Mokar was halfway down the ladder. He reached out his arms for Juanele, carried him up and laid him on deck. The other sailors hoisted Mario on board. Ramon knelt beside him, chafing his hands.

Mario opened his eyes and looked up at him.

'*Estoy bueno* – I'm all right.' His eyes closed, only to open wide again as he sensed someone else kneeling beside him. It was Mokar, with a bottle in his hand, the neck broken and the contents spilling out.

'Drink,' he said. 'It is contrary to our law, but it will help you.' The fire of the brandy choked Mario, but he swallowed it and felt it warm his body. He sat up slowly and surveyed the lighted deck.

'The boy?' he questioned Mokar.

'Safe.' Mokar set the bottle down on the deck. 'And you?'

'Better had I drowned, I suppose.' Mario's hands fell to the deck in a limp gesture of resignation.

'Carry this man below,' Mokar called to two sailors. 'Put him on a mattress. Take the shackles from the black and let him go down also.' He stood up and looked at Mario.

'You did a great service for me tonight. My actions when Juanele fell overboard betrayed my love for him. Such an attachment is not unusual in Morocco.'

Mario nodded his understanding and Mokar continued. 'I am grateful to you, *N'zrani*. The life of my slave is most precious to me, and your having saved that life erases many things. But great as my gratitude is, it cannot erase things not in my power. I can, however, promise you this, *N'zrani*: Mokar ibn Mohammed's gratitude may be able to remove some of the stones from your path.' He reached down and brushed Mario's dank hair back from his eyes.

Chapter Thirty-three

THE SHORT voyage passed quietly and without further event for either Mario or Ramon. They were allowed on deck during the day, and at night shared a mattress in a cubbyhole below. As far as Mario could see, their food was the same as that of Mokar, prepared by Juanele on a charcoal brazier amidships. The morning after his rescue, Juanele had come to Mario and tried to find words to thank him, but only managed to stutter his embarrassed gratitude.

He looked around carefully, scanning the deck from the corners of his eyes, and when he saw that nobody was regarding him he laid his fingers reverently on the sign on Mario's chest and then kissed his fingers. Then he was gone. As for Mokar, Mario did not see him again. He did not appear on deck all the next day nor during the night, and the only time Mario saw Juanele was when he came up the ladder to prepare the meals.

Early in the morning of the fourth day, they sighted land. First it was only a thin, misty strip of blue-green on the far horizon, but, as the hours passed and they drew nearer, they saw tall buildings – white cubes against the sun. A variety of other boats, large and small, passed them now, all manned by tall Moors in a variety of nondescript garments.

As they neared the city, it rose like steps from the water – giant white stairs that led from the harbour up a hill, with what looked like a castle on top. The feathery fronds of palms cascaded over the houses, and the over-all whiteness was relieved by the brilliant cerise splotches of flowering vines. From the sea, the city beckoned them with a promise of beauty and peace, but as the ship entered the harbour a vile odour polluted the salty freshness of the air with the smell of unwashed bodies, decaying carrion, and unnamed offal. Mingled with spices and musk, it was a bittersweet smell that, they were to find later, lingered over all the towns of Africa.

Mokar appeared on deck, hurriedly giving orders to the helmsman and bidding the sailors to attend to the ropes. His snowy white *djellabah* was plastered against his skin by the wind, and flowing out behind him in billowing folds. A turban of spotless white muslin was wrapped carefully around his head. This was the first time Mario had seen him in daylight, and he decided that there was definitely something admirable about the man. Perhaps it was his supreme arrogance, his natural assumption of command, his complete sureness about himself, as though he alone had the right to live – but whatever it was, Mario admired it. And yet when he looked at Mokar's face and noted the cruel lines which marred its sculptured beauty, he felt a stirring of the same hatred that he had experienced on the beach.

Mario walked away from him and stood near the prow, studying the city which they were approaching. He was so intent upon his own thoughts that he was unaware of the soft footsteps which had brought Mokar to his side until he heard the strangely accented Spanish, mumbled so low it was hardly audible.

'I have only a moment to speak to you.' Mokar's brows levelled in a straight line and an ugly scowl spread over his features. 'Attend me well! Remember what I say to you, and while I talk to you, cringe away from me. If I threaten you with gestures, drop to your knees, but pay no attention to those gestures. They are only to convince those who may be watching us. It is my words that count. Do you understand?'

'I do.' Mario stepped back and shrank from the threat of the upraised fist.

'Then listen. There is little I can do to help you, but I shall do what I can. Had Allah willed that the boy Juanele should drown, I should be sorrowing for him. But it was the will of Allah that you should save him. Even had I been able to swim, it would not have been fitting for me to risk my life for a Christian slave. This is Tangiers. From here we shall go overland to Fez, our capital. You, like all Christian slaves, are the property of the Sultan. He will dispose of you as he wishes. Perhaps he will keep you for himself, or perhaps he will give you away. He may even kill you for his own amusement. If I could claim you, I would. But I cannot. First you must be delivered to the Sultan. The life of a slave in Fez is a frightful one, but perhaps I can save you from some of its horror.'

'*Gracias.*' Mario managed the word as the Moor's hand struck him across the cheek. Although it was a glancing blow and he hardly felt it, he fell to the deck. Mokar's foot in its yellow *babouche* feinted a kick in his face. Then he reached down, grabbed Mario's shirt and lifted him up, and, although his features were contorted with fury, his eyes were gentle.

'During the journey to Fez, you will help Juanele in the preparation of my food and my tea. You will learn from him all that he can teach you. Then, when I deliver you to the palace, I shall speak a word to the head eunuch, who is a friend of mine. I shall extol your virtues as a cook and suggest that he put you to work in the kitchens. In this way you will not have to work too hard; you will be out of the weather, and you will have all you want to eat. That is all I can do for you at the present. Later I shall try to persuade His Majesty to give you to me. Now, in case I do not have another opportunity to speak with you, let me give you some advice. Keep your shirt buttoned to your neck, so that the tattoo will not offend true believers. And learn to speak Arabic.'

Again he pushed Mario away from him and Mario fell backwards. As Mokar turned to walk away, Mario reached out a hand and plucked at the hem of his robe. Mokar turned, kicked the hand away, but listened for Mario's words.

'And Ramon?' Mario looked up at him.

'The Negro? Let him learn to cook too. If Allah wills, he can stay with you.' He walked away, shouting orders in Arabic.

They had come alongside the jetty now, and the sailors were busy with the ropes. A single plank was lowered from the ship to the shore. Mokar came back to Mario and Ramon. 'You two and Juanele are the only slaves on board,' he said. 'Juanele is my personal slave – a gift to me from the Sultan. He will remain with me on the upper floors of the *Kasbah* while you will be in the slave quarters below. I shall see to it that he visits you and brings you food. Otherwise you would starve on the slave rations. I shall not see you again until the slave caravan leaves for Fez. Do I have your word that you will not try to escape, if I do not chain you?'

'I speak for both of us,' Mario answered. 'We will not attempt escape.'

Mokar called four of the sailors, spoke rapidly to them, and they accompanied Ramon and Mario from the ship.

The short walk along the jetty led them to the town, and for the first time their feet touched the soil of Africa. But it was the people that Mario noticed. All wore long white cloaks of wool or cotton – the familiar *djellabah* – but many had large pointed hoods over their heads, making the whole city look like a vast convent of Dominican friars. This cloaked and hooded company moved slowly, gravely and silently; men walked in pairs, holding each other's hands, but they seemed to say little, and when they spoke their lips hardly moved. Many were seated or crouched against the white walls of the buildings, motionless, with fixed gazes. The city itself seemed like the inhabitants, cruel, lethargic and dirty.

Their guards led them through a labyrinth of crooked lanes, which were nothing more nor less than outdoor corridors between dazzing white buildings, whose encroaching walls held scarcely a window on the lower story. Only a weatherbeaten door of grey cedar planks, studded with heavy nails, showed the entity of each dwelling.

They walked through a welter of rotted vegetables, feathers, rags, bones and other offal. Sometimes the accumulated garbage reached to their ankles; sometimes they stepped over dead dogs or cats. Mario now realized where the stench that polluted the harbour air came from; it was composed of odours of garlic, dead fish, rotting vegetation, sweaty bodies all bound together by a sweetish smell, which he was afterwards to know as burning aloes.

There was no traffic in the streets, only the shuffling pedestrians through the narrow alleyways, with an occasional Moor riding an overloaded ass with a bleeding back, snarled at by some tailless dog, or avoided by a cat of unbelievable meagreness.

The hot sun shone over all, painting the white buildings an even more dazzling white, steaming the offal underfoot, casting violet shadows from the shuffling Moors, and giving life to all manner of flying, creeping and crawling insects.

From the comparative shade of the slotted paths, they entered a plaza, cut by a wider street than any they had previously traversed. A fountain at one side spilled water into waiting jars and gourds, held by muffled women, and into hairy goatskins, carried by the crouching water sellers. Here out of the confused muddle of Moorish cubes, one or two buildings rose to some proportions. As they passed they were cursed, reviled, and spat upon by half-naked Moorish boys, elderly fanatics, and rough tribesmen, all anxious to earn the gratitude of Allah by despising the Christian swine.

Once or twice Mario caught the watchful eye of some Moor

regarding him from under veiled lashes, appraising him, looking through the rough clothes he wore to the skin beneath. A young Moor, his eyes darkened with kohl, and dressed in a rose silk *kaftan*, only partially concealed by his white robe, saw them passing and called to the sailors. They stopped while he strolled languidly over, stared insolently at Mario, and spoke to him in high, nasal Spanish. 'What is your name, slave?'

'I am the Conde de San Mateo of Spain,' Mario answered.

A corrupt smile showed a row of white, even teeth. 'I should like a count of Spain for my house servant. Perhaps I shall speak to my uncle, the Caid of Zeguta, to ask the Sultan if I may have you.' The breeze blew a corner of his robe against Mario and he snatched at it, lest it be sullied by contact with Mario's dirty trousers. He signalled to the sailors to walk on and they passed him, but his smile haunted Mario. He prayed he would not be presented to the Rose *Kaftan*.

From the square they passed up the wide street and out through two old gates, beyond the walls of the town, to a wide-open space which looked as if it might be a market-place. The littered ground showed many footprints between masses of refuse. A few aloes and figs grew here and there – stunted, dusty bushes which seemed resigned to the struggle for life. A long file of camels passed them, stirring up a thick cloud of dust with their slow, shuffling gait. Under the sparse shade of an almost leafless tree, a circle of Moors, seated around an old man, were listening in open-mouthed wonder to the story he was telling.

Led by their guards, they crossed the open ground to a high-walled structure. Slowly its ponderous wooden gate opened, and they were admitted to a large, bare courtyard.

A Moor in a brown-and-white striped *djellabah* came from the shadows of a doorway, spoke with the sailors, regarded Mario and Ramon with interest, then beckoned them to follow him inside the building.

After the incandescent light of the sun, it was difficult for them to see, but they stumbled along behind their guards for the length of the corridor, then down a flight of steps. Here another iron wicket was opened by the man in the striped *djellabah*, and the sailors stood aside for them to pass through. Once inside the gate, they heard it slam behind them. For a moment they thought they were alone, but then hundreds of voices were raised, and they saw the dirty heaps of rags on the floor move, stand up, and come towards them.

One of them pressed close to Ramon. His words were meaningless, but friendly. Another came up, and still another, babbling in unknown tongues. Finally one appeared who spoke Spanish.

'Welcome to the prison of the Sultan,' he said. 'Here you will find royal entertainment – soft beds, delicious food, yea, even women to amuse you. In truth, we lead a charmed life here – so welcome, Spaniards, welcome to our midst!'

His arm encircled Mario and Ramon, and he pushed them through the crowd to where a window, high in the wall, let in a little light. 'I'm José Gonzales,' he introduced himself, 'onetime sailor on His Catholic Majesty's ships, now a stinking slave of the Maghreb Sultan. And who are you?' He looked at Mario and Ramon through the golden motes that swam in the dusty air.

'My name is Mario, and this is Ramon.'

Another shapeless bundle of rags edged over to Mario. A slender hand was laid on his arm, and, in the half light, he could see a girl's face. Large brown eyes looked up at him. Her lips trembled and tears made a white path through the grime on her cheeks.

'You speak Spanish, *señor*?'

'I do.'

'For a moment, when I heard the name Mario, I thought you might be my brother. He has your name, and he is of your size. But you are not he.' The hand slipped wistfully from his arm.

Mario caught it, pressed it in his hand and gently moved the girl out into the light. As he had suspected, even in her rags, with hair uncombed, and eyes swollen from tears, she was beautiful. He raised her hand slowly to his lips and kissed it.

'That I am not your brother is my misfortune, *señorita*,' he said as he looked down at her. 'But perhaps I can serve you even better than a brother.'

She allowed her hand to remain in his and came closer. 'I am Felita,' she said, 'and now that I see you, I am glad you are not my brother.' Her free hand encircled his waist.

Chapter Thirty-four

BY CURSING and pushing, the sailor, José cleared a space on the floor under the window for Mario and Ramon. Mario's hand had not relinquished his grip on Felita's and, as he sank down to the floor, he pulled her down beside him. Away from the light of the window, strained through the iron grating, the vast cellar receded into dusk. In the shadows there was continuous movement – bodies stood up, walked, talked, sat down – only to repeat the same monotonous process over and over.

Forms emerged from the half light, struggled to get near the window, and stood there for a moment of sunshine and a few draughts of fresh air, until they in turn were pushed away. But José, who seemed to be a man of some authority in the huge prison, managed to hold his place firmly and did not permit either Mario or Ramon to yield an inch. He had established them, and through his influence they seemed to enjoy some strange respect.

José had been a sailor on a captured Spanish ship. Felita had been a lady's maid, caught with her mistress as they were setting off for a hacienda in Mexico. The mistress had been speedily ransomed and returned to Spain, but Felita, whose entire family could scarcely raise a *peseta*, had remained behind. They had, José said, all been there for varying lengths of time, waiting until there was a sufficiently large number to make the long journey overland to Fez. The large number was necessary because so many died on the way that unless there were some hundreds to begin the journey only a few ragged, emaciated, footsore wretches ever reached the palace.

As for food – they were fed twice a day. It was not much, but it had kept most of them alive. Big wooden trenchers filled with boiled wheat or millet were wheeled in and then the scramble began. The strong ate, the weak starved. Every night the Moorish guards came through to see how many had died during the day. Not that the Moors would touch the corpses! A live infidel was bad enough, but a dead one was worse. No, they had to carry out their own dead, far beyond the gates of the town, and there dig graves to put them in.

The day passed slowly. The heat increased the sweaty stench of unwashed bodies and stirred the gamey offal on the floor to a putrid odour. There was nothing to do but sit, talk a little when the desire came to speak, and wait for something – just what, they did not know.

Felita's face pressed close to Mario's, and he could feel the softness of her cheek against his own. It was good to hold a woman in his arms again, to feel the pressure of her flesh against him. He turned his head to meet her lips, which were lifted to his own. She was not asleep in spite of her closed eyes and, when he pressed his lips more firmly against hers, she opened her eyes, looked up into his for a moment, then moved her head until her lips found his ear.

'Tonight,' she whispered. 'I shall be with you tonight if you want me.' A tightening of his arm answered her, and then his eyes closed and he lost himself in sleep. How long he slept he did not know, but he was awakened by a tugging at the collar of his shirt, and when he looked up, he saw the boy, Juanele, standing over him. Juanele's clean white *djellabah*, his scrubbed face and damp black curls looked out of place in the dirt of the cellar.

'I come from Sidi Mokar,' he whispered. 'He has not forgotten you. The slave caravan leaves tomorrow at dawn.'

'And that means. . . .' Mario started to question him.

'It means that if it were not for Sidi Mokar you would be marching on foot for over twenty days, for it is a long distance from here to Fez. But that is not for you nor for the black. Sidi Mokar has not forgotten his promise to you.'

Mario gently eased the burden of Felita from his arm. She was still asleep. He reached over and touched Ramon. He too was sleeping, but at Mario's touch he awoke.

Juanele squatted down beside them, pulling the skirts of his *djellabah* up over his knees so that they would not drag on the floor.

'Sidi Mokar rides on at the head of the caravan and his household follows behind him. Always before his household has meant only me, but on this trip he will also have you and Ramon. You will ride on mules, for it is not fitting that Sidi Mokar's servants walk with the other slaves. You will be fitted out with garments and you will eat of the food of Sidi Mokar's tent. Therefore, when the guards single you out on the morrow, do not be afraid. They will take you from here before the others. But be sure to keep your shirt buttoned so the Moors cannot see that which is pictured on your belly.'

'I'm glad I saved you, boy.' Mario smiled and laid his hand on Juanele's knee. 'But this I do not understand. If Sidi Mokar sets such store by you, why didn't he jump in after you himself or send one of his sailors after you?'

Juanele's smile was wan and unhappy. 'You forget, big Mario, I am an infidel. No true believer would risk his life to save an infidel dog. That is why none of the sailors made any effort to save me. And as for Sidi Mokar – he cannot swim.'

Juanele nodded. 'In the privacy of his tent, Sidi Mokar forgets that I am an infidel.' This time his smile was far from unhappy. 'And I,' he added, 'forget that he is not a Christian.' He stood up, reached under the folds of his *djellabah*, drew forth a package and handed it to Mario.

'You will eat tonight,' he whispered, 'but do not let the others see it. And here,' he reached in the other sleeve and drew out a bottle, which he passed quickly to Ramon. 'Although the believers abstain from Christian wine, there is plenty in Tangiers, and I helped myself to this for you.'

After it grew dark, they drew closer to the wall and, in the darkness, Mario opened the package. Inside were chickens, and oranges, whose juice quenched their thirst as much as the sharp, white wine in the bottle. They ate quietly, passing a bit to their mouths surreptitiously, chewing with satisfaction, and shielding the bottle with their backs as they drank.

Then they stretched out on the hard dirt floor, and, as the shadows enveloped them, Mario's arms sought the sensuous comfort of Felita's body and drew it close to him. It had been too long since he had felt the mounting excitement that the kiss of a woman evoked in him – not since the day he had felt Zaydah's lips aginst his own for that fleeting instant in his bath. Although it was Felita's mouth that he kissed, and Felita's breasts that he cupped in his hands, it was Zaydah he thought about. It was Felita's warm body that brought him release and satisfaction, but Zaydah's perfumed flesh that spent him. He sank back exhausted on the floor.

The moon rose and cast a grated white shadow on the floor. Mario slept, his cheek pillowed on the black hair of the Spanish girl whom he was never to see again. During the night she awoke and looked long at him beside her in the moonlight.

Her grimy fingers traced the outline of the cross on his chest and she wept as she kissed it. Then she calmed herself and smiled. She had tasted Mario and she knew that whatever else might ever happen to her, she would always have these few moments of ecstasy to remember. She too was content.

Chapter Thirty-five

SOME TIME before dawn, two Moors, their turbans almost luminescent in the darkness, strode quickly through the sleeping slaves. They lifted their *djellabahs* high above their knees to keep them from the stinking infidels, who grumbled in their sleep as they were kicked aside. Evidently apprised of the exact location, they made their way directly to the spot by the windows where Mario lay, his arms still tightly clasped around the girl. The Moors halted, looked at Mario's blond head pillowed on the black curls. One of them crouched down, regarded Mario's face carefully, and then scrutinized Ramon. He stood up and spoke a few words to his companion, who confirmed the identification.

'The *N'zrani* sleeps in Paradise,' the first one said, pointing to the girl in Mario's arms.

'With a *houri* to welcome him.' The other laughed. 'Take a good look at that one. She is fair and evidently not unwilling. It will be a long journey to Fez. A man will need companionship and comfort on the way.'

'And take the danger of planting a Moorish son for the Sultan? Ah no!'

'Bah! If a son were to be planted, that has already been accomplished! But wake the *N'zrani*! I'll attend to the black.'

The yellow *babouche* landed firmly between Mario's shoulders. He sat up quickly, letting the girl drop to the floor, rubbed his back and looked up at the Moor. A similar application of the other's shoe had awakened Ramon.

'We are from Sidi Mokar,' the man said, not unkindly. 'We have orders to conduct you to him. The caravan starts at dawn and he desires you to be ready. Come! Do not disturb the others.'

Mario stood up to follow the Moors, but he leaned over for an instant and let his hand linger on the girl's hair. She had awakened and reached for his fingers, held them tightly to her mouth, then bade him farewell with a silent kiss. He left her and followed Ramon and the two Moors through the tangle of limbs spread over the floor to the outer door.

The clean air, free of the foetid smell of the slave pen, was sweet with the freshness of the coming dawn. Somewhere behind the walls of the city, a dog barked at the pale moon which still rode the heavens. They followed the Moors in a single file across the courtyard through an ornately carved and multicoloured tiled archway, up a long flight of narrow steps and across an open terrace. When they reached a narrow door of carved wood, the Moors stopped, knocked and waited for it to be opened. A widening crack of yellow light showed Juanele inside. The Moors delivered Mario and Ramon to him and closed the doors behind them.

They found themselves in a small room, lighted by European candles. Juanele welcomed them with open arms and pointed to a pile of garments on the low divan, which he said were for them. But first, he admonished, they must wash themselves clean of the stench from the slave quarters, and he indicated a large copper tub filled with water for this purpose.

Mario felt a glorious relief in ridding himself of the sweated grime that encrusted his body. The water was cool and there was even soap, which Mario suspected had come from some captured ship. Through long habit, Ramon started to help him, but Mario waved him away.

'As a Spanish count, Ramon, I let you bathe me, but we are both slaves now.' He let a ghost of a smile cross his face. 'And it matters little whether you lay out the black velvet coat or the blue broadcloth.'

'For Morocco you'll like these even better,' Juanele said, holding up the white robes. 'They'll protect you from the heat and keep you warm at night.' He handed them the long white shirts and the voluminous underdrawers, which they put on, covering them with the enveloping folds of a white wool *djellabah*. 'You cannot wear a turban,' he said, 'for, like me, you are unbelievers. But during the day you can put the hood of the *djellabah* over your head and it will keep off the sun and shade your eyes.' He waited for them to dress, and then indicated two pairs of heelless shoes of soft yellow Moroccan leather. Attired as Moors, they left the room and descended a different, broader stairway, leading to an imposing gateway at the front of the palace.

Pale lemon streaks lit the eastern sky. Not far away in the city a voice floated through the still air. Mario did not recognize the words, but he saw the men in the courtyard dismount from their horses, take off their robes and spread them on the ground, all facing towards the growing dawn. Then from the assembled throats went up a mumble of words. Juanele pushed them down on the ground, and they knelt. 'The first prayers of the day,' Juanele whispered. 'Even though you do not pray, it is not well to remain standing while the faithful are at prayer. There are six prayers during the day, all announced by the *muezzin* from the towers of the mosque or by the Iman who accompanies the caravan. When you hear them, dismount, abase yourself on the ground and remain until the others arise. Your respect will not be acknowledged by words, but it will be noticed.' They waited for the prayers to be finished, then Juanele led them to three mules held by an Arab boy. 'Sidi Mokar's servants ride,' he said proudly.

The blast of a trumpet sounded and the big gates of the outer wall opened just as the first edge of the sun spread its rim of gold over the city. The horsemen started with a clatter of hooves against the beaten earth, and Mario could see that the one in the lead was Sidi Mokar. Others followed him, their white robes streaming out behind as their horses galloped through the gates. Then those on the mules started after them until finally Juanele wheeled his mule into the procession, with Mario and Ramon beside him. They rode out of the gate into the big open space in front of the palace. As they rode down the field, they passed the assembled slaves, lined up in miserable rows across the dusty field.

The Moors on horseback dropped behind, leaving only Sidi Mokar and a small band in front of Juanele, Ramon and Mario. Mokar turned around and shouted, and the shout was echoed along the line by the mounted guard that was spaced on either side of the miserable procession, which stretched the length of the field and around the corner of the palace.

They started at a walking pace, riding over a well-travelled road that led them away from the city. It was rolling country, hills with valleys in between. When the road reached the top of a hill, Mario looked back. The sun had risen now, and he saw the long line of slaves straggling behind him. There must have been at least a thousand, some clothed, some only partially covered, some shod and some barefoot. They marched on, and as the sun rose the heat struck the land like a solid thing. Mario was grateful for the woollen hood of the *djellabah*. The peaked forefront shaded his eyes and the thick wool protected him from the blazing rays.

He thought of those behind him, plodding wearily along over the pebbled track. He could hear the shouts of the Moors, the snap of their whips as they kept the column moving, and the agonized screams and surly mutterings of the slaves as the whips bit into weary flesh. When one fell by the roadside, a long, curling snakelike whip wound around his body, lifting him back on his feet. If that didn't suffice, he was left to die by the road. There was no place where he could find shelter, no avenue of escape, no door that would be open to him, no hand that would assist him. The sun, the land, and the people of Morocco were his enemies.

In the early afternoon the column halted at a colony of tents, which had already been erected by an advance party. They were all alike – of black cloth stretched over poles, with one side open to catch the cool breeze. They were for the Moorish guards. But one, facing the temporary street, was larger than the others, and it was to this tent – the tent of Sidi Mokar – that Juanele led Mario and Ramon. Juanele opened a flap in the back and told them to get ready for work.

Mario was sufficiently exhausted after the long ride to have slept immediately; but work, no matter how difficult or distasteful, was infinitely better than having to make the forced march on foot with the other slaves. Juanele showed them chests that were to be opened, and when the cooking pots had been unpacked he taught them how to start a fire in the big copper brazier. That done, they had to fetch water from a stream that passed not far from the tent, and then gather firewood to keep the fire burning.

When all preparations had been made, Juanele showed them how to crush the mint for tea, how to know when the water had properly boiled, the right amount of tea to measure into the kettle, how to brew it properly, the correct way to put the glass cups in the brass holders and arrange them on the tray. Ramon's fingers were deft and helpful, Mario's clumsy and ineffectual, but Juanele was patient with him. When all was ready, he carried the tray through the dividing curtain of the tent, but left a full teapot with cups for Ramon and Mario. They found the tea hot, minty and bracing, and although Mario nearly scalded his tongue, he found it gave him new life and vigour.

When Juanele returned, he bade Mario accompany him down through the street of tents to a smaller tent, one with open sides. Here, placed on wooden slabs, was an assortment of bloody hunks of meat, baskets of vegetables, wooden bowls of coarse white meal, and piles of green herbs. This, Juanelle explained, was the *muna*, a tribute from the local *caid* which he was obliged to furnish whenever a caravan of slaves passed through his territory. It was a tax levied on the territory by the Sultan. He located the tenderest chickens and a hunk of mutton which looked fresher than the rest and sorted out the various vegetables to find the plumpest, freshest, and ripest.

They returned to the tent, the wide skirts of their *djellabahs* filled like panniers. Once inside, Juanele began the preparation of the evening meal, explaining in detail as he worked just how Sidi Mokar liked his *couscous*; how he preferred his lamb roasted; what vegetables he liked best, and how to prepare them. Soon there was an appetizing aroma in the tent, the smell of roasting lamb, the pungent scent of herbs, and the bubbling kettle of *semolina* which was to form the base of the *couscous*.

When the dinner was finally prepared, Juanele piled it in a steaming pyramid in a large brass bowl, covered it with a conical hat of woven reeds, and disappeared with it into the main part of the tent. There was, however, more than enough left behind for Mario and Ramon. Mario thought of the weary slaves, lying on the ground along the trail, and wondered if the girl, Felita, was eating. He wished he might take her a bowl of the hot food and spend another night in her arms. He hungered for the touch of her flesh as he knew she must be hungering for the hot meat – but he was helpless. He was a slave, and he could not leave. It was useless even to think about it.

When Juanele returned, he heated more water to wash the various pots and pans. While the three were washing them, they heard music on the other side of the curtain. Someone plucked on a guitar-like instrument and they heard men's voices singing. Then the music died away and one man's voice alone continued.

'It's the storyteller,' Juanele said, as he burnished the inside of a copper pan with sand.

It was not long before the whole kitchen area was in order again. The fire died down in the brazier, and the pots and pans were lined in shining order on the wooden chests. Juanele laid out the materials for the morning tea and sat by the curtain listening. The voice of the storyteller droned on for an hour or more and then stopped. There were brief exchanges between the men as they departed. All became quiet on the other side of the curtain, but Juanele listened even more attentively. A single silvery chime – a tinkle from a bell – broke the silence. Juanele sprang up. His eyes were bright, his lips parted in a smile.

'My lord desires me,' he said as his hand reached to part the curtains. 'You two shall sleep here, but now I must leave you to sleep beside my lord.' He parted the curtain and walked through. Mario and Ramon stretched themselves out on the wooden chests and slept.

Chapter Thirty-six

MARIO REMEMBERED little of the long journey from Tangiers to Fez. Each day the route became more monotonous – bare brown hills and plains, watercourses that were either dry or showed only a trickle of brackish water. The tiresome amble of the mule, the chafing of the high-peaked Moorish saddle, the short stirrups which cramped his legs – all combined to make every movement a torment. Amid the desolation of the parched plains, the fierce glare of the sun seared his eyeballs and dried his throat painfully.

When they had left Tangiers the line of slaves stretched out a mile or more, but each day Mario had seen it become shorter and shorter, and when they at last arrived in Fez it was only a few hundred yards in length. Now he understood why Juanele had said it was necessary to wait for a large number of slaves to make the journey. Had there been any fewer to start with, they would have made a sorry showing on their arrival.

Towards the boy Juanele, both Mario and Ramon had developed a real affection. He was an ingenuous lad, somewhere in his late teens, with the face of a ravished angel and eyes of deep glowing amber, and in all the Shereefian Empire there was probably no happier slave than he. Orphaned at an early age in Spain, he had fought his way to adolescence on the streets of Malaga, slept wherever he could share a mattress – or, lacking that, on some wind-protected corner – and fed and clothed himself through the favour of sailors of all nations.

He had shipped out as a cabin boy on a Spanish ship before he reached his teens, and had quickly become acquainted with life in the forecastle and the captain's cabin. When his ship was captured by the Moors, he had been thrown in with the other slaves until he came to the attention of Sidi Mokar, who then requested the boy for his own. Now, for the first time in his life, he became a person of some importance; although still a slave, he belonged to someone who loved him and showered him with real affection. To return to Spain was the last thing he wished. Nor did he desire freedom, even though at any time he could have obtained it by accepting conversion to Islam.

Mario found himself increasingly curious about Islam. He had made the declaration of faith more to please Adan than anything else, and he knew it had not made him a True Believer or a follower of the Prophet. But he also knew that from Don Baltazar, Adan, and Zaydah – and now from Sidi Mokar – he had received only kindness, while from Spain it had all been cruelty. So he wanted to know more about Islam, that he might better understand it.

On the last night before they were to reach Fez, Mario was returning from an almost futile search for wood, while Juanele arranged some flat stones beside the tent to form a crude fireplace. As Mario threw down the meagre bundle of faggots, the boy glanced up, his brown eyes asking an unspoken question.

'That's all I could find,' Mario apologized, pointing to the wood.

'It doesn't matter.' Juanele continued to look at him. 'Ramon will find plenty where he went. There's a thicket of aloes and oleander on the other side of the rise. What's bothering me, Mario, is that we must separate tomorrow, for tomorrow we arrive at Fez. You and Ramon will be delivered to the palace with the rest of the slaves. Sidi Mokar cannot claim you at once; you are the property of Suleiman and can only be given away, not sold. Of course, Sidi Mokar intends to ask for you, as he did for me, and his request will probably be granted, since he stands in favour at court, but it would not be seemly to ask for you and Ramon at once. The Sultan is jealous of all his rights.'

'Tomorrow?' Mario sat down on the ground beside Juanele.

'Yes, but do not be distressed. Sidi Mokar will let a word drop to Moulay ben Mansour, the head eunuch, that you and Ramon are both helpful around the kitchen – and you will stand a good chance of being placed there. At least you will have plenty to eat and a far better place to sleep than the other slaves.'

The next morning they broke camp for the last time. It was still dark when Juanele prodded them out of their sleep and set them to preparing tea. Soon the tents were down, the pack mules laden, and the caravan started. As dawn touched the sky, Juanele rode up beside them and pointed ahead. The rising sun topped the earth with dazzling whiteness. Instead of the monotonous stretches of parched land which had greeted them for so long, they saw the city of Fez, lying snugly ensconced in a hollow of hills. The scrawny vegetation of the wasteland gave way to orange, pomegranate, fig, olive and other fruit trees. Little streams of water, tumbling down the hills, were lined with rows of stately poplars.

'Fez,' Juanele said. 'When we enter the main gate, the Bab el Khorbib, we will part for a while, my friends. But, if Allah is willing, we shall meet soon again. Meanwhile, take courage, and if you suffer any hardships try to remember they will be only temporary. *Hasta luego, mis amigos.*' He galloped off to ride beside Sidi Mokar.

As they neared the city the trail widened into a road. They began to pass people, Moors on donkeys and mules, Moors walking in their serene uprightness, with their white robes moulded against their bodies. Moors on horseback, and, now and then, in a curtained litter. When they passed one of these, the curtains would be slightly parted and they could see the shadowy outline of a veiled face with a pair of eyes that regarded the *N'zrani* dogs curiously.

Fortunately Mario and Ramon, mounted as they were on fine mules and dressed as Moors, were not molested. But the gaunt slaves were spat upon, stoned, and cursed with such vile threats as: May God strike you to the ground, accursed ones!' 'May the bones of the unbelievers rot in their graves!' and 'May thy grandmother rot in hell!!'

They rode on, seeing the Moors draw back sneering into doorways and *souks* to avoid contact with the Christian slaves. The street widened and they came out into a broad square filled with light, blindingly intensified by the white-washed walls of a tall building.

Sidi Mokar, the Moorish guard, and Juanele – following behind – rode through the purple shadows of a gate. At almost the same moment, and from the same gate, a man with a conical red hat from which hung a long black tassel, a striped *djellabah*, and embroidered slippers, entered the square. He looked them over from a distance, making an inventory of their number, then disappeared through the shadows of the gate. Immediately a company of soldiers took his place and with whips herded the prisoners up against the palace walls to form them into the semblance of a line. Then they were marched in through a small gate, which closed behind them with a screech of iron.

Once again they found themselves in a long, low room with barred windows on one side, not unlike the slave pen they had occupied in Tangiers. The cracking whips of the Moors lined them up against the wall and then forced them to remain standing for several hours. Finally the gate opened again, and the man they had seen earlier entered. He sauntered casually along the line, inspecting each one with a carefully appraising eye. Occasionally he stopped, went up to someone, squinted at him in the half light and made him step forward. He was choosing the healthiest and the strongest, and by the time he arrived at Mario's place, a group of perhaps a hundred had been singled out in this fashion.

The man's underlip stuck out as he regarded Mario, then shifted his scrutiny to Ramon. His air of boredom changed momentarily as he inventoried their clean robes, their well-shod feet and their healthy appearances. Then he nodded his head slowly.

'You, *N'zrani* dogs.' He spoke a halting Spanish in a sing-song falsetto. 'Are your names Mario and Ramon?'

'Yes, Your Excellency,' Ramon answered for both of them.

The man looked up quickly. 'You greet me with respect, black man. Which one are you?'

'Ramon, Your Excellency.'

'As I thought.' He stepped closer to Mario. 'And you, were you once the Conde de San Mateo?'

'I still am – so far as I know.' Mario returned his glance.

The Moor considered him. 'Well then, so that you may know exactly, I shall inform you that you are not. You're nothing but a slave. No more than the others.' He tossed his head and the pendulous jowls quivered. 'At least, not much more. You have caused us trouble, but we are not the losers, for we have been well-paid. We were told to put you both to the most difficult labour in all Morocco.' A faint smile curled the corners of his fat lips. 'And so we had planned. But it seems that you, Mario, did a great service to a very important person – none other than Sidi Mokar.'

Mario bowed his head.

'And so, Sidi Mokar has made a suggestion about this very

difficult work we are to assign you to. In Sidi Mokar's opinion, the hardest work in all Morocco takes place in the palace kitchen –and who am I to argue with Sidi Mokar? Join the group in the middle of the room, but when they leave, do not go with them. Follow me instead.'

Chapter Thirty-seven

THE DAILY drudgery that was to become a way of life for Mario and Ramon, although not too physically difficult, would have been a living hell had they been compelled to undergo such labour elsewhere. Here in Fez, comparing their lot with the misery of the other slaves, they were indeed fortunate. But the hours were still long – from daybreak until far into the night – the surroundings oppressive and confining, and the work monotonous.

They were stationed in the kitchens, a series of long, low-ceilinged rooms, half subterranean and half above ground. Vast open hearths in the dark interior devoured immense supplies of wood which smouldered and smoked, casting a bluish haze through the rooms. There was no semblance of order and no established routine in the preparation of the meals – which fed anywhere from a hundred to well over a thousand, depending on the whims of the Sultan.

If occasionally there was not enough food, someone in the palace had to be satisfied with a very meagre portion. But none of the slaves in the kitchen ever went hungry, indeed, they were better fed than the Sultan himself. For this abundance Mario and Ramon were grateful, both to fate and to Sidi Mokar. The fifty or more slaves who worked in the kitchens represented a mixed lot. There were Spaniards, Italians, French, a scattering of English and even some Americans. But these whites were outnumbered by the Negroes – swarthy blacks from Senegal, tall Dahomeys from the Gold Coast, Ethiopians with finely chiselled features, black Hamites, and a few from various tribes of the interior. From the ensuing babel of tongues there had emerged a *lingua franca* which they all spoke. It was easy to learn – neither Arabic, Spanish, nor African, but a combination of all.

After several weeks of working in the kitchens, Mario and Ramon began to worry that Sidi Mokar had forgotten them. Occasionally Juanele would come by to reassure them, explaining again how Sidi Mokar was waiting for just the propitious moment to present his request for the two slaves to the

Sultan, who was jealous of his prerogatives and would brook no impatience on the part of his chief slave master.

But as one day dragged on into another, both Mario and Ramon feared the time would never arrive, that they would be condemned to the Sultan's kitchen for all eternity. Their only recompense was gratitude as they watched the straggling line of slaves coming back at night from a day's labour on the walls, the weary workmen stumbling, falling and clutching at each other for support. At least, Mario reasoned, he and Ramon were better off than these poor wretches.

Mario awoke one morning before dawn. In his dreams he seemed to have heard the *muezzin's* call from the mosque, but evidently it had been only a dream. He lay there half conscious of the need to awake, half grateful that he could sleep another hour or so. Then he realized that there had indeed been a call, though not the call to morning prayer. It was rather a banging on the doors of the kitchen; and now, as he listened, he heard the knocks repeated. The doors were opened and he heard the sluff-sluff of Moorish slippers on the tiled floors. Then the ragged curtain was pulled aside and a lantern was thrust into their alcove. In the dim, flickering light, Mario could see an unfamiliar face behind the lantern – dark, saturnine, scowling, half hidden by the cowl of the striped *djellabah*.

'Out, slaves! Out into the courtyard at once! Be quick about it!'

Ramon was awake. He and Mario arose and dressed quickly in the clothes Juanele had given them. Then, mingling with the other kitchen slaves, they groped their way through the dark kitchen out into the palace courtyard, where torches lit up the white walls of the palace with saffron flames. Several of the Sultan's guards pushed them against one of the walls and, as they waited, with the night's cold penetrating their garments, they saw another line of slaves come straggling in.

The workers on the walls had also been aroused and they came limping into the courtyard, clutching their rags around them to hide their nakedness. Mario recognized several whom he had seen on the long journey from Tangiers, although, with their long hair, matted beards, and sunken cheeks it was difficult to realize that these were the same men who had left Tangiers only a few weeks ago.

Within a few moments both the palace slaves and the workers were lined up against the wall. They stood there several minutes while the Moors held a conference in the centre of the courtyard. Then one of the palace guards came down to the section where the kitchen slaves were standing. He dismissed most of them, sending them back to the kitchen, but, when he came to Mario and Ramon, he hesitated, regarded them closely and shook his head.

'You two are but recently arrived?' He looked from Mario to Ramon.

'We are,' Ramon answered.

'You came with the last lot from Tangiers?'

'Yes.' It was Mario's turn to answer.

'Then up with the rest.' The soldier motioned them to close up the ranks of those who had departed. They edged their way along the wall until they stood beside the workers.

'I don't like this, Don Mario,' Ramon whispered. 'Something's gone wrong. I wonder where Juanele is, and what has happened to Sidi Mokar. I'm sure if they had been here, we would have been dismissed with the other kitchen slaves. As it is, I begin to fear.'

Again the Moors conferred with each other, until the tall one who had come to awaken them stepped forward and reviewed the line, his eyes starting at one end and traversing it to the other. He seemed to be counting them, for as he passed each one his head moved slightly up and down. When he had finished the tabulation, the fingers of his right hand made rapid calculations with the fingers of his left. Evidently he had arrived at some arithmetical conclusion, for he called out in scarcely intelligible Spanish, 'Every fifth man step forward.'

There was a hesitation in the line of slaves. As Mario was first, he did not step forward but waited for the fifth man along the line to step out. But the tall Moor, impatient to start the count, walked towards Mario and with a quick, beckoning gesture called to him.

'You, yellow hair! You are Number One. Step out! Then the fifth man after you.'

Mario felt the warmth of Ramon's hand on his shoulder as he advanced several paces to the centre of the courtyard. He little realized that it was the only farewell they would have.

The counting began, and when the end of the line had been reached, the tall Moor, apparently finding he did not have enough men, took some twenty more at random to make up his desired total. As he turned to leave, the soldiers prodded the men and they fell in line behind him. Mario looked over his shoulder. Ramon remained standing against the wall. Their eyes met and Ramon silently drew the figure of the Christian cross in the air. It was his silent benediction – timed to meet the *muezzin's* first call to prayer.

Chapter Thirty-eight

ONCE OUTSIDE the walls, the slaves were lined up four abreast. Mario found himself on the outside of the column, only four or five ranks from the front, behind the Moor who had awakened him that morning. The man had now dispensed with his lantern and was astride a white horse, with soldiers alongside and behind him, guarding the column. As the Moor shouted the order to march, Mario felt a sharp flick of a whip on his back. He was thankful to Juanele for the thick wool of the *djellabah* and also, as they started to march, for the sturdy *babouches* which protected his feet from the flinty stones.

He glanced at the man plodding along beside him, who was naked except for a dirty strip of rag, anchored around his waist by a length of frayed rope. The heavy beard, unkempt hair, and dirt-encrusted body made him look old, but Mario judged him to be about the same age as himself. Mario's nostrils dilated from the stench of the man, a putrid odour of unwashed sweat and excrement, but when the man looked at him, the pale blue eyes were kindly. He smiled then, without moving his lips, and whispered to Mario in the *lingua franca*, 'What's up now, my lad?'

'That I don't know,' Mario answered. 'It's all as much of a surprise to me as to you. I take it you are one of the work slaves.'

The man spat on the ground. 'I'm Jeremiah Cooper, from Barnstable, on Cape Cod.'

'Where's that?' Mario asked.

'In the United States.' He looked back over his shoulder to catch a glimpse of the mounted guard who was several ranks behind them. 'Captured on the schooner *Abigail Ellen*, out of Boston bound for Genoa. First I was taken to Tangiers, then they marched us down to Fez.'

'I was on that journey too.'

Cooper looked at Mario. He noted the clean-shaven face, the decent clothes, and the well-shod feet. Again he spat, this time in the dust at Mario's feet. 'One of the bloody devils must have taken a notion to you,' he said. 'As for me, I'd rather do my stint of work on the walls any day than spend the night in some goddamned pasha's bed.'

'You've got it all wrong, my friend. I slept with no pasha – but I did save the life of one's bedfellow. For that I was sent to the Sultan's kitchen instead of to the work gang. And I was supposed to stay there until Sidi Mokar asked for me and my slave to be his own personal property. That's why I can't understand why I am here.'

'And who are you?'

Mario considered Cooper's question for a moment. Who was he? Surely he was no longer San Mateo, and anyway it seemed simpler to say, 'Mario, of Havana.'

'I've been there,' Cooper said.

'I wish we were both there now,' Mario answered.

They walked on without halting for food or drink until the sun was high in the heavens. Then they halted in the sparse shade of some ragged palms, gratefully sank to the ground, and waited for water to be passed to them from the dripping goatskins. The water was putrid, warm and greenish-looking – but it was liquid, and Mario gulped it down gratefully. Then he lay back on the hot earth. He did not notice the figure standing beside him until he felt the gentle nudge of a yellow *babouche* in his side. He looked up to see Juanele standing over him.

'What's happened, Juanele?' He was on his feet in a moment.

The boy shook his head in despair. Tears appeared in the corners of his eyes and channelled down through the dust on his cheeks.

'We've lost, Mario. Sidi Mokar waited too long to claim you. Now you're on your way to Marrakech – and there is nothing more we can do for you. You're a part of the contingent of slaves that the Sultan owes to the Emir, and even Sidi Mokar does not have enough influence to take you away from the Emir of Marrakech, once you have been claimed by him. These are his men.' He pointed to the soldiers and guards. 'Our men are bad enough, but I fear you can expect no mercy from these. As soon as I heard, I rode out from Fez to talk to you. But, Mario, do not be hopeless, perhaps in time Sidi Mokar can get you back.'

'Marrakech, did you say?' There was a glimmer of hope in Mario's voice.

'Yes, Marrakech. One out of every five slaves that comes to the Sultan belongs to the Emir. He's building new walls around the city – and walls eat slaves, Mario. That's why he's so anxious to get them, and why the Marrakech men came long before they were expected. But I do have some good news: Sidi Mokar sent me to tell you that he has already taken care of Ramon. He is now at our house. Would to God, Mario, that you were there too.'

Mario nodded in agreement, but his mind was elsewhere. Marrakech meant Adan. It also meant Zaydah. Perhaps, if he were lucky. . . . He managed a smile for Juanele. 'Thank Sidi Mokar for me. Take good care of Ramon.' He stopped for a moment. 'Some day, *In'sha'allah*, we may see each other again.'

'I must go now, Mario. But one word of advice: do not uncover your chest. Keep it hidden from the eyes of the Marrakech soldiers. It will go much harder with you if they see the crucifix.'

Juanele's hand lingered for a moment in Mario's; then he turned and walked away. His horse was tethered to a nearby palm. When he had mounted, he turned in his saddle and waved to Mario, then the dust of the road enveloped him, and he was gone.

Once again the slave column started trudging silently along the flinty track. Each day found a few less starting on the march. Each night there were wider gaps in the ranks. Mario was standing it well, and so was Cooper, beside him. Mario's good food in the Sultan's kitchen had prepared his body for the journey, and Cooper seemed to have a way of finding food even when there was apparently none to be found. He usually had a supply of dates, dried meat, or even an orange tucked in the cloth at his waist. Where or how he got them, Mario never knew for sure. But sometimes at night Cooper would slip away, crawling into the darkness like a cat. He never said where he went or what he did, but Mario connected his absences with the extra food; and as Cooper shared the rations with him, Mario was grateful and asked no questions.

It was, however, the warm *djellabah* that Sidi Mokar had given him – the only one in the whole group of prisoners – which eventually caused him trouble. They had halted for the night on a barren stretch of ground and Mario and Cooper had huddled together with the wool *djellabah* over them to gain some warmth from each other and the protective covering. Mario no longer minded the stench of Cooper's unwashed body; his own was equally vile and his nostrils had become accustomed to the smell.

They stretched their weary limbs, finding warmth and rest, but sleep did not come to Mario. At night, with the struggle of the day over, his thoughts seethed in a turmoil of unrest. His one consolation was that each night brought him nearer to Marrakech. But he tried not to solace himself with the hope of reaching Adan. In the status of a slave he would have little means of communication with that exalted world in which Adan moved. Yet there would be a geographical nearness. His mind rehearsed endless possibilities. He might be assigned to work in the palace. He might see Adan riding in the streets. He might rescue Zaydah from some horrible catastrophe. Oh, there were a thousand possibilities, anything might happen.

His concentration was such that he did not hear the soft footfalls approaching him, and not until the Moor was standing over him did he see the yellow *babouches* or feel the brutal thrust of them against his naked ribs. He looked up to recognize the Moor in command – the same one who had routed them out that ill-fated morning with his lantern, the slave captain of the Emir of Marrakech.

'From whom did you steal the *djellabah*, infidel dog?' the Moor demanded, punctuating his question with another kick.

Mario sat up, and as he did so the folds of the robe slipped from his shoulders. His bare chest shone white in the moonlight, and the Moor, seeing it, suddenly dropped on one knee for a closer look. His hand reached out and traced the outline on Mario's chest.

'You affront us, *N'zrani*, with your blasphemous picture. Know you not that your Jesus, who is one of our prophets, was never crucified? Another was substituted in his stead.'

'That I do not know, Moor. I only know I bear this sign unwillingly. It was forced upon me.'

The Moor stood up, and his foot shot out again to kick at Mario. Cooper had awakened now and lay tense and motionless beside Mario. Suddenly the Moor reached down and grabbed the robe with one hand. The other sought purchase in Mario's hair and yanked him up. He called out, this time in Arabic, and a chorus of shouts greeted his words, and figures came running from the soldiers' tents. The Moor twisted

Mario's arm behind his back and pushed him towards the fire which still burned in the centre of the circle of tents.

'Ho! What have we here? An escaping slave? After the *bastinado*, he won't feel so much like running.' The jeering men gathered around Mario. The Moor pushed him into the centre of the group.

'He's no runaway. Even worse! He's a *N'zrani* who publishes his false belief for all of Islam to see – even though he has taken pains to hide it from us, before tonight.' He whipped Mario around to face directly in front of the fire. 'Wast afraid, ignorant son of a she-camel, that the eyes of true believers would profane the filthy picture you carry on your belly? You must be a devoted follower to have undergone such pain as to have this obscene image always with you. Look, men!' He motioned the guards nearer. 'The dog has even stolen a *djellabah* the better to hide the mark of his unbelief from us. Shall we punish him for his impudence?'

'The *bastinado*!' A young Moor approached Mario and spat in his face. The others shouted their approval, but the tall Moor intervened.

'Not that! He would not be able to walk tomorrow. Let him die if he wishes, but we have no authority to kill one of the Emir's slaves. Better that his bones strengthen the walls of Marrakech than bleach here on the road.' He turned to Mario. 'We are ill-equipped here to mete out fitting punishment to you, *N'zrani*.' He smiled and nodded his head slightly. 'But I think we can improvise something which my men will find amusing. Achmed! Bring a saddle here, to the fire.'

He waited until the soldier appeared with one of the tall wooden Moorish saddles. Willing hands grabbed Mario and threw him backwards until his shoulders rested on the saddle, his head falling back on the other side. He felt his arms being pinioned to quickly driven stakes. His legs were spread-eagled and tied to other stakes. He could see nothing but the flames dancing upside down and felt nothing but the thin ropes that cut his wrists and ankles, until the first biting lash cut across his chest.

It was followed by another and yet another, until he lost count and all track of time. Existence became one searing flash of pain after another, punctuated by hoarse screams which he recognized as his own. He felt a warm wetness on his chest as again and again the whip cut into him, until he slipped out of consciousness into a blissful coma where there was no further pain – a coma which lasted until he awoke to find himself once again beside Cooper.

The American did his best to offer comfort, then got up and vanished into the darkness. Mario was alone. He turned over on his back and saw that the stars still shone down on him, but he could no longer look at them. For the first time in his life he was beaten, not only in body but in soul, not only with whips – but out of all courage and all desire to live.

'So this is what it is like to die,' he muttered to himself. 'It is not so difficult as I might have imagined. One closes one's eyes and drifts off.' He closed his eyes and rode on a billow of pain, sinking deeper into that hopeless lethargy where nothing, least of all the struggle to live, matters.

Some time later he felt a presence beside him and recognized the voice of the American.

'This will help you, Mario, my boy.' Something smooth and greasy was being rubbed on to Mario's chest with tender fingers. 'We can thank God these heathen eat sheep. Down where they threw the refuse from tonight's feast, I found the fat of mutton which had not been eaten. My mother always said there's nothing heals a bruise faster than mutton tallow.'

Cooper's body sheltered him from the cold, and gradually the pain eased and Mario slept. The kindliness of a stranger in his extremity had again given him hope for living.

Chapter Thirty-nine

THE NEXT morning, although it seemed impossible for Mario to stand up, let alone walk, he did both, with the help of Jeremiah Cooper. Not only did he stand, but when the march started, by leaning on Cooper's shoulder, he was able to plod along with the others. Now, without the protection of his robe, the tattooed crucifix on his chest stood out boldly for all to see, and the Moorish guards seemed to take a special delight in torturing him. Every time they passed him, as he struggled to keep up with the others, supported only by Cooper's strength, they gave him some mocking taunt, a flick of their whips, or a jet of spit.

He endured it all without a word, for, in truth, words had become meaningless to him. Living consisted of putting one weary foot in front of another, with a grim determination not to fall to the ground. He was through with life, yet he wanted to live. And he could do so only by benumbing all his senses. Somewhere ahead lay Marrakech and, once there, he might find freedom. . . .

The flat dusty plains gave way to hilly country and, as the days passed, the hills rose into mountains, snow-capped in the distance. They were nearing the Atlas range. Some of the slaves who had gained a faint knowledge of the country passed the word around that the mountains were a good omen; Marrakech lay at their foot, and regardless of what might happen to them when they arrived, nothing could be worse than this interminable march.

The hot sun burned Mario's skin, but nightly applications of mutton fat, which Jeremiah always seemed to find, eased the burn and kept his skin from blistering. His beard grew and covered his face with thick, reddish curls. The welts on his chest healed without a scar. He had hoped some scars would disfigure the scrolls of the crucifix and the attenuated figure that hung between his nipples, but the picture unfortunately remained as clear as ever. He avoided looking at it – and, in fact, rarely thought about himself as a person with a body. It was some alien machine which trudged the road, leaning on

Jeremiah when it got tired, grabbing a mouthful of food to feed itself, seeking a place to sleep at night, rising in the morning, and going through the whole weary punishment all over again.

The body eventually carried him to Marrakech, through the wide red walls, through the winding streets, through the dim passages that led to the slave quarters, and there the body rested. Gradually the agony of the body subsided, and the agony of the mind took over, until both body and mind were numbed into a perpetual trance. He rose in the morning, plunged his hand into the wooden trough of garbage to feed himself, then plodded out to the walls with the other slaves.

Through the heat of the day they dug, trundled, piled and tamped the red dirt that slowly rose within its wooden casings to make the walls. Then the wooden forms were moved and more dirt excavated, trundled in squeaking barrows, lifted, tamped and hardened as the high red walls of Marrakech inched around the city. As the days passed into weeks, Mario gave up all hope of ever seeing Adan. Although they lived in the same city, they lived in different worlds – worlds which did not touch each other.

Mario came to curse the crucifix on his body. Its outline on his chest singled him out from all the rest of the slaves for the hardest work, the cruellest taunts, and the promptest punishments. Where the others could seek anonymity in their matted hair, their dirt-encrusted beards, and the universality of a soiled loincloth, Mario stood out from all the rest by the inked scrolls on his body.

Even the sun which turned the whiteness of his skin to golden bronze, even the patina of red dirt which dried with his sweat, could never entirely hide the ever-present picture. It brought him once again the name of *Shaitan* – the Arab word for devil – and he came to know the name as his own. Whenever there was a disagreeable task to perform, some overseer would scream, '*Shaitan!*' If Mario did not answer promptly, he would feel the sting of the long whip, curling around his shoulders, his neck, his belly.

A bond of silent friendship grew up between him and Jeremiah. They seldom spoke to each other but they were seldom separated. There was a certain reassuring comfort in sensing each other's nearness. Their crude shovels kept time with each other when they were digging. Their squeaking barrows followed each other from excavation to wall. They stood beside each other in the endless chain that passed baskets of dirt or pails of water, and their wooden tamps rose and fell in metronomic rhythm on the hardening dirt.

At night they slept beside each other, and at mealtimes they shared whatever meagre food they were able to get. They knew nothing about each other previous to their meeting – neither talked of his life or experiences – but they had built up an interdependence that had become the only stable thing in their existence.

The job which all the slaves dreaded most was the monotonous task of tamping the loose dirt until it became stone hard and weatherproof. No other type of work was quite so tiring or so wearisomely the same. Even the tools were awkward and cumbersome – a section of heavy tree trunk attached to a long pole, one for each man. He lifted it and let it fall, lifted and let fall, lifted and let fall, never stopping until his muscles screamed in agony, but still the never-ending pound, pound, pound must go on.

Nobody dared to stop, not even momentarily to wipe away the sweat that poured down into his eyes, because if he did he varied the regular rhythm and the whip curled out from the overseer's hand making a white mark on his skin that soon turned red and then black, causing an extra ache in the tired muscles. There was only one relief – they were rarely kept at the job for more than one day. Two days was the exception.

Now they faced the third continuous day of tamping. When they marched out to the walls in the morning, instead of the picks or the baskets that they had anticipated, they were once again issued the heavy wooden blocks, and once again they climbed up on the walls to start the monotonous pounding. Aching muscles and taut nerves screamed their protest, but Mario, with Jeremiah beside him, lifted the heavy weight and let it fall, lifted it again and again and again.

Pain awoke Mario's mind from the stupid lethargy to which he had consigned it. Pain and anger and resentment all churned within him. He had already been in Marrakech nearly six months and now he suddenly realized that he would never see Adan. And with that realization, all hope died within him. Why continue on in this useless struggle for mere existence when life, the one thing he possessed, could bring him only pain?

He knew the punishment for lagging – already he could feel the smart of the lash on his shoulder. And he knew the other punishments – the quick death from the blow of a scimitar, with the poor headless body pushed down into the dirt, which the steady tamp, tamp, tamp of the wooden block turned into a bloody pulp, leaving only the bones to strengthen and reinforce the wall. He had heard that the bones of seventy thousand men were embedded in the Sultan's walls at Fez. Surely the second man in the kingdom, the Emir of Marrakech, could afford almost as many.

Mario laid down the tamp, resting the pole on the ground.

'For God's sake, boy,' Jeremiah said, making a lightning grab for the handle and shoving it into Mario's hand. 'Keep working. Do you want them after you?'

Mechanically Mario started in again, but he was out of time with the others. He quickened his stroke to regain the beat and as he did so, he felt the flick of the whip on his shoulders. This time he did not drop the handle. Instead he turned, faced the guard over the flailing arms of the slaves, and threw the cumbersome tool to the ground. He spread his feet wide apart and, with his fists clenched at his sides, he shouted defiance over the bobbing heads of the others.

They sensed his mutiny and, as the overseer pushed his way between them to stand in front of Mario, one by one they laid down their tools and turned to look. In a moment, the whole section of the wall was still. No arms moved; there was no sound of rhythmical pulsation. The stillness under the hot sun and the blue sky was more awful than the noise had been. The Moor advanced to Mario.

The crack of the long lash sounded like a piston as it flew up in the air and descended to wind itself around Mario's rigid body. But he did not flinch. For the first time, he saw the Moor in front of him as a man, not a symbol. He was only a man, not the power of the Shereefian Empire, but only a man. He looked at the thin nose, the pockmarked cheeks, and the wisp of beard that straggled from the chin. Only a man – weak, unintelligent and inferior! As the lash uncoiled from his body and dropped in sinuous circles at his feet, Mario gathered the saliva in his dry mouth, leaned forward slightly and spat in the Moor's face.

The man jumped back with fear in his eyes. He was unaccustomed to rebellion, but he knew there was power in his whip. He lifted his arm to bring the whip down on Mario again, but another arm reached up and snatched it from his hand. The mutiny that had hatched itself in Mario's dull thoughts had suddenly spread to the others. They too had seen the look of fear in the Moor's face and, regardless of the consequences, the slaves had become momentarily the masters.

Their heavy wooden instruments, still in their hands, were raised in unison, and the Moor fell. Immediately the slaves were upon him, pounding, beating, hammering away at his senseless form, each clawing at the other, anxious to strike his one blow. They were so intoxicated with the glorious revenge of the moment that they did not hear the running feet of the guards and the shouts of the soldiers. In a second the Moors were upon them, clubbing the slaves with the butts of their muskets until they had cleared a path to the mutilated lump of blood and mud at Mario's feet, which, only a few moments before, had been a man.

Mario did not move. His eyes, no longer dull and spiritless, glared back at them. He found he had the Moor's whip in his hand. It flew out in a long straight line behind him, then came down on the panting group of soldiers in front. Once, twice, three times he saw the lash cut across their faces before they jumped on him and pressed him down into the dirt.

He felt the vicious kicks and blows, and heard the curses. Through the press of bodies he saw daylight and felt himself being lifted up. Something told him he had little time left to suffer. They would throw him over the wall, and, if he were lucky, he would be impaled on the sharp iron hooks below. If he were unlucky, he would merely hang there, lingering for hours, even days, until death mercifully closed his eyes. He waited for the moment to come, as his body was lifted into the air.

Then, between the cursing and the hissing breaths of the Moors, he heard another voice, speaking with authority, commanding them to put him down. Once again on the ground, he could see the dusty yellow *babouches* retreat from him. He watched another cleaner pair of shoes advance towards him as he felt the hot sun on his back.

'What has happened here?' It was the commander of the guard speaking.

Several screaming voices spoke at once. 'A *N'zrani* slave

has killed one of our own men. We were about to pitch him over the walls.'

'Killed a True Believer? This stinking carrion?' The clean shoes kicked Mario, and a muscular arm reached down and flopped him over on his back. A splash of spittle landed in his face. He opened his eyes and saw the Moorish officer standing over him.

'You fools!' the officer yelled at his guards. 'You were going to toss him over the walls? Why? So he could die an easy death? With one of those iron hooks through his guts, he might die at once. Then tomorrow some other *N'zrani* would defy you. No, we must make an example of this one.' The man bent over and regarded Mario more closely. 'The dog is indeed a *N'zrani*. See, he has the Prophet Jesus on his chest. And crucified too, according to their false beliefs. Well, if he boasts of the death of his god, perhaps he would like to die that way himself. Men have been known to seek death for two or three days, hanging on a cross. They even forget the nails in their hands and feet as they beg for water. Let this dog die that way. Let the carpenters prepare a cross. Here! We will give them a diagram. Strip the picture from his chest and send it to the carpenters.'

One of the guards laid a restraining hand on the officer's arm. 'But, Sidi, we cannot crucify him.'

'And why not?' The officer hesitated. 'You are right. We cannot do it ourselves. Only the Emir can order an execution.' He motioned to the man whose razor-sharp dagger was already entering Mario's skin. 'Leave it for the Emir to see. We'll flay him afterwards. Now pick him up. Carry him to the palace gate. I'll go on ahead and prepare the Emir. It will not be long before the dog will be hanging on the cross he loves so well.'

Brutal hands picked Mario up. Two of them carried him by his ankles, his knees bent over their shoulders, his head hanging down in back, his arms dragging on the ground. Thus they dragged him through the shadowed streets and across the Djmaa el Fna, and then dumped him in the dust before the palace gate. The officer who had gone on before was awaiting them.

'The Emir does not want to come out in the sun. He says to bring the stinking *N'zrani* into the palace.'

Once more Mario was hoisted, carried through the hot sun of the courtyard into the cool marble whiteness of the palace, up a long flight of stairs and into a semidarkened room where he was once again dumped belly down, on the floor. This time he welcomed the coolness of the marble tiles under him. He opened one eye and saw the veiled marble, then lifted his head a little – enough to see the silken draperies of a divan, spreading over the floor, and two pairs of *babouches*, elaborately embroidered with gold and pearls.

'You say this dog killed a Moorish guard?' The voice from the divan was that of an elderly man. 'And you desire my permission to crucify him? But why crucify him? Even that is too easy. Flay him! Strip the skin from him and toss him on a heap of camel dung. Let the flies devour him.'

'We would flay him before we crucify him.' It was the guard speaking. 'He bears, stained on his chest, the Christian cross with the Prophet Jesus on it.'

'On his chest? How do you mean, on his chest? This I would see.' This voice from the divan was that of a younger man. Mario barely understood the harsh Moorish words, but he hearkened to the voice itself. 'Turn him over on his back,' the voice commanded.

That voice! Mario opened his eyes as he was flopped over, and looked up at the men sitting on the divan. The elder he dismissed with a glance; but the younger! As he looked, the young Moor met his gaze, but that which was such a joyful revelation to Mario apparently meant nothing to the young Moor – clean, cool, immaculate in his snowy white *djellabah* – whose hand pointed down to Mario.

'Give the order for the crucifixion, my father. Let this one feel a cross on his back as well as the one he flaunts on his belly. But, my father, the suggestion of the Captain of the Guards is a good one. Before he is crucified, let us take the skin with the hated picture from him. Have it sent to the *souks* of the leather workers. I would have a pair of gloves made from it.'

Mario listened to the familiar voice and once again he saw the moonlight streaming through the windows of Don Baltazar's house. Slowly and painfully, he raised himself on one elbow. With the other hand he wiped the blood and slaver from his lips and tried to moisten them with his tongue. One word only. Would that some God would grant him the ability to say that one word. He must speak it. It welled up in his throat, his lips parted and slowly shaped it. It became a sound.

'Adan.'

'You call my name, *N'zrani* dog?' The young Moor leaned forward.

Mario had to speak one other word. This time it was easier. He opened his eyes wider, searching the cruel but familiar face above him for some sign of recognition. Finally the word came.

'Mario.'

'Mario?'

'It's Mario, Adan.'

'Mario!' Adan's voice screamed the name. 'Not ... by Allah! It could be!' He slid from the divan to the floor and knelt before Mario. 'It is! It is you, Mario! Oh, Mario, Mario, Mario!' He turned to the Emir. 'My father, it is he I told you about – my brother from the house of Don Baltazar.'

The Moorish guards fell back as they saw the white-robed figure of the Shereef Adan, Prince of Marrakech, stretch out his arms and pillow the bruised and filthy head of the despised slave on his knee. They saw his clean, perfumed fingers push back the matted hair and part the dirty beard. They saw him take a kerchief from his sleeve and wipe the blood and spittle from the lips, and then they saw him lean over and kiss the dirty forehead. The Emir of Marrakech rose and stood by his son.

'Is it he, Adan?'

'Allah be merciful, my father, it is he.'

'But why the cross?'

'That I do not know. I only know it was not there when we parted in Cadiz. Mario became a Moslem. Therefore, my father, I suspect Spain.' He looked down at Mario. 'Can you hear me, my brother? Was this cross put on by your wishes?'

Mario heard the words, but he could not answer. He could only shake his head.

'We shall learn the story in time, my father. I would have him nursed back to health. He is my brother.'

'We shall wait for the story. That he is your brother, I have no doubt. That he is a Moslem, we shall wait to see. Call slaves. Have them bring a litter. The execution is delayed by order of Prince Adan.'

When the slaves came running in with the litter, no one must touch Mario but Adan. Tenderly he eased Mario on to the litter, and when it was lifted, Adan rose. Mario had lost consciousness and his arm dangled over the side. Adan clasped the inert hand in his and gave the order for the slaves to carry Mario out. He walked beside the litter holding Mario's hand. For the first time, the Moors of the Court of the Emir of Marrakech saw another Moor weep over a Christian slave.

Chapter Forty

SOMEWHERE in the far reaches of consciousness, Mario felt the clean touch of perfumed water as a female slave washed his wracked body. Did she recoil when her sponge touched the figure of the crucified Nazarene? He never knew. Nor did he feel the soft slipperiness of the oils, smell the sharp herbal odour of ointments rubbed into his body, or hear the words of the learned physicians that were summoned.

Gradually the tired muscles of his body relaxed and a natural sleep came to him. Once, for a brief moment, he regained the ability to think, and slowly opened his eyes. Adan was on the divan beside him. He was reassured; it was no dream. Again he closed his eyes and slept – how long he did not know, but when he awoke the shadows of the room had purpled into dusk.

Near him he could hear the cool musical splash of a fountain. It was the first sound he was able to distinguish, and its regular rhythm would have sent him back to sleep had not a hand stretched out in the dim light and stroked the hair from his eyes. The hand was cool and smooth, and he saw the slender fingers, the hennaed nails. His eyes slid up the rounded bronze arms to the swelling breasts and above them to the slender face of a girl. Her teeth made a crescent of white against the full dark lips. There were words, soft, hushing, comforting words, but he could not understand them. An intermittent breeze cooled him as she waved a fan with the other hand.

'Adan?' For the time being he could say no more.

Her fingers rested lightly on his lips, and she nodded in understanding. Slowly she arose from her knees, letting her filmy garments straighten out in long folds as she stood up, leaned over, touched his cheek lightly and then sped from the room. He was alone.

With a twinge of pain, he raised himself slowly on his elbows and looked around the room. Before he fell back on the pillows, he had time to see the shadowy walls of coloured tiles, the twisted marble pillars that framed the outside twilight, and the plume of water that sparkled dimly in the bronze basin in the centre of the room. That was enough. He was free. There were no bars on the windows, no chains on his ankles, no bands of iron on his wrists.

His right hand crept slowly to his face and slid over the clean smoothness of his chin, instead of tangling in the thick mat of curly hair that had covered his cheeks. He noticed that his fingernails were trimmed and clean. His whole body smelled faintly of roses, instead of the putrescence he had become so foully accustomed to. The ghost of a smile hovered on his lips and he spoke aloud.

'Another life, Mario. What will this one be like?'

'Better than all the rest, I hope.' The voice came from behind him, but it didn't speak either Spanish or Moorish. It was the *lingua franca* that he had been accustomed to for so long and, as the voice materalized into a white-robed figure, he recognized Jeremiah.

'You here too?' Mario asked in astonishment.

Jeremiah nodded. 'I've exchanged those for these.' He held out his arms. Where the bands of iron had calloused his wrists there were now only thin silver bracelets.

Mario looked to him for an explanation.

'Well' – Jeremiah smiled as he shrugged his broad shoulders – 'it seems that instead of being a slave on the walls, I'm now the personal slave of the Emir's son, and I don't mean the young chap that brought you here. I mean you, you lucky devil – you, *Shaitan*, you! Why didn't you tell me you were the Emir's son?'

'I had forgotten I was. There's a lot more to it, Jeremiah, and some day I'll tell you.'

'Can't say as I care particularly, so long as I'm here. It's a hell of a lot cleaner, with much better food, and a damned sight pleasanter, if you ask me, which you haven't. But I don't suppose that, as the Emir's son, you care much what happens to a *N'rzani* slave. And lest I forget what I came here for, I'm to tell you that your exalted brother, the Prince Adan, will be here in a moment. The fellow's been with you all day, waiting for you to come to yourself; but the minute he leaves you woke up. But he'll be back. In fact, here he is now.'

The filmy curtains at the other side of the room parted and Adan entered. He ran across the tiles, sank down by Mario's divan, and slipped one arm under his head sufficiently to raise it.

'Can you talk to me, Mario?' There was a catch in his throat which betrayed his anxiety. 'But no, Mario, don't talk now. Sufficient to know that you are here and you are safe and nothing can ever happen to you again.' He turned to Jeremiah. 'That is all; you may leave now.' Then he turned back to Mario with a smile. 'You see, my brother, we work fast here.' He pointed to Jeremiah's retreating figure.

'Damn fast, but thank you for helping Jeremiah. He's been a good friend to me.' Mario held up his hand and beckoned to Jeremiah to return. 'So you're my slave now, *Señor Americano*. Well, man, it will not be difficult. I've been a slave myself and, I assure you, you won't find my ownership irksome. Yes, go, Jeremiah, and later on we'll talk together; now I have much to tell my brother Adan.'

As Jeremiah left, Adan withdrew his arm from behind Mario and piled extra pillows behind him. But Mario pushed them away, sat up slowly, and managed to get his feet over the side of the divan. The tiles had a welcome coolness to the soles of his feet. His body ached from numerous bruises, but his strength and vitality had returned. One hand rested on Adan's shoulder, and he stood up. As he rose, Adan stood beside him. Mario reached for his hand, took it silently and clasped it in both of his own.

'What are words, Adan? There are none in your language or in mine to tell you what is in my heart now. Perhaps, as time goes on, I can prove to you what I would like to say and cannot. Do you understand me, Adan?'

'I do, Mario, I do. And words are not necessary between us. But now that you are able to get up, you must have clothes.' His hand touched Mario's chest and his fingers delicately outlined the scrolls of the crucifix, although they did not touch the figure impaled thereon. 'Tell me about this, Mario. It is something I must know about. Are you then, in the months since I last saw you, become such a Christian fanatic that you must wear the sign of your god on your body?'

'The sign was forced on me, Adan. It was put there against my will while my hands and feet were tied and my body stretched near to breaking. I shall tell you about it, so that you will understand, but what I have to tell will take a long time, so some time when you are not busy —'

'Busy?' Adan laughed. 'With you suddenly recovered to me?'

'But Zaydah must be here in Marrakech now as your wife.

And, after all, even a long-lost brother cannot compare in importance with a new wife.'

'Of course, Zaydah is here and we are married. I have just finished telling her about you, and she is overjoyed that you are here. She would like to see you, but she realizes that is impossible.'

Mario was silent for a moment. It was hard to realize that Zaydah was really here, separated from him by only a few walls, a few rooms, a few corridors. But that was another part of his life which he must forget. His love for her could be nothing but hopeless now. She belonged to Adan. He half stifled the sigh that rose in his throat, and changed it to a smile. 'That is why I asked if you were busy. Surely the arrival of a brother could not —'

'Take me away from my *hareem*?' Adan lifted his hand to slap Mario's back, but the welted sores stayed his movement. 'Listen, Mario. Besides Zaydah there are some forty girls in my *hareem* already, and before many months have passed the number will probably be doubled. Think you that I am not already surfeited with women? They are there, waiting for me, any time of the day or night that I wish to visit them. But how often do I have the chance to welcome a brother – particularly one whom I had just ordered crucified? Oh, Mario! Suppose I had not recognized you? It was the will of Allah. Everything that happens, happens only through the will of God. *In'sha'allah*. Allah is great. Allah is merciful.'

'Allah is compassionate,' Mario added.

There was a faint scratching on the heavy cedar door. Adan clapped his hands and the door opened. The girl who had been attending Mario entered, her outstretched arms piled high with garments. Mario stepped back, ashamed of his nakedness, and reached for the silken covering of the bed, but Adan snatched it from his hand with a laugh.

'Oh Mario, you need not be ashamed in front of Lallah. She already knows all there is to know about you, for it was she who bathed you this morning. She is yours, Mario. The beginning of your *hareem*, if you will overlook the fact that she once belonged to me. Now I'm only one wife and thirty-one concubines ahead of you! But soon you will catch up with me, for when the sheiks and the shereefs, yes, even the Sultan himself, hear about you, there will be many presents of girls – girls of all colours, and every one more beautiful than the one before.'

Lallah walked across the room, circling the fountain, and laid the clothes on the floor beside Mario. She knelt before him. Suddenly her arms were around his legs, and her head was thrown back so that her hair streamed to the floor behind her. Mario listened to her in mounting embarrassment. He feared the effect of her flesh against his own. Although her words entreated and implored, they were unintelligible.

Adan reached over and pushed her away. 'She is trying to tell you that you may take her life if you wish. Just another way of saying that she is yours and is overjoyed to belong to you.' He smiled at Mario. 'Which must be construed as a doubtful compliment to me, for truly, I believe I have never lain with her.'

The girl drew garments from the pile and one by one she held them up and put them on Mario. First the thin baggy trousers of fine white muslin, then the long shirt with the gay embroidery at neck and sleeves. She held up an amethyst-coloured *kaftan* of bold-embossed silk and slipped it over his arms. With a sweeping motion she gathered up the folds of the fine white wool *djellabah* and slipped it over his head. Kneeling once more, she placed his feet in the soft yellow slippers, then bade him sit on the divan while she wound the white turban around his head. She turned to Adan and spoke a few soft words in Arabic.

Adan's hand darted out quickly and caught the girl on the cheek. A red mark appeared where he had struck her, but she did not change her smile.

'Why, Adan?' Mario was puzzled. 'Why did you strike her? Surely she has done nothing to deserve it.'

'No? She had the impudence to refer to the tattoo on your body. She has been told that she must never mention it. If she does, she'll have her tongue sliced off.'

She stood up and her smile was gone, but her eyes sought Mario's and he gently cupped her chin in his hand. 'Bid her be gone, Adan. We have much to talk about you and I and it will take many hours for me to tell you everything. Also, I am hungry. It has been many months since I have tasted decent food.'

'It is waiting for you outside the door. Go, Lallah, fetch the dinner and then leave us.'

'Will she come back later?' Mario asked.

'That is as you wish, my brother. She is yours. Do with her

as you wish. If it is your desire that she share your divan tonight, it will be her pleasure.'

'Adan, do you remember one of the last nights you were in Cadiz, when we visited the gypsy girls?'

Adan nodded slowly. 'Yes, Mario, it was your idea.'

'Then let me tell you that outside of one poor slave who slept in my arms one night in the dungeons of Tangiers, I have not felt a woman's flesh against mine since that night in Cadiz. I desire her for tonight, Adan.'

'That is for you to decide, my brother.'

Chapter Forty-one

MARIO'S TENURE of the silken couch lasted, much to his surprise, far longer than he had anticipated. His invalidism was not due to the bruises he had conceived, nor were Lallah's caresses responsible for his remaining in bed. For perhaps the first time in his life Mario was to find himself indifferent to the charms of any woman, even one so consummately skilled in the arts of love as Lallah.

He relished the touch of her cool hands as she bathed his body, but when her lips touched his skin, it sent the hot blood coursing through his body and caused him such exquisite pain that he pushed her from him with curses. Her absence would endure only a short time, just long enough for her to leave the room and return with something which she imagined might whet his appetite – a silver dish of black figs, speckled with globules of honey, pale green grapes which had come from Spain, a fish delicately cooked in a sauce of almonds, or a tempting dish of *couscous*.

Then she would be beside him again, the fragrance of her body in his nostrils and the touch of her fingers lingering on his body, until the excitement of her nearness once more brought the stab of pain. Lallah had not forgotten the first night they had spent together, during which he had responded so ardently to all the training she had received. She was anxious for that first night to be repeated. So was Mario. But for the time being, he could only curse her for her attentions and anticipate the time when he could once again prove to her that he appreciated her artistry.

Scarcely had Lallah quitted his divan that first morning when Adan appeared, cool and immaculate, to gaze down on Mario lying satiated and exhausted among the rumpled sheets. Adan was full of plans – plans which he outlined to Mario with mounting enthusiasm.

First, Adan assured him, he must be received by his father, the Emir, but for the present the Emir could not come to him as Mario was not, according to the strict tenets of Islam, a True Believer. But that would come, Adan hastened to add. Fortunately, in his ignorance, Mario did not think to question the method by which it would arrive. Then, Adan continued, there must be daily lessons in Arabic for Mario. As the son of the ruling Shereefian house, he must speak the language perfectly. This Mario did not feel apprehensive about, as he already understood some Arabic and found that he had no difficulty in learning it.

Next there must be daily instruction in the creed of Islam, and here Mario would be most fortunate; he was to be taught by one of the great doctors of the Koutoubia Mosque – the one whose pink tower gleamed outside the window. To this too Mario agreed with enthusiasm, as it seemed only fitting that, having professed Islam, he should learn about it.

A third proposal which Adan advanced was even more entertaining to Mario. It was the matter of Mario's home, which Adan informed him was to be a small palace adjacent to Adan's own. Naturally Mario must have an establishment of his own, for the women of his *hareem* could not mix with those of Adan; nor could he remain in the Emir's palace.

In all these things Mario echoed Adan's enthusiasm, although it still seemed like a miracle that he, who only the day before had been a despised Christian slave pounding dirt on the ramparts, was now discussing his own palace, his servants, and his position as the son of the Emir. However, he gratefully accepted all the facts, threw back the tumbled sheets and started to rise only to be pushed back on to the divan by Adan.

'Not so fast, my brother Mario. This morning I fear you will not arise from your bed.'

'And why not?' Mario started to rise again, only to feel Adan's restraining hand. 'You say there are many things to do – my house to put in order, my lessons in Arabic to begin and my instructions from your learned doctor. With all these things ahead of me, it certainly behoves me to get started.'

'Ah yes.' Adan's smile was not as gay as before. 'All these things must be attended to. But, before we start on them, there is one little item which I have not mentioned. It is not, I am afraid, as pleasant as the others.'

'Then what is that thing, my brother? Come, tell me! I have had many unpleasant things in my life of late, and one more cannot make too much difference.'

'This, however, is something you must do of your own free will. I can only suggest. It is for you to make the decision.'

'Is it something you desire me to do?'

'More than anything else in the world.'

'Then, Adan, before you ask it, I shall tell you that whatever I can do that will please you, I will do it.'

Adan bit his underlip as he regarded Mario thoughtfully. 'Some day, my brother, I shall remind you of what you have just said. Some day when I have the courage to ask you for something which has been uppermost in my desires for a long time, I may find the words to ask you. But that will have to wait until later. What I have to ask you now is something quite different. I want you to remain here in Marrakech with me and be my equal in all things. I want you to be the son of my father, my own brother – a sheik in your own right, honoured and respected by all of Marrakech. These are the things I want for you, my Mario and, in order for you to have them, you must become a True Believer.' He paused and looked directly at Mario. 'But do not fear, Mario. We Moors are well-versed in surgery, particularly along the lines I am about to suggest.'

Mario's thoughts raced back to the smoky tent of Sidi Mokar, to a conversation he had had with Juanele. 'To be a Moslem,' Juanele had said, 'one must be circumcised. It is nothing for a child, but on a grown man it is painful and dangerous. That is why Sidi Mokar has forbidden it for me.'

'I think I know what you mean,' Mario said, smiling at Adan. 'Very well! I am ready. After all, the operation cannot be too painful. I imagine it is just a quick slice, a little blood, and that is all.'

'You know, then?' Adan seemed relieved.

'Yes. Juanele, Sidi Mokar's boy, told me about it. It is nothing that I would particularly choose to undergo, but if the loss of an inch or two of useless skin will make you happier, and give me the standing here in Marrakech that you desire for me, then it is indeed a small sacrifice.' He looked at the blue lines on his chest. 'How strange it is, Adan, that a belief in God can do such tortuous things to my body. First I am painted with the Christian God for denying Him, and now, to accept your God, I must suffer more pain. At least, let us hope that the trifle I am about to lose will cancel the addition that was forced upon me.'

Adan's hand rested lightly on Mario's head and he bowed low and whispered in his ear. 'Do not fear, Mario. You are not a Christian who has professed Islam to escape from slavery.

When they are operated on it is pretty brutal – a slice of the knife and, if they bleed to death, who cares? No, yours will be much different. You will feel nothing, and when it is over you will be glad, for you will be a man after our ancient tradition. Remember, even the Prophet Jesus was circumcised, for he was a Jew.' He walked to the door, opened it and clapped his hands.

An old man entered. He was completely enveloped in a dark brown *djellabah*. Two tall Nubians followed him, each bearing a tray which was covered with a white cloth. At a nod from Adan, they approached the bed. The old man carefully removed the cloth from one of the brass trays. Mario caught a glimpse of delicate steel knives. A few quick words in Arabic from the old man brought the slave with the other tray, which he placed on a low table near Mario's divan. This held a round glazed pottery jar. The old man uncovered it, took out two pellets and handed them to Mario. His muttered words were unintelligible, but Adan interpreted.

'It is opium, Mario, distilled from the white poppies of Persia. Swallow these and you will drift off into beautiful dreams, peopled by the *houris* of Paradise. When you awake it will be all over. Again I tell you, do not fear, for I shall not leave you, not for a moment. And you can trust Sidi Abdullah; he is not only a great surgeon in the eyes of all Morocco, but he has also studied medicine at the University of Bologna in Italy. He has some strange and unusual ideas about surgery, but they have made him very successful.'

Mario swallowed the pellets and watched as one of the slaves brought in a small charcoal brazier, lighted it, and set a small brass pan of water on the coals. When the water was boiling, the old Moor placed his delicate knives in it. After a while he took them out with a pair of pincers, shook the moisture from them, and waved them in the air to cool them. He knelt beside Mario's couch.

In his pleasant drifting into another world, Mario felt the sheets being lifted and sensed the light touch of an exploring hand, but his mind was too far away from his body to care. He dimly realized that something was about to happen, but it scarcely seemed to make any difference to him. Once again, he was being troubled by a name – a name which he must remember and repeat to Adan before he drifted farther into these delightful dreams. With difficulty he raised one hand, and Adan stepped near to the head of the divan.

'Something you wish, my Mario?'

Mario had discovered the name. 'Ramon.'

'A messenger is already on his way to Fez to fetch him.'

Mario let his hand fall back. He was aware that somewhere a sharp knife was cutting into his skin, but it mattered little to him. Somewhere one hand clasped another tightly, but Mario was beyond feeling or caring. He had indeed passed into some other world where there was no pain, and he remained in that world until he opened his eyes to find the sun streaking across the floor. His hands sought the soreness of his body and encountered only a thick bandage. He stretched and slept again.

Later in the afternoon he awoke to find both Lallah and Jeremiah beside him. Lallah sped quickly away and returned with Adan.

While she was away, Jeremiah poured a glass of cool water from the porous pottery jar and handed it to Mario. 'Well, my boy,' he said, grinning, 'if what I hear is true, you're less of a man than you were this morning.'

'Or perhaps more of one,' Mario answered. 'How about you, Jeremiah? It's your turn next.'

'Not by a damn sight.' Jeremiah laughed. 'I'm not like you. I've got to keep all I've got!'

There followed the long quiet days on the divan, with either Lallah or Jeremiah always in attendance and Adan running in and out. Not that Mario was sick; he was not even troubled with pain, except when Lallah's kisses warmed his blood; but the old Moorish doctor had insisted he remain in bed.

After the second day, Mario had other visitors. There was the learned doctor from the mosque, who read from the sacred Quoran, translating the harsh Arabic words into sibilant Spanish so that Mario would fully understand them. Following him was a jolly little fat man with eyes like plump raisins in a well-baked loaf of bread.

Where the old doctor taught with all the seriousness of his deep reverence for the Quoran, Mario's Arabic tutor bubbled over with jokes and small witticisms, most of which, when translated into Spanish, lost their meaning – but Mario laughed along with his teacher rather than disappoint him. Each day, when he departed, Mario found that he had added a store of Arabic words to his knowledge.

Mario had been on the divan for several days when a knock on the door produced one of his biggest surprises. The door opened slowly but, instead of the slim, lithe figure of Lallah in her clinging silks or the hulking form of Jeremiah in his enveloping *djellabah*, another stepped in – a face so well-remembered, so welcome, so terribly missed. He looked up to see Ramon coming across the tiles, with Adan following.

All the words which he wanted to say stopped in his throat. He felt Ramon's calloused palm inside his own, saw his white teeth between the full purple lips, and heard the soft Spanish words. In spite of the doctor's orders, Mario kicked back the sheets and stood up. He felt Adan's hand on top of his own and looked down to see three hands linked together – brown, black and white. Surely, never before in his tumultuous life had he ever been quite so happy. Now he had everything he wanted. There was Adan his brother, Jeremiah whose strength had upheld him during the tortuous miles from Fez to Marrakech, Ramon the faithful, who brought back a memory of Havana, and Lallah, whose kisses no longer provoked a stab of pain. Surely he had everything he could want – surely.

But his thoughts crept out beyond the cedar door of his room, down the long corridors of the palace and across the sunny courtyard to Adan's palace. There in imagination, he entered the *hareem* of his brother and saw Zaydah sitting. His love for her welled up within him, but he forced it down again. She was lost to him forever. Continents and oceans could not have separated them more than the short distance of the sunny courtyard and Adan's face, glowing now with pleasure.

Zaydah! Let him mention her name but once more in his thoughts, and then try to forget her. He walked across the room, sat down on a low stool, and pointed to the folded clothes on the floor. Ramon smiled with gratitude, picked up the clothes and shook them out. Once more he dressed Mario, giving the same care and attention to the silk *kaftan* and the woollen *djellabah* that he had once given to the white trousers and the blue coat with the long tails.

Chapter Forty-two

EACH DAY started with the howling cry of the *muezzin* from the top of the Koutoubia tower, as the dawn painted the snowy peaks of the Atlas with shifting tints of rose and orange. Each morning, in obedience to the call Mario rose from the warmth of his divan and the soft arms that encircled him, shivered as his bare feet touched the cold tiles, and knelt on a soft rug of Persian wool, his face towards the Holy City of Mecca.

He, like so many recent converts to a faith, had learned his prayers so thoroughly that he repeated them with their true meaning rather than by rote. For the first time in his life, he felt a nearness of Deity – the presence of some vast power outside himself – and, as he prayed the sonorous words of the Arabic prayers, they were mixed with his gratitude and devotion. Allah was great! Allah was merciful! Allah was compassionate!

Life had finally ceased to be a struggle against overwhelming odds, and the peace that he had tasted in Don Baltazar's house had now increased a hundredfold as Mario gloried in his own home – the palace that was his in Marrakech. Although it was not as large or as imposing as Adan's palace, and although it did not have endless corridors and countless rooms like the vast establishment of the Emir across the courtyard, it was exquisitely beautiful, with its tiled walls in jewelled colours, its carved doorways, and its honeycomb ceilings of fragrant cedar wood.

Where the money came from to support all this luxury, Mario never knew; nor were questions to Adan of any avail, for Adan could only shrug his shoulders and confess he did not know how his own establishment was financed. The money came from somewhere – and there seemed to be an endless supply of it constantly flowing from the purse of the Emir.

Although Mario seldom had even a copper penny in his pocket, he knew that all he had to do was ask, and whatever his demand might be, it would be granted. He was, in truth, the son of the Emir, and as such he became recognized throughout all Marrackech, and gradually in all Morocco. He was the acknowledged son of the most powerful man, outside of the Sultan himself, in all the sprawling north of Africa.

As soon as he was able to walk with sufficient ease – the operation having healed successfully – he prepared to be received by the Emir himself. His clothes had been specially tailored, and were far finer in quality than anything he had ever worn before. There was a *kaftan* of gold tissue, a *djellabah* of heavily corded white silk, and a turban of fine white muslin which entirely hid the gold of his hair.

But before donning these garments, Adan had accompanied him to the *hamman* where they had soaked, sweated, bathed, rinsed and anointed themselves, and where Ramon had come, to rub greater suppleness into Mario's muscles. Adan had insisted on Ramon's attendance. Only Ramon should attend Mario in the bath, because the tattooed crucifix must be kept a secret. Adan, Ramon, Jeremiah and Lallah knew about it, but they were all sworn to secrecy.

As Mario's *hareem* had increased, a serious problem regarding the tattoo had arisen. At first Mario had admitted the girls – who came as gifts from the Emir's tributary sheiks – to his bed only when the jalousies of his windows had been tightly shut against the moonlight. He had awakened them before the *muezzin* called the first prayer of the day, and sent them back to the *hareem* courtyard.

This he found to be a most unsatisfactory arrangement. The pale light of a candle increased his pleasure. He wanted to see as well as feel, and he also discovered that, when the time arrived to dispatch his companion of the night, that would often be when he desired her the most.

It was Ramon who solved the problem. Now Mario wore a thin silk shirt at night, and when stray fingers crept under it he quickly pushed them outside. It was a cross to bear both literally and figuratively and, each time he glimpsed it, it brought all the cruelty and barbarity of Spain back to him. But gradually he was able to forget it. For days at a time he never noticed it, and even the memories of its infliction were becoming blurred as the full life of Marrakech pushed such thoughts into the background.

When the day of his presentation to the Emir arrived, he was carefully dressed by Ramon, then quitted his palace alone with Ramon and Jeremiah, followed by the twenty-four white-veiled concubines, who now composed his *hareem*, at a respectful distance behind him. From the sun of the courtyard, he stepped into the dark coolness of the hall and walked unchallenged past the slouching guards and the palace hangers-on who squatted on the floor.

Here the fluttering *hareem* was herded by an elderly eunuch down a dim corridor to a hidden courtyard, where they were to have tea and nougat with the Emir's women. Ramon and Jeremiah stayed behind as Mario mounted the marble stairs to the second floor. He was wishing that Adan could be with him, but Adan had preceded him and he was now alone.

The guards on the second floor, smartly dressed in the pleated white skirts of the Turkish uniform, were lined up along the length of the corridor. In contrast to the guards below, these were ramrod stiff, with the eyes straight ahead, and, although they glanced at Mario as he passed, they gave no sign of recognition.

As he neared the end of the long hall, carved doors of nail-studded cedar wood swung open at his approach, and he beheld a long strip of carpet which led down a huge room to a divan at the end. He was aware of figures standing in the shadowy recesses, of a blur of white *djellabahs* and white turbans, with here and there the green turban of a *hadj* – one who had made the pilgrimage to Mecca.

Mario's eyes were centred on the divan at the end of the carpet, and on the man who sat there, with Adan standing behind him. There were a few silver hairs in the man's beard, the lines around his mouth were deeply etched, and his face was tanned to a darker olive, but the luminous eyes were those of Adan and the voice and mannerisms were so nearly Adan's that Mario felt no strangeness with this man who was Adan's father.

Mario recalled the intricate instructions that Adan had given him. As he came within a few paces of the divan, he dropped to his knees and stretched his body out flat on the floor, with his head between his extended arms. There he remained motionless, his eyes hidden.

'My father,' he heard Adan's voice speaking beside the divan. 'This is my brother, in whose veins flows my blood. And, as my blood is yours, illustrious father, it is your own blood which gives life to this man. If it is the will of Allah, will you acknowledge this, my brother, as your son?'

'Is this man a True Believer? Has he acknowledged Allah as the one God and Mohammed as His prophet?'

'He has and does, most illustrious son of the Prophet.' This Mario recognized as the voice of the doctor from the Koutoubia Mosque who was teaching him. 'Not only does he now place himself among the ranks of the True Believers, but he has been one for some time, even before he came to Morocco.'

'Is this true, Adan?'

'It is true, father. Even while we were at the house of Don Baltazar in infidel Spain, my brother Mario professed to Islam. For that deed of faith, he was tried and persecuted by the *N'zrani* Inquisition in Spain, horribly branded and sold into slavery to His Magnificence, the Sultan. Here is a man, my father, who was not taken a slave by right of conquest, but was branded with a faith he had repudiated and forced by his own uncle into a life of degradation. Naturally the Sultan was not informed as to my connexion with this man, but as you know, he has since expressed his deep grief that one so recently converted to Islam should be so misunderstood by our own people.'

'And now His Magnifience makes up for it by sending him five of the most beautiful girls in his *hareem*.' Mario heard the older man chuckle. 'Ah, 'twas almost worth being persecuted by the Spaniards to receive such a magnificent gift.' He laughed, and throughout the long room there was a polite echo of the Emir's mirth. He waited for it to die out, and then his voice became serious one more. 'What is the barbaric name that this, your brother, has been called, my son?'

'Mario. It is a Spanish name.'

'Then, before I receive this man as my son, we must change his name. Have you a suggestion, my son?'

'He would like to bring honour to the name of the Prophet; therefore he would choose the name of Mohammed.'

'Quite fitting. Through you, he is of the blood of Mohammed, a descendant of the Prophet. And in order that there may be no question as to his ancestry and his sonship he shall bear my name also, as you do, Adan. He shall be called Mohammed ibn Ibrahim.'

There was a movement on the divan and Mario opened his eyes a little. On the jewelled tones of the carpet, he saw a foot descend in a *babouche* of gold-embroidered leather. Then another foot, similarly clad, was placed beside it.

'Arise, Mohammed ibn Ibrahim! Arise and embrace your father.'

Mario got to his feet and saw the Emir, with Adan beside him.

The Emir's eyes twinkled and he opened his arms wide and drew Mario to him. 'My son,' he said, 'welcome to your father. You have come to him by a long and tortuous road, but now you are home.' He released Mario and turned him around to face the assemblage of nobles in the hall.

'I speak to every man here.' The Emir raised his voice so that it echoed from the lofty pillars. 'To every sheik, every pasha, every *hadj* and every *sidi*. This is my true son, Mohammed ibn Ibrahim, once a *N'zrani* of infidel Spain, but now my son and second only to the Prince Adan. Today Mohammed ibn Ibrahim is raised to princely rank in my Court and also in the Shereefian Empire. To him you will all owe homage, as you do to me and my son, Prince Adan. He is now the third man in my kingdom and to him is due your respect, your loyalty, and your devotion. Today he becomes a commander of my cavalry. Let me hear your responses, my men.'

A mighty shout arose from the hall. '*In'sha'allah* – as God wills.'

The Emir took Mario by the hand and led him back to the divan, indicating a place for him to stand on his left as Adan stood on his right. Mario remembered the careful coaching that Adan had given him. He dropped to one knee, took the silver-sheathed dagger from his belt and laid it on the floor in front of the Emir. Slowly he withdrew the curved damascened blade from the silver scabbard and laid its point against his heart. He then reached over and took the Emir's hand and placed it on the dagger's hilt. Mario had learned the words perfectly, but as he spoke them, he found that he had never meant anything quite so sincerely before.

'I am all too unworthy, illustrious father, to be called your son. It is an honour which my life can never repay. Therefore from this moment on, I place my life in your hands, as it is now. Press on the dagger, if you will. Let it penetrate my heart and spill my blood at your feet. My life is yours. If it is the will of Allah that I may serve you better dead at this moment than alive, you have but to press the blade an inch. But, my father, if I can serve you better living, then let me live to add honour and greatness to your name.'

The thin hand relinquished its hold on the hilt, and the dagger clattered to the floor. The hand sought Mario's and lifted him up. The Emir rose from the divan and walked towards the door. Adan and Mario fell into step behind him. Then one by one the minor princes of Marrakech, starting with the oldest, who looked older than Adan, to a toddler of about four years, followed the lead of the Emir towards the door.

This time, as Mario passed down the carpet, he could see only the tops of their turbans as the foreheads of the sheiks of Marrakech and the High Atlas and the Berber country beyond were all pressed to the floor in silent homage to the Shereef Mohammed Ibn Ibrahim, Prince of Marrakech, Sheik of Morocco, Lord of the High Atlas, Son of the Prophet and a True Believer in the ancient creed of Islam.

Chapter Forty-three

ALTHOUGH SEVERAL weeks passed before Mario ventured to straddle a horse, particularly now that he had no choice but to use the high Moorish saddle, he had been pleasantly surprised one morning, on going to the stables with Adan, to find one of the grooms leading forth a familiar sight. It was difficult for him to credit his eyes, but it was certainly Zuleika. She had not forgotten him during his long absence, and her affections had not been alienated. As she approached him, she lifted her hooves daintily, pranced coyly sideways, and pirouetted in a minuet at the end of her halter rope until she reached him.

Mario gave his foot to the groom and, mindful of his recent painful experience, eased himself into the saddle. But before he could touch the reins, Zuleika was off. He clutched frantically for the leathern straps, managed to get them in his hands, and then let her gallop down the dusty street. She skilfully dodged donkeys heaped high with faggots, itinerant peddlers, water carriers and street urchins until she had carried him beyond the city gates, whereupon she halted suddenly, arched her neck and gave him a sweeping look which informed him that, although she willingly acknowledged him as her master, there would certainly be times when she would do as she pleased.

Once again, as in Cadiz, the days marched by in a golden parade, but here in Marrakech the nights too passed in a splendour of perfumed eroticism. Throughout the day Mario and Adan rode, hunted, talked, slept or just passed long periods of silence in the marble-columned coolness of the palace.

Occasionally they would seek some thyme-cushioned valley high in the mountains and eat their lunch of bread, dates, and cheese, which they washed down with the icy water of a mountain brook. They hunted in cedar-scented ravines below the snow line or raced their horses across the dusty plains outside the city. Sometimes, after hours of riding, they would stop to bathe in some mountain torrent, ever mindful that the accompanying soldiers would remain at a distance, for Adan insisted that nobody should see Mario's body.

One afternoon, when Mario was leading the way, they rode higher than usual into the mountains, and Adan, as soon as the narrow ledge permitted him to come abreast of Mario, insisted that they return. This, he informed Mario, was dangerous territory. Although his father was nominally the Emir of the mountain Berber tribes, many of them had not accepted him. A bitter enmity of many generations had existed between some of the Berbers and the Moors, and, in their mountain fastness, the Berbers steadfastly maintained their independence, refusing to bow their knees or kiss the hand of the Emir.

Although the path ahead seemed as safe and empty as that over which they had just ridden, Mario turned at Adan's bidding. They retraced their road down the mountain until they were once more able to see the three golden balls on the Koutoubia tower gleaming in the sunlight.

As Mario's knowledge of Arabic increased, he took over the command of his company of cavalry. His leadership was really only nominal, because the Moors under him were all independent agents; they regarded him more as a figurehead of authority than a disciplinarian. At first the men all appeared alike to him – a collection of swarthy faces under the shadows of their hooded burnooses; but gradually they became separated into individuals, and soon he came to know each man by name.

There was no rank among them. They considered him their commander because he was their Emir's son, but each man gloried in his own individuality and his independence. Mario wondered how efficient this independent spirit would be in war. It might mean that every man would ride off in a different direction of his own choosing to encompass the enemy. But of one thing he could be sure – their bravery. He knew that in times of stress they would not fail him. They were ready to follow him willingly either to death or to victory. Death would mean an immediate entrance into the arms of a waiting *houri* in Paradise. Victory would entitle them to their share of the captured loot.

So passed Mario's days. When the purple shadows of the mountains fell across the city and the last call of the *muezzin* splintered the still air, Adan always left him. Through the wooden lattice of his second-story window, Mario would watch him cross the courtyard to the black shadows of his own doorway. Adan always paused for a moment and looked back regretfully at the blank façade of Mario's palace.

The pause would sometimes lengthen and, more than once, Mario saw him turn and start to retrace his steps. Then he would decide against it, and walk slowly to his house. Mario sensed his loneliness. One night he opened the shutters, watched Adan's slow progress across the courtyard and, as Adan turned, Mario waved to him. Adan's smile was his reward and, after that, he always watched him leave and waited for Adan's raised hand, held high with the sleeve of the *djellabah* falling back from his arm. Mario's hand would go up in answer, and it had become a good-night ritual which neither ever overlooked. Mario realized that it had a deep meaning to Adan.

There was something Adan greatly desired but never asked for. Neither ever mentioned it, although both Mario and Adan recognized it. They had resolved to let nothing mar that friendship. Both realized that the desire of one could never be the desire of both. Mario was grateful for Adan's reluctance to press the matter, and that evening wave of his hand was a tacit expression of his gratitude.

Mario had sensed this underlying desire on the part of Adan ever since the first moment he had seen him—that time in the house of Don Baltazar when he had caught Adan spying on him from the little door above his bed. At first glance he had mistaken Adan's finely chiselled features for those of a girl, and even with their ripening acquaintance he had never been able to dispel entirely the aura of femininity which clung to Adan.

Mario was well aware of Adan's size, vigour and masculinity. He had seen proof of his ability to beget offspring. He knew of his muscularity, his horsemanship, his ability with the sword and with the hawk. But even with this visual evidence, Mario could not disabuse himself of his own concept of Adan's androgyny.

Adan was far too beautiful to be a man, and, especially with the turban wound around his head, hiding his hair, he became altogether too pretty. There was a softness about him which his muscularity belied. His lips were too bee-stung, his lashes too long, his eyes too languorous. Mario did not object to Adan's good looks – he enjoyed them – but he did not relish the underlying sadness in Adan's eyes nor the unexpressed thoughts he knew existed in Adan's mind.

Although he never questioned him, Mario was sure that Adan found relief, if not satisfaction, in his nightly companions from the *hareem*. But he also knew that something was lacking in Adan's life. Something had always been lacking. Even the fight on the salt mounds, which Adan had instigated and for which Mario had never seen any logical reason, had been inspired by Adan's inner need, and by his unwillingness to declare his real sentiments to Mario.

Blood brotherhood with Mario had never seemed to satisfy Adan fully. He longed for more, but did not want to lose what he had by claiming more than Mario might be willing to give. He was aware of the Christian prejudice for what that more might entail. He knew that Christians frowned upon sexual relations between man and man, and although Mario had presumably shed all his Christian convictions and become a convert to Islam, he had grown to manhood under the restrictions of the Church.

Adan was wise enough to realize that Mario unconsciously retained some of these Christian ethics, particularly those that would involve affectionate advances from another male. He knew the hypnotic effect that Mario's face and body had on women. They affected him the same way. But where women could respond freely, and even make advances, to Mario, Adan must always dissemble. Mario's brotherly affection was far too valuable to throw away on the chance that it might be replaced with another stranger and a more vital love.

Mario understood, and although he pitied Adan, he too kept silent; he wanted to preserve the ever-increasing bond that daily grew stronger between them. He loved Adan, but he realized it could never be the degree of love that Adan desired. He was neither so structured nor so natured. Women and women alone sufficed him. They were all he wanted, and he had never been so surfeited with them that he desired new and stranger ecstasies.

Possibly he could have endured, even without repulsion, closer physical contact that he had previously had with his brother. He could picture the joy in Adan's face if he were to grab him, draw him close, plant his lips on Adan's, and let him feel the hardness of his body pressing against him. He pictured Adan's joy if their heads were to share the same pillow. But any such gesture would have been one of pity, and pity only, on Mario's part. He loved Adan but he was not *in* love with him.

And, even as he thought about these tentative embraces, he shrank from them. He knew that if he encouraged him, Adan would demand more than he could willingly give.

Yet, every night when Adan halted on his way across the moonlit courtyard and turned and waved to Mario, Mario recognized the suppressed longing in that lonely gesture. He knew how much it would have meant to Adan to be invited to stay. One word from Mario and he would turn quickly, come running up the stairs and burst through the door into Mario's room. He would see a look of joyous contentment on Adan's face such as he had never seen there before. Together they would spend the night – Adan ecstatically happy in the strength of Mario's arms. But, although Mario was tempted, he never spoke the word to the figure in the white *djellabah* below. The sacrifice of one night with Lallah or any of the others would mean little to him compared to the joy a night with him would give Adan. But once begun, the relationship could not be ended. So the words never came and, much as Mario hated himself for withholding so simple a gift, he knew he was preserving something far more precious. And he felt that Adan knew also and was perhaps grateful for the unspoken word.

When the shadows of the doorway had swallowed Adan, Mario would close the shutter, cross the room and open a latticed door on the other side. This door led out on to a balcony, screened with a thick curtain of vines, which hid him from the courtyard beneath. From his hidden vantage point he had a perfect view of the courtyard and of his *hareem*, the occupants of which had increased in number. At this hour of the evening, the members of his *hareem* promenaded slowly back and forth around the fountain. Each one had spent the long afternoon hours perfecting her beauty. Each one did her best to outdo the others; she who was fortunate enough to be chosen for the night would become the queen of the *hareem* for the following day.

Mario's choice was not limited. In the nightly procession there were girls from Senegal with skin like polished ebony, blue-eyed girls from the Berber tribes of the Anti-Atlas, a slim Persian who moved with the feline grace of a cheetah and had left Mario with long red scratches from her sharp and hennaed nails. If he desired he had his choice of various girls who had been captured on the seas – girls who spoke Italian, English and Spanish as their native tongues, but who now spoke Arabic or the *lingua franca*.

They were all his, awaiting his word. There were some with passions so fierce that they devoured him; others whose meek docility demanded mastery. Some there were whose favours he had to beg for, and some that he had to force with a whip to acquiesce. Some poured out their desire for him in strange kisses, others denied him their lips. His was the choice, depending on his mood of the evening, whether he desired to master or be mastered. He savoured this nightly parade of multicoloured flesh, considering first one and then another, recalling certain delightful sensations of this one's hands, of that one's mouth, the smooth roundness of another's breast or the slow undulations of her silken hips.

When at length he had made his choice he would clap his hands. The grinning, uplifted face, and tubby, silk-clad torso of his *hareem* eunuch would appear, and Mario would call out a name to him. In a few moments a key would grate in the lock of Mario's room. The door would open and the one he had chosen would enter, walking slowly across the tiles with lowered head, or throwing herself in his arms with wild abandon.

Occasionally, however, after a long day spent in the mountains on Zuleika, Mario would step out on to the balcony, and without looking at the silken parade below him, toss a kerchief through the vines. As it fluttered to the ground, a hush would fall over the courtyard below, there would be a murmur of disappointment, and Mario could hear the sluff of their slippers as they returned to their rooms.

On those rare nights, Mario slept alone. Ramon served him his dinner and he and Mario sat together, speaking in the familiar Spanish and reliving the tortuous path that had brought them to Marrakech. Ramon was now the head of Mario's household, as Jeremiah was the chief groom of his stables. Between the two of them, the whole establishment ran with an easy perfection. Meals always appeared promptly and, when Mario was surfeited with the inevitable *couscous*, Ramon prepared a real Spanish dish – a thick hearty soup, *arroz con pollo* or *paella*.

It was on one of those nights when fatigue had caused him to throw the handkerchief down from the balcony and he and Ramon were finished their evening meal that the door of his room opened and Adan entered without knocking. It was the first time Adan had ever returned after their early evening farewell, and Mario sensed that something unusual must have occurred to cause Adan to break the established ritual. One look at Adan's face convinced Mario that, whatever the reason might be, Adan was the bearer of good news. Not only the wide smile and the shining eyes, but the quick, nervous steps that carried him dancing across the floor, betokened his joy.

'My brother! My brother! Allah has blessed our house!' His hand reached out to Mario's and his arm clasped Mario's neck.

Mario smiled indulgently. 'He certainly must have, to cause you to explode like this. What has happened? Have you suddenly been made Sultan of Morocco, or have you received a new and even more exotic addition to your *hareem*?'

Adan's face wrinkled in displeasure. 'As for the first, I would not be happy if I were to be sultan. Too many have died with a towel around their necks. And as for the second – bah! One girl in my *hareem* has come to look much like another.' The flame in his eyes rekindled. 'No, Mario! Nothing as ordinary as that. Tonight I am a father. The father of a son!'

'But that has happened before. You yourself told me that the court of your *hareem* was already crawling with babies of many different colours.'

'But oh, Mario, this is different! This is my son, my heir! Born of Zaydah! I've seen him, Mario. Now, as I am the first heir of my father, our line of succession is assured. Now there is a legitimate son, with the blood of the Prophet in his veins!'

Mario regarded Adan in silence for one brief moment. He had forced the image of Zaydah far back into his consciousness, trying hard to forget that she was only a few steps away from him. Now once more he brought her forth, allowed himself to feel the imprint of her kiss on his lips, feel her perfumed hair cascade over him as it had that night in his bath at Cadiz. But only for a moment. The poignancy of his memory must not dilute the joy he knew he must express in Adan's great happiness. He clasped the hand that was in his own even more tightly.

Adan's joy was complete. 'And now, Mario, you must see my son because, as you are the son of my father, you are my son's uncle, and you must share in the good fortune of our house. Come, Mario, dress and come to my palace. Tonight, in my great happiness, I shall forget the customs of my people. You shall enter my *hareem* where no man except myself has ever stepped before. Come, Mario, you must see my son, and see him now!'

Ramon lit the lamps and helped Mario on with his robe, while Adan paced the floor with quick impatient steps. When Mario was dressed, they ran down the stairs, waking the nodding sentries who dozed at their posts. He followed Adan down a long corridor and paused with him before a massive door of cedar with polished brass bosses. Adan's loud knock caused the door to swing cautiously open and Mario saw the fat moon face of a eunuch staring at him incredulously. Adan shoved the man aside and they entered, as the door banged closed behind them.

The courtyard inside was larger than that of Mario's palace, with many more rooms leading off the encircling verandah. They crossed the marble pavement, circled the splashing basin, and mounted a few steps which led to a series of apartments on a higher level than the rest. Adan knocked on a door and it opened.

The room inside was brilliantly lighted with Spanish candles, but Mario had eyes only for the spread of black hair which flowed over the pillow and for the dark eyes that looked up at him from under lowered lashes. That was all he could see of Zaydah's face, for a thin veil covered the rest. But the eyes were those of Zaydah, and they looked at him with mingled fear and joy. Adan rushed to her divan, slowly and tenderly pulled back the sheet to show Mario the tiny head that was nestled in Zaydah's arm.

Mario forced his eyes away from Zaydah's to the little head. He saw the black down of hair, the red puckered face and the tiny hand that, half curled, lay still against Zaydah's breast.

'My son, Mario! My son!' Adan's voice was triumphant.

Mario knelt beside the divan and placed one strong brown finger inside the tiny ones. Immediately they curled tightly around it. He felt the slight pressure on his finger, but his eyes were not on the little hand. They were looking down into Zaydah's. In that one brief glance, they said many things to each other – things which could not be put into words. When Mario did speak, his words were commonplace enough.

'It is a long time since I have seen you, my sister.' He found it easier to speak in Spanish.

'A long time, brother of Adan. I have heard your story, and my heart rejoices that you are safe.'

He gently disengaged his finger from the white petals of the little hand, and stood up. He must keep from looking at Zaydah.

'He even has fingernails, Adan. He's so . . . so complete. I've never seen a newborn baby before. Somehow I never thought of them as being born with fingernails and everything. What a marvel! Oh, Adan! I'm as happy as you are. I almost feel as though he were my own son – this little bit of life that has come into the world.'

Adan motioned to Mario to stand beside him. His mood changed. The look of wild joy faded from his face, and his eyes, which had danced with wonder, grew larger. A single tear welled up and rolled down his cheek.

'I have brought you here tonight, Mohammed ibn Ibrahim, to exact a solemn promise from you. This, my son, must live. Someday he will be Emir of Marrakech. From tonight on, I shall devote my life to him. And so must you, my brother. Promise me! Swear to me, Mario, by all we hold sacred in the world of Islam, that if anything should happen to me, you will be a father to my son. Swear to it, Mario, before the mother of my son, that she may know your oath and depend on it.'

'I swear, Adan. I do not know the solemn words of your Moslem oaths whereby to make my words more binding to you. But even more binding than any oath I could swear to you is my love for you and the debt of gratitude I owe you. That is the foundation of my oath. If anything should ever happen to you, which Allah forbid, I swear that I will not only care for your child as a father, but I will protect and guard his mother as well.'

'It is sworn, Mario, and if there has ever been in your mind any idea of a debt between us, that debt is now cancelled. I sensed from the first moment I saw you in Cadiz, when I opened the little door between our rooms and saw you lying on the divan, that our lives would be drawn together. That is why I desired that your blood mingle with mine and mine with yours. I have not been mistaken in you. Outside of my father, you are the only man I can trust.'

He took Mario's arm and led him from the room. But as the door opened for them to go out, Mario turned back. Zaydah's eyes were on him and, as he passed through the door, he saw her perform a curious act. Her fingers traced the sign of the cross from her forehead to her breast and across her shoulders.

Chapter Forty-four

MOHAMMED IBN ADAN cut his first tooth at the age of eleven months. In another month he was walking, and his first hesitant steps were between the outstretched arms of his father and Mario. Although Mario did not see Zaydah again after the night that Mohammed was born, he now received frequent messages from her through Adan, some verbal, some written in careful, convent-phrased Spanish. But all of the messages related to Mohammed and whatever he might have done in the *hareem* when neither Mario nor Adan were watching.

As he developed from a squalling, red-faced infant to a sturdy child, Mario found his interest and his love increasing. He was awkward and clumsy with the child – half afraid to touch him – but Ramon clucked over the baby like a mother hen. He had become adept at whisking off wet cloths and substituting dry ones, a delicate chore which neither Adan nor Mario felt qualified to do. Jeremiah toted the baby on his back by the hour, or at least until Ramon found some excuse to take him.

He grew to be a man's child. Naturally he was spoiled. Even before he had passed his second birthday he was aware of the power he had over these men. The only harsh words that ever passed between Mario and Adan were occasioned by a smart slap on the young Mohammed's bottom, which Mario delivered. During the argument that followed, Mario finally convinced Adan that some sort of discipline was necessary. In the end Adan agreed, but he would never punish the child himself. That was Mario's task, and many times Mohammed screamed in anger at Mario's well-directed spanking. When the tantrum was over and his bottom stopped smarting, he would crawl into Mario's arms, beguile him with kisses and love him more than ever.

Mario had found peace. He grew taller and broader, with hands and face a deeper bronze from the hot Moroccan sun. He came to look like a Moor, and few there were who would suspect that he was not, for the gold of his hair, close cropped and hidden under a turban, did not betray him. His language now was Arabic, fluent as that of Adan – even more so, for Mario could curse more obscenely and love more passionately than Adan. Occasionally he lapsed into Spanish with Ramon; otherwise he would have forgotten his mother tongue.

Islam had answered many questions for Mario. It was a religion which suited him – lusty and sensual, glorifying the joys of the flesh in a way that the pale asceticism of Christianity did not. As he developed in Islam, he achieved the same fanatical hatred for the *N'zranis* as all the others had. When he passed the Christian slaves toiling on the walls, he spat on them with bitter vengeance and cursed them as dogs of infidels. Had he not reviled them, he might have pitied them. But pity was an emotion he could not afford.

His *hareem* had increased until every one of the cubicles was now occupied, and it was necessary to weed out and sell off those women of whom he had tired. The old eunuch in charge of the establishment had advised adding several more rooms, but to Mario variety was more important than numbers. If a girl did not please him, she was led away to the slave market and, with the money she brought, Mario shopped around for one who had greater erotic possibilities.

But in spite of his search for new sensations, he called more and more and more for Lallah – she who had first dressed his wounds and tended him, she who knew the secret of his body. Although the others offered spice and variety, it was Lallah who offered comfort and relaxation. In the smooth security of her arms there was no need to prove himself the master. She understood him and loved him.

When he was with her, the whips, the thin steel chains, and the cunning fetters remained in the big carved chest. Mario slept contentedly in her arms. With no wife in charge of his *hareem*, Lallah became its mistress, coaching those under her in more subtle ways to delight their master, but confident of her own ability to please him more than all the others.

One morning when the shadows from the sun had crept nearly across the floor, Ramon came bursting into the room. Mario, exhausted from his diversions of the night before, had dismissed his companion at the call of the *muezzin* and then crept back into bed alone. Now, he realized as he wakened, the morning was half spent. He looked up drowsily at Ramon, half grateful for his awakening, half resentful of having to open his eyes.

'What now, Uncircumcized One? Are the Berbers storming the gates of Marrakech? Leave me alone.' He reached down to the floor and let his questing hand find a brass goblet which, with a sudden unsuspected movement, he flung across the room, making sure that he would not hit Ramon but aiming near enough to cause the other to duck his head.

Ramon picked up the goblet, noted the dented lip and placed it carefully on a tabouret.

'And if the Berbers were storming the gates, my Lord Mohammed, of little use you would be to protect us. You, Mohammed ibn Ibrahim, son of the Emir, lying exhausted in bed after a night's tussle with the new slave girl.'

'Ay! But she was a wise purchase, Ramoncito. Be on the lookout for another like her.'

Ramon nodded as Mario continued. 'And why may not the son of the Emir lie in his bed when he has a grand vizier such a you to attend to all his business?'

'Because, my lord Mohammed —'

'Oh, how you love titles, Ramon! Once I was "Your Excellency" and then for a little while I was just "Mario". In our misfortunes, I was Mario. Now I have become "my lord Mohammed"! Stop putting me on a pedestal, Ramon. Stop being a slave.'

Ramon waited patiently for him to finish.

'Sidi Mokar and his slave Juanele have just arrived from Fez. The Emir is away from the palace, having gone to the water gardens outside the gates, and Adan accompanies him. That leaves nobody to welcome the noble messenger from the Sultan but yourself.'

'Sidi Mokar and Juanele!' Mario shook his head in disbelief, as Ramon held a clean shirt over him. As his head appeared through it, he laughed. 'Methinks Sidi Mokar will not ask me to gather firewood for him today. Nor will Juanele show me how to scrub copper pots with sand. Think you, Ramon, that they know me and who I was?'

'All of Morocco knows you, Mario – who you are and who you were. Many are jealous of you, and there are some in the palace itself who resent you and would do away with you, but they fear Adan and through him the Emir. But come! Stand still and let me finish dressing you; Sidi Mokar awaits you in the grand hall.'

Mario paid special attention to his dress that morning. Today he was not satisfied with the plain brown-and-white striped woollen *djellabah* or the simple white muslin shirt and white *kaftan*. He sent Ramon to the cedar wardrobe for other clothes, and Ramon returned with a *kaftan* of ribbed sulphur-yellow silk, heavily encrusted with silver threads, a *djellabah* of the finest white wool, yards of gold metallic cloth to wind into a turban, and yellow *babouches* solid with stitches of gold.

'We owe much to Sidi Mokar and Juanele, Ramoncito. You must accompany me.'

Ramon acquiesced. For once he was willing to share Mario's splendour. He opened the door and preceded Mario down the hall. The big double cedar wood doors of the reception hall were closed, but Ramon opened them both and stepped inside. Mario saw him sink to one knee, and glimpsed a seated figure at the other end of the room, with a second familiar figure standing behind the divan. He heard Ramon's sonorous words, in perfect Arabic.

'My lord, the Shereef Mohammed ibn Ibrahim, Prince of Marrakech, Caid of Tameslout in the High Atlas, Sheik of Derdouri and Calipha of Talat, bids you welcome.'

As Mario walked passed, he could not refrain from whispering to Ramon, 'How many of those titles did you make up?'

A whisper answered him. 'None, my lord. They are all yours by grace of the Emir.'

But Mario had no time to ponder titles. He was far too amazed to see the mighty Sidi Mokar flat on his face on the floor, and the boy Juanele also prostrate. He walked over to where Mokar had flung himself in obeisance, reached down and picked the man up. Mokar arose and, although his face was filled with the correct amount of reverence and respect, a ghost of a smile hovered on his lips. The formal words of the Arabic greeting came slowly and reverently. Then his smile broke forth.

'It is an honour to be received by the Prince Mohammed – he whose mighty hand once caused this most unworthy nose to bleed.'

Mario's lips were smiling too.

'It is an even greater honour to receive you, Sidi Mokar. What would you that I do for you today? Shall I gather faggots of argon and oleander to light your fire? Shall I go with Juanele to fetch a haunch of mutton for your *couscous* this evening, or would you prefer that I make your tea with just the amount of mint that you like?'

Sidi Mokar's smile broke into laughter. 'Ah, Mario, for I alone of all Morocco can call you by that name, you have come a long way since the night you hurled me on the ground on some nameless beach in Spain. But it is I that shall always be indebted to you.' The toe of his *babouche* nudged the prostrate boy beside him. 'May so mean a person as my *N'zrani* slave gaze upon your exalted face?'

'If you mean that uncircumcized brat, Juanele, whom I once fished out of the ocean and who afterward proved such a hard taskmaster, I do not know, Sidi Mokar. My father, the Emir, has countless dungeons under his palace. Sometimes at night we can hear the hopeless groans of the prisoners confined there. Were I to look on Juanele now and remember the cruel taskmaster he was, I would most certainly consign him to those dungeons immediately.' He winked at Mokar. 'But no – the only thing I can think of is to open my arms and embrace him, infidel though he be.'

Juanele sprang up and took two quick steps to Mario's side.

'Oh, Mario, Mario, Mario! How good it is to see you and see that you are safe. And you too, Ramon. But, Mario, how grand you look. Even the Sultan at Fez does not wear such magnificent clothes.' His fingers tested the fine wool of the *djellabah*. 'Oh, Mario, I'm so happy.'

'And I, boy, I am happy too, and I owe much of it to you, Juanele. Now, with Sidi Mokar's permission, I would like to do something for you.' He waited for Mokar's nod. 'Take Juanele, Ramon, and lead him to my wardrobe. Let him have his pick of anything there. Then open the chest of jewels which Adan gave me and let Juanele choose from among them. Do not restrict him, Ramon. Anything that I have is far too poor to repay the debt I owe him.'

They waited for Ramon and Juanele to leave, and Sidi Mokar remained standing until Mario had taken his place on the divan and motioned for Mokar to be seated.

'I come from His Magnificence, the Sultan,' he said, 'with a special message for the Emir. This I must deliver today, as I should start at the *muezzin's* call in the morning to make the return journey to Fez.'

'Horsemen have already been sent to fetch the Emir and Prince Adan. They will arrive soon. Until they come, Sidi Mokar, let me make you comfortable. This is your house. Would you bathe, eat, refresh yourself? Would you enjoy the company of one of the slaves from my *hareem*?'

'My *hareem* accompanies me, My Lord Mohammed, since it was the will of Allah that you fish him out of the ocean. But I thank you for the offer, as I once thanked you for saving Juanele's life. No, there is nothing that I want except to talk to you. And, in addition to the message I have for the Emir, I have a message for you. The Spaniard who paid me to take you away is dead.'

'My uncle? How do you know?'

'The Court of the Sultan has many informers at the Court of Spain. He was killed by his own brother, Frontera Baja.'

'My father!' Mario searched Mokar's face. 'But have you any more news of him?'

'No, Mario, none. Old Don Baltazar Ruiz has been ill for months in Cadiz, and he was our chief source of information. Spain is in a ferment now. The old order has passed and a new one has taken its place. The King and Queen of Spain no longer rule. They have fled Spain and gone to Rome to seek sanctuary with the *N'zrani* Pope. The nobles of Spain have fled too. Their estates have been confiscated, and they are impoverished. And Spain is just another dominion of the Frankish Emperor who today dominates all Europe – the great Napoleon. He has placed his brother Joseph on the throne, but it is Napoleon himself who controls the destiny of the country. It is for that very reason that I am come to see the Emir – and from the commotion outside, I would guess the Emir has arrived.'

Sidi Mokar was right. In a few moments, Ramon opened the doors and the Emir and Adan entered the hall. As Mario and Sidi Mokar knelt before him, the Emir waved away their formalities and bade them arise. A messenger such as Mokar was too important to warrant a waste of time in dignified formalities. Sufficient to give the usual Arabic praises to Allah and then get down to business. The Emir seated himself, while the others remained standing.

'Speak your words to me, my worthy Mokar, for I am an old man and consumed with curiosity as to what His Magnificence might want of me.'

'It is not of you that he requires a service, my lord Emir, but of your son, the Prince Adan.'

'And what does His Magnificence desire of my son?'

'He wishes him to go to Spain as an ambassador of the Shereefian Empire.'

'To Spain – our ancient enemy?'

'But now an enemy no longer, my lord Emir. Today the Spanish nation no longer exists. It is now nothing more than a Frankish province – a part of the empire of the Frenchman Napoleon.'

'I have heard of him. He has already destroyed half of Europe. Good! Let him destroy the rest of the infidels and then destroy himself.'

'*In'sha'allah.*' Sidi Mokar bowed. 'But in the meantime the cursed English harass our coasts. They have eyes on our city of Tangiers, which they would make into a naval base for operations against the French. This the French do not want. It is bad enough for them to have the English on one doorstep; worse if they are on two. Therefore, this Napoleon would discuss the matter with the Sultan, and he has invited the Sultan to Spain to talk about it.'

The Emir spat on the floor. 'The insolence of the man! Was he not a mere Corsican corporal before he plundered and pillaged his way to being emperor? Naturally the Sultan will not go.'

'Naturally. He wishes no traffic with unbelievers. But our Sultan is a wise man, my lord Emir. He desires to be allied with France, rather than to be plundered by both France and England. It will help us protect our coast and keep the infidels from taking Morocco. Therefore, he would send an ambassador to treat with this upstart Napoleon. We must sound him out – what he will do for us and what he expects us to do for him. Then, when the ambassador has returned to Fez, the Sultan will weigh the matter and consult with his counsellors.' Mokar bowed slowly in Adan's direction. 'The Prince Adan has been in Spain. He speaks the tongue, and he is wise with the wisdom of his illustrious father. He will talk little and listen well, and bring back the words of Napoleon to our Sultan.'

'Then I answer for my son, Sidi Mokar. He will go to Spain and meet this Frankish upstart. Does he accompany you to Fez?'

'If Allah is willing.'

'Then grant me one more day with my son before you leave. There is much that I would discuss with him. Give me tomorrow, Sidi Mokar. Do you agree?'

'If it is your wish, my lord Emir.'

'It is. Tomorrow I shall be closeted with my son the entire day, and you shall leave the day after. But today, Sidi Mokar, we would show you the hospitality of Marrakech. What can we do to make your stay here pleasant? Would you review my troops? Shall I stage a *sortie* for you? Shall I hold a conclave of the nobles of my Court? Or' – he lowered his voice – 'would a shaded room in my palace with one of the slaves of my *hareem* be more acceptable?'

Sidi Mokar's hand passed over the pointed beard on his chin. He looked up at the Emir and smiled slowly.

'You ask me what I would like to do, my lord Emir. Therefore I shall be so bold as to tell you. There is one desire I would like granted more than anything else, while I am here in Marrakech.'

'You have but to name it.'

'Snow, my lord Emir.'

'Snow?'

'Yes. As many times as I have been here, I have looked up to the noble mountains of your Atlas and seen their tops covered with snow. I have seen it white at midday, rose-coloured at dawn and purple in the evening, but I have never really seen it, my lord Emir. Just once before I die, I would like to see snow, pick it up in my hand, taste it. Many times as I have journeyed under the burning sky, across the wastes of Morocco and into the wide stretches of the Sahara, I have dreamed of snow – cold, white, glistening and pure. Now I crave to know it. Would that be possible?'

'Alas, Sidi Mokar,' the Emir said, sighing, 'if all my guests were so easily satisfied! You shall see snow. It is not too long a ride up the mountains, and the snow at this time of year comes far down into the ravines. My sons shall accompany you – the Prince Adan and the Prince Mohammed.' He looked from one to the other and they both nodded willingly. It was their favourite trip – the ascent from the heat of the city to the icy cold of the snow-filled ravines.

'Then I beg leave of you, Sidi Mokar. My slaves shall prepare a dinner for you and transport it to the mountains so you will have refreshments on your return. You shall most certainly see snow, Sidi Mokar, and, that you may see it in comfort, I shall send you my heaviest *burnoose* to wrap yourself.'

He walked across the room, not turning to notice their obeisances.

Chapter Forty-five

A GALA HOLIDAY air accompanied the group that sallied forth from the high red walls of Marrakech that afternoon. Adan led the way, blissfully unmindful of the sweating slaves that worked on the battlements. Sidi Mokar rode abreast of Mario, the heavy *burnoose* of the Emir strapped behind him on his saddle. As always, Juanele followed directly behind him; and after them rode four soldiers from Mario's company. Straggling along at the end of the procession were half a dozen slaves on mules and donkeys, their full panniers stuffed with provisions for the repast on the mountain.

Soon they had left the city-encircling palms behind and started up the mountain. A few oleanders, sparse-leaved argon trees and withered grass covered the sides of the hills; they mounted higher, seeking the hidden valleys, made greener by the snows above them. There they found deep grass, mountain thyme, rose laurel and, as they mounted higher, tall cedar trees. Their objective was a wild valley where a bold promontory gave a clear view of the city far below. It was a favourite spot of Adan's and Mario's, where they had often come hawking or spent the afternoon, sprawled in the sun on the fragrant, springy bed of thyme which carpeted the ground. The last time they had visited it, a trickle of snow still remained in the fastness of the ravine, but this day, when they arrived, the snow had entirely disappeared.

They reined in their horses and contemplated the empty ravine. Sidi Mokar was ready to apologize for having brought them so far on a fruitless search but Adan, mindful of the obligatory hospitality of the Moor and remembering his own debt of gratitude to Sidi Mokar and Juanele for their kindness to Mario, insisted that they accomplish their mission, even if it necessitated riding to the nearest summit. For as he insisted, if Sidi Mokar wished to see snow, then he should see snow, even if they had to send the slaves on ahead to bring it to him in the copper pans they would use for the *couscous*.

Mario, however, had a better idea. Why not leave the slaves, whose slowness hampered their progress, here in this delightful spot to prepare the meal? He, Adan, Sidi Mokar and Jeremiah would proceed up the mountain to the snow. Then, when they returned, tired after their climb and descent, the fragrance of thyme would be mingled with the dinner odours and they would need no sauce to whet their appetite. The idea was enthusiastically received by all except Juanele, whose lower lip drooped in a pout when he found he was not included.

The air had already begun to cool, so they donned their heavy woollen *burnooses*, pulled the hooded caps over their heads, and started on up the mountain. It was a narrow, precipitous trail, one that was so difficult to follow they had to go in single file. At times they skirted the edge of cliffs, and the loose stones that their horses dislodged rattled over the edge and fell in a nerve-shattering racket to the bottom, sometimes several hundred feet below. They let the horses choose their own way, let them have time to test their footing before they took a step. Gradually the way widened until they reached a level spot where the trail divided. Here all except Adan dismounted to rest their horses. Adan kept his seat in the saddle.

'Sidi Mokar,' he said, pointing up the narrow trail which led around an outcropping of granite, 'if I am not nistaken, that path leads to a deep ravine where there should be snow. But for the moment I am confused. Perhaps we should follow the other trail. I am not certain. But rather than lead you on to another disappointment, let me go on, while you rest here. In a few seconds I shall know better where to guide you. Wait here for me.'

He turned his horse towards the ascent and Mario watched him until he rounded the corner of the huge rock. Sidi Mokar sat down, reached in the folds of his *djellabah* inside the *birnoose*, and produced several thin cigars. He looked a question at Mario.

'Are you so faithful to Islam that you do not break the rule of smoking, my lord Prince?'

'My adherence to that rule, Sidi Mokar, is not one of piety. I have not smoked since I left Havana, and now I feel no desire.'

The tinderbox flamed in Sidi Mokar's hand and he drew a deep puff from his cigar, settled back against a boulder and smiled ruefully at Mario.

'So my kitchen helper has become the son of the Emir of Marrakech – a tale that could well have been included in the

Thousand Nights and a Night. Surely no magic carpet or Aladdin's lamp could be more miraculous than the transformation of the lowest *N'zrani* slave to an emir's son.'

Mario held up a warning finger. 'Ah, but you are wrong, Sidi Mokar. I was not a *N'zrani*. Although I bore the sign of that religion on my body, I had already proclaimed Allah as the one God and Mohammed as His prophet. Yes, long before I met you, when Adan and I were in Cadiz together.'

'Then why didn't you tell me?'

'Ah, but I did, Sidi Mokar, and, if you will remember, you did not believe me. But how could you? I was a walking advertisement of Christianity, as much as the urchins who walk the streets of Havana with a pennant urging all to visit some new *cantina*. No, Sidi Mokar, it was not your fault. I cannot blame you.'

Mokar inhaled deeply from his cigar. He carefully examined as much of Jeremiah's face as appeared below the hood of the *burnoose*. 'And you, man, were you in the same company as Mario, the group that marched from Tangiers to Fez under my command?'

'I was, Your Excellency. I was one of the miserable wretches who survived. Day after day I marched, until my feet were masses of cuts and bruises. I wrapped them in rags, I padded them with leaves. I stuffed the rags with grass and hobbled on to Fez.'

Sidi Mokar shook his head doubtfully. 'I have been in this business a long time. One would think by how that I would be callous to all the suffering. But I am not. Perhaps contact with so many Christians has made me as white-livered as they are. Once in a while I can do something to better the lot of a few of them, as I did for Mario — or should I say the Prince Mohammed? But alas, there are too many of them — far, far too many — and if I gained the reputation of softness with them, then another, more cruel than I, would take my place. . . .'

Jeremiah's hand on Sidi Mokar's arm cut off the rest of his sentence. He lifted his other hand to enjoin silence.

'What is it, Jeremiah?' Mario asked.

'Quiet, Mario.'

Sidi Mokar shook Jeremiah's hand from his arm. 'I think your slave is too familiar, Prince Mohammed. First he puts his infidel hand on me and then he commands you to be quiet —'

'Quiet, goddamn it,' Jeremiah silenced Sidi Mokar. 'Listen!'

Then all three heard it – faintly at first, losing itself in the echoes as it bounded from rock to rock. It was a call and it repeated one word: 'Mario, Mario, Mario.' Then silence.

'It came from there.' Jeremiah pointed up the mountain. 'It must be Adan.'

Mario had already leaped to his feet. He ran to Zuleika and vaulted into the saddle. Without a word he started up the trail. He did not wait for Zuleika to pick her way. For the first time he used a whip on her – a branch of shrub which he had picked up from the ground while he was sitting. He turned the corner of the rock but saw only the trail winding upward.

As he rode, he felt the chill of ice in the air, and in a few moments he came to the brink of a ravine, black with cedar trees but with a glimmer of white at the bottom. Mario spurred Zuleika on. Now they were in the snow which had overflowed the sides of the ravine and made a thin covering of white on the rocks. Below him Mario saw the tracks of another horse. He was sure it was Adan's. The tracks veered to the left, where the ridge of the ravine was broken, and led down the steep slope.

Mario pulled Zuleika up short. Behind a cedar tree, a short way down the ravine, he saw the black tail of Adan's horse. He jumped down, finding the snow up around his bare ankles. As he started to run towards Adan's horse, he lost both his *babouches*. But he did not bother to retrace his steps, for as he came closer he saw a form beside the horse – a dark brown *burnoose* sprawled on the white snow.

'Back, Mario, back!' The voice that hailed him was weak. 'Do not come to me.' Punctuating Adan's call, a shot rang out in the still mountain air. This was followed by a fusillade of others. Mario dropped flat on the ground, knowing that his heavy dark cloak made a conspicuous target on the snow.

'Adan,' he shouted, 'can you hear me?'

The voice was fainter. 'Mario! There are Berbers behind the farther ridge. How many I do not know. I am badly wounded. I cannot move, but do not come to me. Protect yourself.'

'Nothing can keep me from you!' Mario slipped out of the brown *burnoose*, confident that his white *djellabah* would protect him by its colour. He crawled over the snow, hiding as much as possible under the low-lying cedar branches, until he reached Adan's side.

Mario noticed the crimson spot on the robe. 'Are you badly hurt?'

'It is hard for me to breathe.' Adan's words brought a froth of blood to his lips. 'Mario, I am dying. It is the will of Allah that I die, but Mario, my brother – oh, more than a brother – let me say this. I die happily in your arms. Hold me, Mario. Tighter! You have never held me this way before. Let me feel the strength of your arms, to give me strength to die.'

'You will not die, Adan.' Another fusillade of bullets drilled small round black holes in the snow. 'You cannot die. You mean more to me than my own life, Adan. I cannot let you die. Breathe, Adan, and live. Live for me.'

Adan's head pressed against Mario's chest. 'Mario, your words are sweet to me. There is much I have always wanted to tell you, Mario, but now it is too late. Too late.' Blood spurted from his mouth and made a red stain on Mario's robe. He sank back in Mario's arms. Mario's hand reached inside Adan's *burnoose*, feeling under the *djellabah* and the silk *kaftan*. He felt the warm stickiness of blood.

'Mario.' Adan's words were faint and laboured. 'The little Mohammed. Your promise. He must live. Guard him. Oh, Mario. It darkens and I cannot see you, my Mario. I feel your arms about me. Hold me, Mario, hold me. The love of a brother. ... my Mario. ... *In'sha'allah*. ... Mario.' The last faint whisper was drowned by a rattle of musket fire.

Mario laid Adan's body tenderly on the ground. For the moment he was numb to sorrow; it was overwhelmed by an all-consuming black hatred, so great that it swept everything else before it. Kill, kill, kill! Let his hands find flesh to tear!

He crept away from the cedar tree and crawled down the slope, seeking shelter behind rocks and bushes. From the protection of a huge boulder he looked back up to the crest of the ravine. He saw a dun-coloured mound on the snow. It was the Emir's *burnoose* and the bright red stream that came from it told him that Sidi Mokar was dead. A few yards away was another heap in the snow. Jeremiah! The second fusillade had been well-aimed. Now Mario alone was left. All the others were too far down the mountain to be of immedate help – even assuming that they had heard the gunfire.

He sloughed off Mohammed of Marrakech and San Mateo of Spain as a snake sheds its skin. Once more he was El Rubio, stalking his prey in some midnight alley in Havana. He had lost none of his cunning. The silent snow under his belly gave no warning of his progress and the white *djellabah* made him one with the snow. He crawled from tree to tree, inching across the bottom of the ravine, then up the other side. Only once did he stop, and that was to assure himself that his dagger was still fastened to the cord around his waist. The sweeping snow-encrusted branches of cedar gave him momentary shelter as he crawled from one tree to another, up the precipitous side.

He saw something move. Parting the snowy branches, he peered out. Only a few yards away, cautiously scanning the opposite rim of the ravine, he saw the figure of a man. Evidently he was waiting for the reinforcements which he thought must be following, for his head moved from one side of the stone to the other, looking across the ravine to where Mario could see the bodies of Mokar and Jeremiah.

Mario slid out from under the tree. With his knife in his teeth, he bellied along the snow until he was able to spring on the unsuspecting Berber. His hand grasped the blade and he jumped. As he landed, his knife sought the man's throat. It was over without a sound except for the last twitching of the man's feet in the snow and the spurt of blood from the gushing artery.

That was one! From the shots he had heard, Mario knew there must be others hiding out on the hillside. His only task was to find them. He took the long musket which was still clutched in the dead man's hand, turned the lifeless body over and cut the cord of the powder horn, found a small leather bag of bullets and reloaded the musket. Now he was better prepared. Then he stripped the ragged blue *burnoose* from the dead Berber and put it on over his own head, pulling the hood down over his eyes. Then he rolled the body over the snow until it was hidden by the rocks.

He had only a few moments to wait. A crouching figure ran towards him, bending low to avoid the trees, and, although he could not understand the words that the man mumbled as he ran, Mario knew they were words of triumph. Mario beckoned the man on, imitating the anxious movements of the man he had killed, until the second Berber sank down beside him. His whispered words were the last he uttered, for once more Mario's knife sought a stringy brown throat and ripped it open. The man rolled his eyes in fright, gurgled, and died. That made two. These had been easy; the rest might be more difficult.

Now, with the protective cover of the blue *burnoose*, Mario left the rocks, running between the trees until he heard a low hail. It came from a third Berber, lying on the ground, his musket trained to the spot where the trail came to the rim of the ravine. He waved to Mario to come nearer, and Mario ran over and dropped down beside him on the snow. He saw the man's puzzled look at his unfamiliar face, saw him open his mouth to scream a warning, and then Mario's knife plunged into his back. Three! That at least evened the score – one for Adan, one for Mokar, and one for Jeremiah.

Where to next? As he was contemplating which way to go, he saw the figure of a rider silhouetted against the opposite rim of the gully. It was one of his own men, followed by another. They were here; they had heard the shooting! Now the soldier spied the bodies of Mokar and Jeremiah and was dismounting from his horse, while he called to the others to hurry. But, as he called, a single shot rang out and the man fell to the ground.

Mario did not watch to see if the man was dead. Instead, his eyes turned in the direction of the shot and he saw a fourth man, hidden by a thick growth, reloading his musket. As the Berber's fingers fumbled with the powderhorn, he peered out from between the branches, unable to explain to himself why his had been the only shot.

As Mario ran to him, the Berber gesticulated wildly, pointing across the depression to the other horsemen that were gathering there. Mario nodded and pointed in the same direction and, as the Berber lifted his long musket to take aim, Mario's musket came up to his shoulder. He sighted and fired and saw the man drop. Four of them. And as the Berber's shot had been the only one, Mario was sure that he was the last of the lot.

Dropping the gun and the Berber robe, he ran out into the open and yelled across, 'My men! Do not shoot! I have killed them all. One of you come over here, armed with a sword.' He waited, standing near the dead Berber, until the man arrived. Mario pointed to the dead man. 'Cut off his head,' he muttered, 'and when you have finished, there is another one down there.' He pointed to the clump of trees below. 'Farther up on the side of the hill you will find two more. Decapitate them and bring the four heads back to me. They have killed Prince Adan.'

'The Prince?' The soldier's face blanched.

'Yes, and Sidi Mokar, and my man Jeremiah, and one of your companions too, I think.' Mario started to run down the slope, but the soldier called after him, 'Then who killed all four of these men?'

Mario stopped his descent abruptly to hurl one word back at the soldier. 'I.' Then he continued his mad race to the bottom of the gully and up the other side. Juanele was lying on the ground, the head of Mokar in his lap. His eyes, glazed with tears, looked up at Mario. 'He is dead, Mario.'

'You are not alone in your sorrow, boy. My heart is as heavy as yours. Down there in that clump of cedars lies the still heart of Adan. I go to fetch him.'

Tenderly Mario picked up Adan's cold body and cradled it in his arms. Somewhere in his mind, crazy half-formed thoughts made him believe that the warmth of his own flesh would remove that terrible chill and bring life back to Adan. But Adan was dead. He staggered up, burdened more by the heaviness of his heart than by the body of Adan. One of the soldiers came down to help him, and together they placed Adan over the saddle of his horse. Then they lifted Mokar, with Juanele still clutching his hand, and then Jeremiah and the soldier. Ramon came to Mario to help him mount Zuleika, but Mario waved him away. He pointed down the ravine to where the soldier was struggling up, burdened by the four heads.

When the soldier arrived and deposited his gruesome burden on the ground at Mario's feet, Mario reached down and clutched the long hair on one of the Berber heads, lifted it up and gazed into the sightless eyes. He screamed curses at the head, but they were merely wordless sounds. His free hand slapped the face, hitting it so hard that the lifeless flesh of the cheeks turned purple. Still cursing, he took out his knife and carved out the eyes, slit the mouth and tore out the tongue. Then Ramon came to him and loosened his frenzied grasp; the head fell with the others on the ground.

Ramon led Mario over to Zuleika, but Mario refused to mount the horse; he wanted to walk beside Adan. Mario did not feel the icy cold of the snow nor the sharpness of the stones. He stumbled along beside the horse; his tears blinded him so that he could not see.

Chapter Forty-six

IT WAS a dark, sad journey from the winter of the snow-filled ravine to the date palms that surrounded Marrakech – a journey in which each slow step of the horses fell like the blow of a hammer to pound the anguish deeper into Mario's numbed consciousness. He knew that he was not alone in his sorrow. It was shared by Juanele, behind him. Each of them had lost something infinitely precious to him, not only a friend but a protector. Now they were both alone in the large world of Islam, a renegade Christian and an unbeliever.

As they neared the city gates, passersby on the road noticed the strange procession, with the dangling arms and legs of the dead men across the horses, and Prince Mohammed limping beside one of them. Questions to the soldiers identified the victims, and, when these men of the road discovered that it was the son of the Emir, they followed, some on donkeys, some on foot. A shrill, mournful wailing commenced, timed in macabre cadences to the plodding hoof-beats of the horses. At the city gates, the watchers stopped them, incredulous at first. Then, shocked into belief, they admitted the long procession. It gained in followers as it passed through the narrow streets and out into the big square of the Djmaa el Fna, increasing to a dirge-howling mob which reached its keening tentacles far back into the *souks* and alleys.

They halted in front of the Emir's palace, and Mario lifted his head for the first time. He would allow none other to touch the body of Adan but himself. He eased it tenderly from the horse, took it once again in his arms, and pillowed it against his chest.

The big doors opened for him silently and he entered the long hall. Step by step he staggered with his burden up the marble stairs. Word of their arrival had preceded them, for the Emir awaited them at the head of the staircase. He looked down silently as Mario ascended, reached out one hand and grasped Adan's cold fingers in his own. The door of the Presence Room was open. Without speaking, Mario carried Adan in, laid him tenderly on the state divan, straightened the stiffened arms, and crossed Adan's hands on his chest. Together he and the Emir knelt beside the couch.

'Sometime later, my son, you shall tell me what happened.' The Emir had difficulty in controlling his voice. 'I know you have avenged Adan's death. But we shall discuss that later. Now we who love him must bid him farewell and turn him over to the women. As man comes into the world through woman, so does he depart. Look long at Adan, Mohammed ibn Ibrahim. Imprint those fair features on your mind forever, for now we bid him farewell. After this he will be only a memory. I would that my son might have lived, but it was not the will of Allah, and Allah is the all-wise, the all-knowing, the all-compassionate. We must not mourn for Adan, Mohammed ibn Ibrahim, no matter how much our hearts may miss him, for now, while we thus grieve, he has already heard the gates of Paradise close behind him. We should not wish him back.'

'But he is gone, my father.' Mario strove to keep the tears from his voice.

'No, he lives, my son. As long as we breathe there will be an image of Adan in our hearts. I loved him as only a father can love a son. You, Mohammed, loved him for the friend he was and for the great love he bore you. No, Adan is not dead, for over in his *hareem* a crying infant continues his life for him.'

'And to that life, my father. . . .' Mario looked up at the old man. 'Is it possible for me still to call you father?'

'More than ever now,' the Emir assured him.

'Then, my father, let me swear now, holding the hand of him whom we both loved, that my life, poor as it is, belongs to the young Mohammed. Do you accept the oath I once gave Adan?'

'I do, and I thank you for it.'

Mario leaned down for one last look at Adan's face. For a fleeting second he thought he saw the eyes open and look at him, saw the lips part in the well-known smile, and heard Adan's words. They were strange words that raced through Mario's brain, but he obeyed them. He pressed his lips against the cold lips of his brother. The chill seemed to depart from the lips and they grew warmer. Mario arose. His head spun and he would have fallen, had it not been for the arm of the older man supporting him. Arm in arm they walked across the aisle of carpets to the door where Ramon was waiting. The Emir gently disengaged Mario's arm and delivered him to the Negro, who led him down the stairs and across the courtyard to his own palace.

Deaf to the cries of mourning, Mario sat silently on his divan. The glass of hot tea which Ramon brought him steamed the room with the sharp odour of mint, then cooled and grew cloudy in the glass, but Mario did not reach out his hand for it. Over and over again his eyes traced the intricate pattern of the tiles on the opposite wall. His familiarity with Arabic script now enabled him to translate the cursive writing on them, and he repeated endlessly their flowing characters. 'There is no God but Allah, and Mohammed is His Prophet.' He read it over and over until the lamps of argon oil flickered and went out. Still he sat immovable, as the moon rose above the Koutoubia Tower and strained its lights through the slatted jalousies.

Some time during the night, Ramon came to him, removed his clothing, took off the silk *kaftan* with the dried blood-stain, laid Mario back on the cushions of the divan, and covered him with a warm blanket. He tiptoed out and came back with a glass of snow-cooled water, which Mario drank silently. The opium which Ramon had put in it brought sleep to Mario, but not a dreamless sleep.

Adan reappeared to him, not the lifeless body with the dangling arm which Mario had brought down from the mountain, but a young, laughing Adan, the same who had sat with him on that moonlit night in Don Baltazar's house in faraway Cadiz. Then he felt Adan's lips pressed against his own, but this time they were not cold, they were warm and seeking. In his dream, he opened his eyes to find that they were not Adan's lips but those of Zaydah. She stepped back from him, and he saw her hand make the gesture he had so often seen his mother Ana make as she knelt before the little shrine back in Havana. Then Zaydah faded away and became Adan again, sitting beside him on his bed.

Mario slept. When he opened his eyes the grey light of morning was creeping through the window. He heard the dawn cry of the *muezzin*, but this morning, for the first time since he had lived at the little palace, he did not rise and prostrate himself towards Mecca. His hand crept to his breast and he forced his eyes down to the hated picture he bore there. The God of the Christians had failed him, and now the God of Islam had deserted him.

Ramon, sitting in the shadows on the far side of the room, had seen the movement of Mario's arm and he came over to the divan. 'I would not disturb you so early were it not that I know you are awake. Come, Mario! You must dress and attend the Emir, for the coffin of Adan now lies in the great hall of the palace, with the Emir sitting stony-eyed at its head. An empty stool awaits you at the foot. You must attend him who is your father and share your grief with him.'

Ramon washed off the encrusted blood from Mario's hands, then dressed him carefully in a dull grey *kaftan* and an even darker grey *djellabah*. Today there were no yellow slippers; white ones took their place. When Mario had finished dressing, Ramon took a piece of charcoal from the brazier and smeared its black ash on Mario's forehead. They walked together across the courtyard and up the stairs to the palace.

At the door of the Presence Room, Mario left Ramon and walked down the carpet aisle between the bowed heads of the Moroccan nobles. He saw the stony face of the Emir on the right of the plain cedar box. He noted the leather hassock at the other end. Behind the box that contained Adan there were many people standing – boys and young men, the sons of the Emir's concubines. A screen of fretted wood had been placed at the side of the coffin and from behind it Mario heard the soft sobs and the stifled wails of the *hareem* of his brother. As he seated himself, he wondered if Zaydah was one of those moaning behind the screen, and his thoughts turned to his dream of the night before when Adan's lips had become hers. Guiltily he dismissed the forbidden thoughts and stared straight ahead in unblinking silence.

Much happened which he did not entirely comprehend. He remembered rising and walking behind the Emir down the carpeted strip as they followed the cedar coffin. He felt the hot sun as he quitted the palace, and then the cool shadows of the mosque. He saw the red dust of Marrakech encarmine his white slippers as he walked through the narrow streets, and he felt the damp coolness of the royal tombs, saw the heavy stone lid lifted from the black opening. Then the wooden box sank from sight and the stone was replaced. The prayers of the Iman ceased and the cold dampness of the tomb changed to the heat of the streets, then to the shadows of his own palace. Ramon's hands took away the grey clothes and brought cool garments of thin white muslin for Mario to put on.

He sat through the long afternoon without speaking. When a knock came at the door, he did not arise, nor did he turn in the direction of the door when Ramon opened it. The first thing he heard was a childish cry and then the voice of the Emir.

'My grandson frets because he has not seen his uncle. Knowing that it was his father's custom to bring him here daily, I have come with him.'

Mario knelt on one knee before the Emir and would have placed his forehead on the floor, but the child ran across the room and put his arms around Mario's neck. The obeisance would have been impossible.

A wan smile momentarily lit up the Emir's face. 'The little one knows that there is no need for you to bow before me. Our grief has brought us too close. I deliver the lad to you, Mohammed. Take good care of him. You must bury your grief in the tomb where Adan now lies and give your smiles to the living. And, Mohammed, I would speak with you.'

Mario gathered the boy into his arms. 'May your words give me some task to do, my father, that I may forget my grief. Do I head an expedition into the mountains to annihilate the rebellious Berbers?'

'Something more important than that, Mohammed. Tomorrow you leave for Tangiers, and thence to Spain.'

'For Tangiers? Do you disown me? Do you send me into exile away from you and him?' He clutched the boy tighter.

'Only for a little while, Mohammed.'

Mario loosened his clasp as the little Mohammed wriggled from his arms.

'But why to Spain?'

'As you know, His Magnificence the Sultan requested that Adan go to Spain to meet the Frankish Emperor. Alas, Adan cannot go. But you, his brother, must take his place, for you know the ways of the *N'zranis* far better than Adan ever did. You know their cunning words and the traps they set for the guileless. Once they drove us from Spain, Mohammed. Now they ask us to come back. They seek an ambassador from the Shereefian Empire. You shall be that ambassador, Mohammed.'

'You remember the conditions under which I left Spain, my father. It is not that I fear for my own life in returning but I remember my promise to Adan and to you, regarding him.' He pointed to the baby playing on the floor.

'This time, my son, you travel under the holy flag of Morocco. You are an ambassador from the Sultan himself and, as such, your person is sacred. No one will dare lay a finger on you, and you will return safely. Of that I am certain.'

'If it is your wish that I go, I shall go.'

'It is my wish. In Tangiers you will meet the representatives of His Magnificence. They will instruct you. Even now your caravan is being prepared. You will go in proper style, not only as the ambassador of the Sultan but as the Prince of Marrakech. It is our intention that you dazzle the eyes of Europe so that they will understand the vast riches of the Mahgreb.' The Emir turned to leave. 'Keep the boy Mohammed with you for a while today. Already he calls for his father. You must fill that empty space and' – he paused for a moment as Ramon held the door open – 'may Allah go with you, listen for you, speak words of wisdom with your tongue, and bring you safely back to Marrakech.'

Chapter Forty-seven

WHENEVER HE had a spare moment to think during the teeming bustle attendant on his preparations for departure, Mario came to recognize the wisdom of the old Emir's insistence on his leaving. He was kept so occupied from sun-up to far into the night that he was forced to relegate his sorrow to the back of his mind. He realized that by the time he did find the leisure to grieve the full sharp bitterness and sorrow would be softened.

Then, moving suddenly through his grief for Adan, came the realization that Zaydah was now free. This knowledge did not lessen his grief, but it added a new hope to his life. He had renounced her, buried his love for her, blotted the memory of her kisses from his mind, but now, in all conscience, he was able to think of her once more.

Mario was sure that, in loving Zaydah now, he was depriving Adan of nothing he had cherished. Zaydah had fulfilled her role. She had produced the son that Adan desired. Until her death she would have remained the first wife of Adan's *hareem*, but it was entirely possible that Adan would never again have had any desire to share her divan. Mario was free to desire her, and he allowed his thoughts to savour this new freedom.

He recalled the only time he had seen her since that last night in Cadiz. Something still puzzled him. The Christian sign! Did she still believe him to be a *N'zrani*? Was there something deeper? But even Zaydah could not occupy all his thoughts; there was work to be done and preparations to be made.

In spite of Ramon's stubborn insistence, Mario refused to permit him to make the journey. In the eyes of Spain, Ramon was still a Cuban slave, and therefore without rights. Although Mario did not believe that the long arm of the Inquisition would dare to reach out and touch a slave who belonged to the Moorish ambassador, he did not wish to take the gamble.

'And who will dress you, my Mario?' His worried look followed Mario about the room. 'And awaken you in the morning and prepare your bath for you and' – he hesitated – 'counsel you?'

'Nobody as well as you, I realize that. And yet perhaps I can find a substitute in Juanele.'

Ramon shook his head. 'He is too young.'

Mario ignored the remark. 'He mourns over Sidi Mokar and his grief is inconsolable. Now he is alone and he needs someone to whom he can give his loyalty. It will help him to have another master, and we both owe him much. Do not be jealous, Ramon; he will not take your place.'

Ramon relinquished his jealousy with a nod. 'The boy is Spanish, Mario, and still a Christian. Perhaps once in Spain, he would decide to remain there rather than return here. It is an opportunity for him to regain his homeland.'

'Right, Ramon, and once there he can decide. As long as he stays here without embracing Islam, he will be a slave and a part of Mokar's property. Who knows what will become of him?'

'Then ask the Emir if he cannot arrange to have his ownership transferred to you.'

Mario acted on Ramon's advice and the matter was easily settled.

At the same time Mario was being outfitted, each of the soldiers and slaves who were to accompany him must be dressed with equal resplendence. The *souks* were despoiled for new uniforms in the Turkish style, with finely pleated linen skirts. To these were added gem-studded silver daggers, ivory-hilted swords, scimitars of damascened steel in gold scabbards, and spears that sported long silken pennons. Zuleika must make the long journey back to Spain. Each of the soldiers must ride a white horse, with the result that any noble who owned a white horse of the required length of mane and tail found it missing from his stable.

They left at dawn. Mario broke early bread with the Emir, and fondled the baby as he ate, holding him in his lap and feeding him pieces of bread dipped in the sweet mint tea. The boy sensed his departure and he bellowed when Mario put him down, but the Emir called Ramon, who carried him off on his shoulders. The long cavalcade was drawn up in front of the palace. Mario and the Emir walked down the stairs and across the courtyard to where Juanele held Zuleika, harnessed in red Morocco leather studded with silver bosses. The Emir himself helped Mario mount and then, for perhaps the first time in his life, he spoke to a Christian slave.

'You were the slave of Sidi Mokar?' he demanded of Juanele.

Confusion robbed the boy of speech, and he sank to the ground, touching his head in the dust of the courtyard.

'Then, boy, as you were faithful to Sidi Mokar, so do I put my son, Mohammed ibn Ibrahim, in your charge. If it is ever a question of your life or his, you are not to hesitate – let it be yours. My son has many enemies in Spain. Guard him. Taste everything that is prepared for him to eat before he touches it. Sleep at the foot of his couch every night, and sleep there fully armed. Let not a curtain of the thinnest gauze be between you. Stay by his side wherever he goes. Never leave him. Do you understand?'

Juanele's head bobbed in acknowledgement, but the Emir was not done.

'Even when he meets the Frankish Emperor, you must be with him. Should the Corsican upstart deny you entrance, tell him to his lowborn face that I, the Emir, have so instructed you.' He smiled down at the prostrate figure. 'And remind him, if necessary, that my ancestors were lords of the High Atlas when his were grubbing garlics in Corsica. Is that clear?'

Words were impossible for Juanele, but he crept forward and kissed the toe of the Emir's *babouche*. The Emir gently nudged him with his foot to stand up and take his horse.

There was a moment of silence, broken only by Zuleika's champing. It was the moment of departure. The old Moor came closer to Mario, laid his blue-veined hand on Mario's knee, and blessed him with the protection of Allah. Then he turned quickly and, without looking back, retraced his steps across the courtyard.

Mario, pillowed high on Zuleika, thought of the other journeys he had made in Morocco. First the comparatively easy one from Tangiers to Fez, thanks to Sidi Mokar and the boy who was now beside him. Then the days of living hell on the walk from Fez to Marrakech, which had been made endurable by Jeremiah. Now Jeremiah was a part of the red soil of Marrakech. Being an infidel, he had not been allowed burial inside the city; but he rested in a casket of cedar wood, and a stone, engraved with his name in Arabic script, marked the spot outside the gates where he slept.

On this journey, Mario rode in command. Every one of the hundreds who accompanied him was along for his use – to protect him, serve him, and anticipate his every whim. They travelled on, over a passable road, beyond the palms of the city, out into the barren country. As all their animals had been chosen for speed, health and endurance, they made excellent time, pausing only at the crossing of rivers, now full from the melting snow, to water their horses.

Early in the afternoon the heat became unbearable, and the baggage mules were cut out to gallop ahead with an escort of soldiers. Within an hour they came upon the encampment – an orderly street of tents, with the big tent that belonged to Mario at its head. He handed Zuleika over to a groom and went inside. The walls were lined with costly shawls from Cashmere, lengths of brocade from Persia and heavy damasks from Italy and Spain.

One side of the tent – that facing away from the sun – was open, with the raised wall of the tent forming a protective awning, supported by silver-tipped poles. The rough ground had been covered with thick rugs, and for furniture there were a broad divan, low tables inlaid with nacre and silver, and tier after tier of cedar chests piled against one wall. All this for Mario – for one person for one night. Tomorrow it would be the same, and the next night and the next, until they reached Tangiers.

Juanele, experienced in anticipating the wants of Mokar, soon had things in even better order. Mario found hot water for his bath, fresh clothes laid out to replace the sweat-soaked garments he was wearing, a delicious meal prepared, and always Juanele to wait on him. He would have enjoyed the boy's company at his meals, but it was not fitting that a slave break bread with the son of the Emir. Mario insisted, however, that Juanele remain in attendance during his meals so they could talk together in Spanish.

Later, after Juanele had cleared away the remains of the meal and had eaten his own supper in the back part of the tent, he came in with Mario and produced the chess set which had belonged to Sidi Mokar. While he was setting the ivory pieces on the squares, Mario noticed that tears rimmed the boy's eyes, but thought it better to disregard them. He shoved his ottoman over to the chess board and moved one of the pawns in an opening gambit. Juanele followed and, during the game, his tears stopped. They had to finish playing by the light of the argon oil lamps. When it was over, Mario yawned and motioned for Juanele to leave.

'Dawn will see us starting, boy; better get some sleep.'

'Yes, Mario.'

'Well, then, *buenas noches, muchas gracias* and *duerme bien*.'

'*Buenas noches*, Mario. I trust that you dream of the *houris* of Paradise.'

Mario waited for him to pass through the curtain into the other side of the tent, but the boy remained standing.

'Then go to bed.' Mario waved him away again.

'I go, Mario, but first I must prepare my bed. Do you remember what the Emir said? I must not leave you. I must be your shadow. Not even a curtain of the thinnest gauze can separate us, for someone might crawl into your tent in the night.'

He unrolled a mattress which had been covered with a strip of brocade, and placed it at the foot of Mario's divan. 'Here is where I sleep from now on, with this.' He pointed to the slender blade of Spanish steel which he placed beside the mattress. 'And this.' He took a slim pistol from his belt and laid it beside the sword. 'Even the red *djinns* that fly at night will not be able to touch you while I am here.'

'And have you magic to keep the *djinns* away?' Mario laughed at the boy's boast.

'I kept them away from my master – always. Only when he left me did they succeed in destroying him. The magic is this.' He reached inside his *djellabah* and pulled out a battered crucifix. 'Even Mokar, a true believer, trusted in this to keep the *djinns* away.'

Mario tore open his light shirt and exposed his chest to Juanele. 'Think you that this has protected me? No, Juanele! Since I have had this I have been damned, and now I hate that bit of brass you hold in your hand. I am condemned to wear this hateful thing the rest of my life. I can never get away from it, and you see what it has done to me.'

'Yes – I see you rich and powerful. I see you at the head of a company of picked soldiers. I see you a prince of Marrakech, the son of the Emir. And, Mario, as I look at you, I do not see that you have suffered overmuch. Your face is as young, as healthy and as handsome as ever. Your limbs are strong, your chest is broad and deep. Now you return to Spain, not as the miserable slave who dove from the prow of a boat to save my life, and who welcomed even the small favours a slave boy could do for him to make his life more bearable. Think, Mario! Think well what that mark you bear, which you call so hateful, has done for you. Then look at it again and remember who you are and what you are today.'

Mario glanced down at his chest. Somehow, after Juanele's words, the indigo scrolls did not seem to repel him quite so much. He buttoned the shirt and lay back on the divan. Juanele blew out the flickering flame and the silver moonlight etched the black shadows of the tent poles across the carpeted floor.

Soon there was no noise in the tent except Mario's deep and regular breathing. But Juanale did not sleep. He thought of other nights in other tents. He gazed, open eyed, at the shadows of the tent poles until they disappeared with the sinking moon, and then stuffed the sleeve of his *djellabah* in his mouth so that his sobs would not awaken Mario.

Chapter Forty-eight

THEIR ROAD led over barren wastes and rolling hills to the fertile plains near the coast, and at length to the little fishing village which even today the Moroccans call by the Spanish name of Casablanca. From Casablanca Mario and his men continued along the richly fertile coastal plain to the larger city of Rabat. Here they were welcomed by emissaries of the Sultan, who informed them that the Grand Vizier himself was awaiting them at Tangiers with condolences for the death of Adan and the instructions that were to have been transmitted to him from the Sultan.

There was a good road between Rabat and Tangiers and they were able to make good time, even over the mountains. Soon they had the blue Mediterranean before them and they could see the white towers of Tangiers in the distance.

'We come again to Tangiers, Juanele.' Mario pointed to the minarets of the city, shining in the sun.

'We do indeed, Sidi Mohammed.'

'Am I not the same Mario who once rode out of this city with you?'

'To me you are the same Mario, but to all the rest of the world you are not. You are something much more, and I must remember to call you Sidi Mohammed and bow to kiss your slippers when there are others present.'

'And I must remember to be Mohammed and not Mario.'

As they neared the gates, a double line of the Sultan's black guard drew themselves up in line. Mario's men raced ahead to announce him, and the guards' horses galloped towards them in a cloud of white dust. When they neared Mario, they wheeled, circled him and raced around him, shouting and waving their spears in the air. Gunfire crackled from the high walls, and it seemed the entire city was on a holiday to greet the son of the Emir.

The captain of the guard disentangled himself from the mêlée and rode up to Mario, to welcome him in flowery metaphors and to ride beside him. Under the cool shadow of the gates, another soldier – this one a Turkish janissary in a white skirt of voluminous pleats and a gold-embroidered jacket – relieved the captain and took over the escort until Mario and his train had managed to squeeze through the streets and enter the first of the palace gates. They crossed the familiar square which Mario remembered from so many dawns before.

'This time you enter at the front door,' Juanele whispered.

And, through the front door, under the arched horseshoe of filigreed marble, they went. An old man in the green turban of a *hadj* greeted them and conducted them down a long hall where the strong light, strained through windows of coloured glass, painted their faces and robes with brilliant splotches of colour. He bowed them into a large apartment, bustled about to open windows, flick imaginary spots of dust from polished tables, and open doors to baths, dressing rooms and terrace.

Waiting only for Mario to acknowledge his services, he slipped out with a knowing grin and reappeared almost instantly with four girls, whose silken draperies did little to conceal their charms. They huddled in a little group, eyeing Mario expectantly until one, bolder than the rest, came over and knelt before him. Her eyes slowly travelled up from the toes of his *babouches* as though they were able to penetrate the folds of his *djellabah*. When they had reached his face, she smiled – an impudent, knowing smile – and addressed him.

'We are at your service, my lord Mohammed. We have been especially chosen by His Magnificence to add to the pleasure of your stay in Tangiers. If we succeed' – her smile widened – 'and we shall try our best, we shall accompany you across the water if you desire, so that you will not be tempted by the wiles of infidel maidens.'

Mario answered her smile with one of his own. His hand under her chin drew her nearer. His lips met hers and found them soft and yielding and her hands, making swift motions under his robe, were warm and experienced. Ah, Tangiers was a place where a man was lucky in love. Even as a penniless slave he had found love there once before. Now it was being offered to him in a quantity almost to surfeit him. His hand crept slowly down her back and slapped her gently as his words, 'Night comes, my sweetheart, and I shall put you to the test,' sent her giggling back to the group, who were regarding him from under veiled lashes.

He pointed to the heavily grilled door that had opened to admit them.

'Get them out of here now, Juanele. If they stay longer I shall forget everything else. And, boy,' he called to Juanele, who was herding them back to the door, 'think you that my father, the Emir, considered this when he bade you sleep every night at the foot of my bed and never leave me?'

'I do not see in the darkness, my lord Mohammed.'

'Ah, but you can hear, Juanele.'

'But not if I sleep, my lord Mohammed.'

'And would you sleep, Juanele?'

'I would sleep, Mario, because I would know that you were happy, and that is important to me.'

'But there are four of them, Juanele. They are unveiled and belong not to my *hareem*; therefore, to keep your hand from being tired, from shielding your eyes, I would share one of them with you. Then perhaps you would not wish to go to sleep.'

Juanele laughed, but denied the offer with a shake of his head. 'Let me have my dreams, and they will not be peopled with your unveiled *houris*. However' – he looked at the wide divan – 'if you wish, I can hang a curtain between your bed and mine, even though it would be disobeying the commands of your father.'

With the arrival of the multitudinous boxes, Juanele became occupied with their reception. The room was filled with slaves and porters, coming and going. In the midst of all the confusion, a tall Moor, dressed in the black of a holy marabout, entered. He held up his hand for silence and the activity stopped. With only a slight obeisance, he addressed Mario.

'The Grand Vizier of His Magnificence has sent me to welcome you, O Prince Mohammed of Marrakech, and to say that he will see you after the sunset prayers. He wishes to condole with you on the great sorrow that has come to your father's house and to talk with you about your journey across the water. He will await you in his apartments.' He touched his forehead lightly and left as the confusion and activity started all over again.

In time all the boxes and baskets and hampers had been received and stowed away by Juanele, who had checked each one off on a long sheet of paper. They were at last alone. The jalousies were closed to keep out the sun and there was quiet and peace in the room. Mario threw himself on a couch and watched the boy rummage through the chest for the clothing for which he was searching.

'Shall we blind the eyes of the Grand Vizier with my magnificence tonight?' Mario asked.

'No, I suggest a plain white *djellabah* with a *kaftan* of white linen and a turban of white muslin. That will dress you, and *you* will be more important than your robes. Come, let's start! If you are to meet him after sundown, we should begin to get ready. You have eaten nothing since morning. I will send for food, heated water and tea.'

Juanele had only to clap his hands and whatever he asked for arrived. First food, then copper cans of steaming water, and finally glasses of hot minted tea. By the time the *muezzin* had called – Mario was certain that it was the same one whose voice he had first heard in Tangiers – and Mario had spread his rug and said his prayers towards Mecca, he was ready to leave. Juanele's clapping hands summoned a palace slave to conduct Mario to the Vizier's apartments. They traversed the same multicoloured gallery, but now the lengthening shadows had robbed the windows of their brilliance and the glowing reds, greens, and yellows were greyed by the evening light. The slave tapped with a wooden wand on a door, and at a reply from inside opened the door and admitted Mario.

It was a small room, dominated by a single divan and that in turn dominated by the man who sat cross-legged upon it. He was old, so old that Mario noticed his hands tremble as he lifted one to his forehead. Mario dropped to one knee but the old man, impatient of formality, motioned to him to stand up, turned on the divan with some difficulty, and indicated the cushion beside him. When Mario sat down, he shifted even more, so that he could face Mario more directly.

'It is with deep grief that we have heard of the great sorrow that has come to our good friend, your father.'

Mario inclined his head but did not answer, for the other continued.

'But we are honoured that your excellent father saw fit to send his other son.'

'Thank you, Your Excellency.'

The Vizier's eyes studied Mario's face. His scrutiny was bold, direct and unflinching. He drew his lips into a thin line and, without taking his eyes from Mario's, he spoke.

'We were unaware of the substitution of yourself for Prince

Adan until after you had started. Had we known, Prince Mohammed, we might have directed you to remain in Marrakech and sent another to Spain. Shall I be frank with you?'

'Please do, Your Excellency.'

'To have dismissed you would have been an affront to your father, and we regard his friendship highly. Therefore we have permitted you to come here to Tangiers. We are prepared to send you to Spain and place full responsibility on your shoulders.'

'As Allah wills, Your Excellency.'

'As Allah wills, and as the Sultan wills, Prince Mohammed.' For the first time, the Vizier let the ghost of a smile appear on his lips. 'However, since we received news of your departure, we have not been idle. We have thoroughly examined your life in Morocco. It has meant interviewing many people in a very short time. There have been those who were with you in the slave caravan when you first appeared in Fez from Tangiers, whose who worked with you in the Sultan's kitchens, slaves who had been with you on the walls of Marrakech, and even members of the Emir's household – his lords, his sheiks and his soldiers.'

It was Mario's turn to smile. 'And what, my lord Vizier, were the results of these investigations?'

The old man cautiously allowed his smile to widen.

'Most estimable! According to all reports, you possess the courage of a lion, the beauty of the Angel Gabriel, the wisdom of a Solomon, and the devotion to Islam of a marabout. In fact we have been unable to pry out one black mark against you. I am forced to gaze in wonder at the one perfect man Allah ever created.'

'You compliment me, my lord Vizier.'

'So we bow to the superior knowledge of your father. We are proud to have you represent us in Spain, which, Allah be praised, is now no longer Spain, but only a colony of France. Now, Prince Mohammed, attend my words. Europe wants Morocco. Europe's greedy paws have always itched for the Mahgreb. Why? Because we control one side of the Mediterranean. Since the time that Carthage threatened Rome, Europe has never felt secure with the opposite side of her sea in hostile hands. When Rome conquered Carthage, she spread her heathen influence over all of Northern Africa, and this became a Roman province, until the cursed Christians grew so weak and impotent that they were conquered by Islam. Then we were stronger than they and we drove them out of Africa, across the Mediterranean. We followed them into Europe and became firmly entrenched in Spain, but we lost that realm after ruling it for eight hundred years.'

'And now the Spaniards have lost it.' Mario's words were rich with pleasure at the thought.

'Ah yes, but the French have it, and beware of the rascally French, young prince. They are worse than the Spaniards. All the Spaniards ever wanted was gold, and after they discovered the New World, they had it. But the French are ambitious. They want the world, and only the English hold out against them. Yet I had rather see the French here than the stubborn English. They never give up an inch of soil once they possess it. Give them a toehold and they spread over the land like a plague of locusts.'

'So they all want the Mahgreb – England, France and Spain; how, Your Excellency, shall we hold it?'

The Vizier shook his head sadly. 'We cannot. As they grow strong, we grow weak. We fight only amongst ourselves – tribe against tribe – until we bleed inwardly from a hundred wounds. Inevitably Europe must engulf us. We can only hope for time. But' – his eyes lighted up – 'we can play one off against the other. Let England control the Mediterranean – our sea. We cannot stop her. But we can entrench the French on our seacoast to plague her. Give the French just a little. It will satisfy them. For instance' – he pondered for a moment – 'there's Casablanca, with its cursed Spanish name which seems to stick to it. We'll let the French into Casablanca where they can harass the English. We'll *give* the miserable place to them instead of letting them *take* all of Morocco. Now attend me!'

The instructions were long, minute and detailed, but when the old man had finished Mario saw the wisdom and the cunning of his thinking. Give a little to the French here, a bit to the British there, perhaps a small slice to the Spaniards. Then let them feel that each one was the most important. Flatter them, cajole them with bribes, but keep them all in their places. In that way, Morocco would be safe from all but minor penetration. The infidels could have their worthless places on the coast, but all the rest of the Mahgreb would be Moslem. It was giving an inch to gain a mile.

The sun had sunk and the lamps were lighted when Mario left the Grand Vizier. Back in his own apartments, he found that the cool breeze of evening had fanned the heat from them. Juanele was waiting for him.

He pointed to the grilled door. 'There is much speculation in there as to which one will be favoured tonight.'

Mario grinned and slapped Juanele on the back. 'My boy, although I have been talking matters of state, my mind has been wandering behind that same closed door. If I remember rightly, there were four of the charmers?'

'Four, my Mario.'

'And we have been many nights on the road, with only you in the tent with me.'

'Many nights, my Mario.'

'Then tell them, Juanele, that not one of them will be disappointed tonight. Open the door and call them all in.' He stopped Juanele's rapid crossing of the floor. 'The curtain?'

Juanele pointed to a length of shimmering gauze that hung from the ceiling at the foot of the big divan.

Chapter Forty-nine

MARIO HAD often heard the old men of Marrakech repeat the Arabic proverb to the effect that to him who walks in leathern shoes, the whole world is carpeted in leather. He discovered how true it was, for, to him who is an Arab prince, the whole world bends a knee. The ship that carried him to Spain was far different from the small boat which Sidi Mokar had commanded on Mario's former trip across the Mediterranean. It held the some hundred members of Mario's escort, with their horses and equipment, even their tents and pack animals. Four small cabins aft, together with a part of the deck which had been screened from the rest of the ship by fretted wood, were for the four girls who made up Mario's temporary *hareem*. The Moors were invading Spain again for the first time since Ferdinand and Isabella sent Boabdil weeping from his beloved Alhambra.

Mario had a lofty cabin, panelled in carved oak, with gilded touches in the carving and, for the first time since he had left Ponta Delgada, a real bed. Accustomed as he had become to the soft divans of Morocco, it presented a too-hard mattress and too-tightly stuffed pillows to suit him. Nor was it to the liking of his *hareem*, for they complained about the board-like qualities of the bed and swore that its rigidity hampered the full and professional performance of their duties. When Mario informed them that all Christians slept in similar discomfort, they could only express pity for the unfortunate *N'zrani* women. They had heard they were cold and frigid. No wonder!

The ship had set its course for Malaga. As they neared that Spanish port, Juanele, standing on the deck beside Mario, grabbed his arm and pointed to a deserted stretch of beach. It was, so he informed Mario, the identical spot where Sidi Mokar had landed that fateful night in the darkness when Mario and Ramon had been brought on board. As usual, whenever the boy recalled incidents of the past, he saddened, but he managed to force a smile for Mario's benefit; slowly, during the journey, Juanele's loyalty was being transferred to Mario.

'You return, Mario. Almost to the same spot from which you left.' He reached down and picked up a fold of the fine white cashmere of Mario's *djellabah*, let it slither through his fingers, then touched the gold-embroidered muslin of Mario's turban. 'But . . . methinks your adventure in Morocco has paid well.'

Mario stared at the sandy shore. He too let his fingers wander over the soft cloth and remembered the patched cotton trousers he had previously worn on that deserted strip of sand. Yes, Morocco had been cruel. He remembered the whips of the slavedrivers across his stomach. But Morocco had also been kind; he remembered Adan and the Emir.

'From what place in Spain did you come, Juanele?' he asked.

'From here – from Malaga.'

'Then, Juanele, you shall remain in Malaga.'

The boy turned quickly and looked at him. 'But why, Mario? Why? Do you abandon me here?'

'Let us not say abandon, Juanele. When I leave you in Malaga you will have enough gold to make you comfortable the rest of your life. You will seek out your family and live once more in a Christian country, because you are still a Christian. You never changed, as I did.'

'Oh no, Mario! *Por dios*, no! Christian I may be, but Spain – no! What have I here? Nothing! As for my family, I never had any. What would I do in Spain? No, Mario! I have been very happy and, although I still mourn for that happiness, I know I shall be happy again. My days of slavery in Morocco have been far better than my days of freedom in Spain. Here, although free, I was the slave of poverty. I begged for a crust of bread and found my rest on the hard stone steps of the cathedral at night. Think you that poverty is an easier master than my lord Mokar was?'

'But Mokar is dead.'

'Which means that I have now become your property.'

'Good God, boy, I don't want to own you.'

Juanele laughed. 'There you have no choice. You must, my Mario. As a Christian in Morocco, I can never be free. And I will not stay in Spain and be free. How stubborn the little Juanele is, what? So I return to Morocco with you.'

Mario looked at the boy and placed his hands on his shoulders. 'No, you remain in Spain.'

'No, I return to Morocco as your slave.'

Mario let his hands slide from the boy's shoulders and turned again to the rail.

'Although I do not comprehend, I accept. You are free to remain in Spain; but if that displeases you, then you are free to return with me. And, although in the eyes of Morocco you will be my slave, I assure you your slavery will be only nominal. You have made your choice.'

Juanele turned and pointed to the shore. 'Look you well, Mario. We enter the harbour of Malaga. See, up there on the left, climbing up the hill, the old castle of the Moors, and see' – he turned in the opposite direction and pointed to the twin towers of the cathedral – 'there under those towers was my Spanish bedroom. Ay, Mario, but the bed was hard and the steps of the cathedral were draughty. But even then, there was always someone to whom I looked for protection, and even though the stones were cold there was always the warmth of another body curved against my back.'

Mario looked out the other side of the ship over the narrowing blue water to the white city with the high mountains behind it. This was Spain and somewhere in the mass of mountains and high plains and deep valleys his father might be. His father! He had only seen him for one short interval, but he remembered how they had met in the marble lobby of the hotel in Havana. His father had been proud of him and he had been proud of Frontera Baja.

It was evident that they had been expected. Their ship had been sighted in time for the city authorities to assemble a company of soldiers at the quay, and, as the boat warped in, a military band began to play. Mario saw the long line of soldiers drawn up in rigid, white-trousered lines. After the ship tied up, the band started again, with a blare of trumpets and a rattle of drums. No sooner had the wide plank bridged the gap between the deck and the stones of the quay than a beplumed and shakoed officer tripped across it. Mario stood waiting for him, the Spanish breeze moulding the folds of his *djellabah* to his body. The officer hesitated a moment, then advanced to Mario and offered his hand in greeting. But Mario ignored it.

The officer's hand dangled clumsily in mid-air. He glanced

at Mario, whose expression had not changed, dropped the hand to his side and mumbled an introduction.

'Major Etienne Beauchamp of His Imperial Majesty's Fifth Chausseurs,' he began in fluent Spanish and then added, 'at your service.'

Mario neither spoke nor recognized him. He turned to Juanele beside him and spoke a few rapid words in Arabic to the boy. Juanele, with an understanding nod, turned to the French officer.

'The ambassador of His Magnificence, the Sultan of Morocco, His Highness Prince Mohammed ibn Ibrahim of Marrakech, Caid of Tameslout in the High Atlas, Sheik of Derdouri and Calipha of Talat, is quite willing to pardon the ignorance of Major Beauchamp, but wishes to advise him that he can accept only a full obeisance from him. If, therefore, *señor*, you wish to be acknowledged by His Highness, it will be necessary for you to kneel and touch your forehead on the deck.'

'A major of His Majesty's Army kneels to nobody, young man.'

'Then very well, *señor*, you had best return across the plank, and we shall give orders for our ship to return to Morocco.'

'But you can't do that. You have business with the Emperor.'

'Can't?' Juanele raised his eyebrows. 'Would you tell the Prince Mohammed what he can and cannot do? Unless, of course, you intend to detain us by force?'

The major struggled to free himself from his dilemma. 'No, but. . . .'

'Then kneel, infidel.' This time Juanele commanded.

The major looked up at Mario, who pretended not to have understood any of the conversation. His high black boots creaked as he got down on his knees on the boards of the deck. His tight white trousers seemed about to split at the seams as he bowed forward, and Mario, gazing at the white cloth stretched so tightly across his rump, suppressed a smile as he wondered if the stitching would hold. A bare-assed French major kneeling before him might provoke serious diplomatic maneouvres. But the man, plumed shako on the deck before him, touched his forehead to the hot boards, then managed to get himself erect, in spite of the long boots and the tight trousers.

Now Mario allowed himself to smile. He acknowledged the major's presence with a slight nod.

'It is indeed kind of you, Major Beauchamp, to extend the courtesy of a welcome to me.' The look of surprise on the major's face at Mario's perfect Spanish caused his mouth to open and close like a dying haddock. 'In the name of His Magnificence, my Sultan, I accept your welcome.' He led the way to the gangplank. As he stepped up to cross it, the major touched Mario's elbow to assist him. Mario turned, feigning a look of anger.

'Am I the first Moor you have ever met, Major?'

'The first, Your Highness.'

'Then learn something, Major. The touch of a Christian pollutes a Moslem. Even your shadow cast across my body brings a curse on me, although for convenience' sake I am willing to disregard the matter of your shadow. But let us understand one thing. The hand of an infidel must never touch the body of a True Believer.'

The major nodded dumbly in agreement. 'I was about to assist Your Highness.'

'Better a death by drowning than pollution by your hand.'

Mario stepped into the high-sprung open carriage – the first time he had ridden in an open carriage since the night he and Adan had visited the gypsy café in Cadiz. He settled himself back against the cushions and motioned to Juanele to sit facing him. Then he moved over as far as possible to the side to allow the major to sit beside him. Neither he nor the major said a word during the short ride.

They stopped at a pillared palace, glittering in a coat of fresh pink stucco, and walked past smartly uniformed French sentries, up a broad flight of marble stairs to a vast series of salons and chambers, furnished – evidently in a hurry – with the clumsy ormolu-mounted furniture which Napoleon's reign had made popular. The heavy brocades at the windows showed a design of laurel leaves encircling a Roman 'N' and the chairs and sofas also featured the same initial. Mario inspected one or two of the rooms, with the major following closely behind. At the door of the bedroom he dismissed the soldier.

'We shall be very comfortable here. I presume in your gracious hospitality you have provided servants.'

'The house is fully staffed.'

'Then may I ask that you dismiss them all. I have my own

suite with me. My major domo here' – he indicated Juanele – 'will inform you of what food we desire. Please see that the tradesmen render a bill before I leave.'

'But my orders are, Your Highness, to furnish everything for you.'

'Again my thanks, but it will not be necessary. Please see to it that all of the horses of my men are stabled and food and fodder are provided for them.'

The major recognized the tone of dismissal, saluted smartly and turned to leave, walked a few steps towards the door, then stopped, turned slowly and retraced his steps back towards Mario. Once more he nearly split his breeches in his low obeisance, touched his head to the carpeted floor and then arose and backed out of the room. Mario tried hard to stifle his smile until the man had gone, and he dared not look at Juanele. But, when the major had managed to get himself through the door without looking where he was going, Juanele, unable to control himself any longer, doubled over with laughter, in which Mario joined.

'The bastard!' Mario tried to control himself enough to speak. 'The damned little French popinjay! The next time he'll know how to greet a Moorish prince. But, Juanele, I had a reason. We do not come crawling on our bellies to the great Napoleon begging for favours. Now this tag end of a bitch's litter will run all the way back to his barracks, and, before an hour, couriers will be starting off to wherever the Corsican is to tell him that I have arrived, and that the only correct way to greet me is to grovel in the dust before my *babouches*. So you see we have already taught the French a good lesson. Perhaps we'll teach them more later.'

The old palace quickly came alive with Mario's followers. The kitchens echoed to the rattle of pots and pans. Household slaves arrived and took up their position in the halls. A carriage wheeled up to the door with Mario's *hareem*, now discreetly veiled and swathed in voluminous robes so that, except for the dark eyes that gazed out, fascinated by the strangeness of Spain, they looked like bundles of linen. Two of Mario's soldiers were mounted on their horses in the shade of the pillared entrance. Gradually the Spanish palace became a Moorish one.

All the rest of the day Mario received official delegations – from the French Army, the Spanish *alcalde*, members of the various guilds. It was amusing to see each delegation go through the same performance he had insisted upon from the major. They were learning fast.

So passed his first day in Spain, and so passed the second. He entertained – having had Juanele direct his men to remove the long dining table and the stiff chairs – with his distinguished guests sitting on cushions on the floor and eating their *couscous* with their fingers. Mario was an affable host and did not even notice the stained uniforms after his guests had dined. In return he was invited out, but he sent his apologies through Juanele, and hinted to his prospective hosts that His Highness could not eat infidel food.

The only group which was lacking on his list of guests was the clergy. Neither black-robed priests, violet bishops nor red-clad cardinals honoured him by calling. Mario wondered what the effect would have been had they been present and he were to open the neck of his shirt and show them the tattoo on his chest. What consternation that would have raised! A heretical Moor with the crucifix on his belly! All of Spain would have yammered and yapped.

The King and Queen, he heard, were in Rome. The Prince of the Peace, at first in favour with France, had fallen from the Emperor's good graces, and was also in exile, but not with Their Majesties. Mario wondered who was studding Maria Luisa, but he felt certain that Papal Rome had been able to supply some staunch Italian who would try to satisfy her. He heard no news about Cleora, but she, like all the other Spanish titles, had fled Spain, despoiled of their property. He imagined his father must also be among the exiles.

On the morning of his third day Mario was scheduled to leave for Granada, where the Emperor was to meet him – or, rather, where he was to meet the Emperor.

The snow-capped Sierras beyond Granada welcomed him, and he felt he was back in Marrakech with the Atlas towering behind the city. Also, when he arrived and found that he was to be quartered in the old Moorish palace of the Alhambra, he felt sure he must be back in Morocco; it was, in all respects, a piece of Morocco transplanted to Spain. He remembered that for many years it had held the Moorish sovereigns of Spain. Here were the same tall cypresses, the plentitude of roses and the tinkling fountains in the gardens. Inside were the same darkly cool rooms with tiled floors and walls.

They settled in comfortably; even the soldiers and Mario's slaves felt quite at home. Mario sipped his mint tea in the shady portico and listened to the splash of water in the fountain of the lions. Any nostalgia which he might have had for Spain and his own people had vanished. He was glad to be back in the soft Moorish atmosphere. Now he was, in truth, Mohammed of Marrakech. He put the glass of fragrant tea down carefully on the tiles and lay back on his cushions. His eyes had closed, and he was beginning to feel the first forgetfulness of sleep, when Juanele came running across the courtyard, leaping over the gutters that carried off the fountain's overflow. Mario sat up as the boy approached.

'And now what is it?'

'Tomorrow, yes, tomorrow, Napoleon comes.'

'Well, we've been expecting him.'

'But, Mario, he comes here to us. We do not go to him. That is an honour!'

Mario yawned and agreed that it was. He pushed the pillows back and stood up. With a motion of his hand that invited Juanele to follow him, he disappeared through a doorway and walked down a long corridor until he came to another courtyard. He waited for Juanele to arrive.

'My memory may not serve me correctly, boy, so tell me, what do they call this court?'

'The Court of the Ambassadors, my Mario.'

'How fitting! Then it is here that we shall receive the little Napoleon tomorrow.'

Chapter Fifty

MARIO DISPATCHED Juanele down the hill from the palace into the sprawling city, with instructions to find the two biggest and most ornate armchairs in all Granada. Hours later, Juanele returned, dangling his legs from the tail of a creaking oxcart which held a pair of gilded monstrosities that must have been designed for a behemoth and its mate. Where they were not gold they were crimson damask and, where the ingenuity of the carver had found no place for another fat cupid, a rose, or a shell, the gilder had merely burnished the gold to a brighter lustre. These chairs Mario had moved to the shadowed loggia at the far end of the Court of the Ambassadors. He had ordered them hoisted up on a raised dais which had been covered with a violent shade of violet velvet. The result was awe-inspiring, imperial, and atrociously ugly.

Mario envisioned the pair of thrones as only a background – his own splendour would complete the picture. Napoleon had come in contact with many monarchs; he would not be easily impressed with a minor Moroccan prince, certainly not after having conquered Egypt. After long consideration Mario finally settled on a *djellabah* of stiff white Persian taffeta; *akaftan* of turquoise silk, heavily embroidered in silver and pearls; a turban of silver-shot white muslin; and scarlet *babouches* encrusted with silver and moonstones. Juanele suggested several ropes of pearls, each pearl the size of a chick pea, but Mario declined them.

In rummaging through the steel-bound jewel casket, he discovered a mammoth ruby the size of a pigeon's egg. This he had Juanele fasten in his turban as a clasp for an aigrette of heron feathers. The effect of the gleaming coal of fire was exactly what he required. Let Napoleon match the riches of the Mahgreb which lay behind the understatement of that single ruby.

A few moments before the hour scheduled for the Emperor and his suite to arrive, Mario took his place on one of the thrones – that on the left-hand side, out of deference to majesty. Juanele adjusted the folds of the *djellabah*, separating it just enough so that the *kaftan* gave an inch-wide hint of its richness. Mario's soldiers, each in the pleated skirts and rich satin of the Turkish *Bashi Bazouk*, lined the loggias under the arched portico. In the hot sun of the central courtyard, surrounding the central basin, he had Juanele marshal all the household slaves, each in a snow-white *djellabah*. Napoleon, he was sure, would not be able to distinguish between slaves and Moroccan nobles.

Seated in lonely splendour on his baroque throne, Mario heard, a long distance away through the tortuous halls and the hidden courts of the Alhambra, a commotion at the lower gates. Gradually the babel of voices came nearer and then, from under his shadowed vantage, he saw a man step from the pillared loggia into the white sunlight of the courtyard. He was short, brusque, and impatient. He wore a simple uniform – a green coat and white trousers – with only one decoration, the white enamelled star of the Legion of Honour. Mario did not need the loud announcement of the slave to tell him this was the Emperor.

The resplendent uniforms behind him halted under the loggia, and the Emperor crossed the courtyard alone. He had no time to waste on formalities. His simplicity put to shame Mario's gaudy pretensions to grandeur, but he took comfort from the fact that Napoleon did not even notice them. As far as he was concerned, Mario might be sitting on a kitchen chair.

Mario watched Napoleon's quick steps coming across the courtyard, saw him come nearer, ascend the single step into the shadow and look up to where Mario was sitting on the throne. Only then did Mario rise; his right hand indicated the empty chair beside him. Napoleon did not pause but strode up to the dais, ascended the step and sat down abruptly beside Mario.

'Welcome to Europe, Prince Mohammed.'

'And welcome to Morocco, Your Majesty, for, although we may be in Europe, this is Morocco.'

Napoleon allowed himself a brief look, gave one short decisive nod as if to acknowledge the truth of Mario's statement, turned sideways in his chair, and regarded Mario. He sucked in his lower lip, appraised Mario quickly but carefully, and then spoke, his words bouncing with impatience.

'Let's forego the flowery speeches about our individual healths and all the unnecessary flim-flam. Convey my regards to your sovereign, and now, Prince Mohammed, let's get down to business.'

'Your Majesty.' Mario could be abrupt too.

'First, do you want Morocco to be French or English?'

'Neither, Your Majesty.'

'Well, it has to be one or the other. Either we protect you from the English, or the damned Britons move in to protect you from us. Believe me, Prince, you'll get better treatment from the French than from the English. We'll live *with* you. They'll rule you.'

Mario shook his head. 'But, Your Majesty, we in Morocco intend to live under our own rule. We are an independent country, under our own sovereign —'

'Bah! So was Naples, so was Spain, so was Portugal, and Holland, and many others I could mention.'

'Ah' – Mario held up a warning hand – 'you are now speaking of Christian nations. Remember, Morocco is not a Christian nation – it is Moslem.'

Napoleon twisted in his chair to stare more insolently at Mario. 'So! Morocco is not a Christian nation. Neither was Egypt. What difference does it make? Not the slightest! I tell you it's either France or England. Take your choice.'

'But His Magnificence, the Sultan of Morocco, does not choose to make that choice, Your Majesty. When you conquered Egypt you did not conquer a sovereign state; it was under the rule of the Sublime Porte. But Morocco is a sovereign state, and to us our Sultan is supreme. If he gives, we are willing to stand by his decision. But we shall not accept any demand that is forced upon us. I mentioned that Morocco is a Moslem nation.'

'Yes, yes, I know.' Napoleon spat out the words.

'Then if you know that' – Mario turned sideways and stared back at Napoleon – 'you also know the meaning of a *Jehad*.'

'I do.'

'And have you ever fought one?'

'I saw the beginning of one in Egypt.'

'Then, Your Majesty, let me tell you a little more about it. A *Jehad* is a holy war. It is not fought by men but by fanatics – men to whom life means nothing and death is desirable, because it gains for them immediate entrance into Paradise. It is not fought according to the rules of modern warfare. There are no generals, brigades or regiments – neither artillery nor infantry. Instead there are hordes of men, each man fighting individually for his God and Prophet. You'll never meet them in a battle, Your Majesty. Instead they will decimate your army in the passes of the mountains, in the chill of the desert night, in the false safety of the oases. They creep upon your men silently and slit their throats and mutilate them, stuff their dismembered organs in their dead mouths. Then, like shadows, they are gone.'

Napoleon shifted uneasily in his seat. He had given the young Moor the advantage and there was no stopping him. There was a wild gleam in Mario's eye, as though he himself were a fanatic, fighting a *Jehad*.

In his excitement, Mario forgot that the man beside him was accustomed to fawning princes. He raised his voice and pounded on the arm of his chair.

'Land your regiments in Morocco! Yes, land them! And in spite of all your sentries and your precautions, where ten men stood there will be only nine, and the next day only eight, and each day there will be another missing. March your regiments from the coast. See them die from thirst, because every well will be poisoned, every stream polluted. Make camp at night and watch your army melt away as you see, every morning, a ring of mutilated corpses around your tents.'

'Do you think I am afraid of your half-trained brigands?' The Emperor's lower lip protruded even further.

'You asked me a question, Your Majesty, and I shall answer it. My answer is "yes". Because if you are not afraid of them, you should be.' His arm swept out towards the courtyard. 'Look at these men! Regard them well. Do you see any smiles on their faces? No! Do you see how they look at your pretty officers with hatred? Just one soft word from me, and they would fall upon you and your soldiers without regard for consequences. They would hack your men down in a moment and decapitate you with a swing of the sword. Why? Because you are Christians and they are Moslems, and the hatred they bear you knows no equal emotion in Christendom.'

Napoleon seemed to be making a mental count of the number of French soldiers in the courtyard. It was easy to see that they were outnumbered. His voice lost its impatient brusqueness.

'Then you prefer that the English take Morocco?'

'Oh, no! To the English I would say the same as I have

said to you, but I would add more to it. I would tell them that while Morocco was fighting a *Jehad* against them, the whole Arab world would rise – all of North Africa, all of Asia Minor, all of the far corners of Islam. The English would find themselves engaged with not one enemy but millions. Half-crazed Moslems would pour into Europe through Turkey, they would cross the Atlantic from here and land at Lisbon and Cadiz. They would use the islands of the Mediterranean as stepping stones to Italy. Then, Napoleon, you would see the English scuttle back to their little fog-bound island. But you would not provoke a *Jehad*. You are far too clever, Your Majesty.'

Napoleon's fingers worked inside his tight cravat and loosened it. He unbuttoned his waistcoat, sighed, slumped down in his enormous chair and considered the toes of his boots.

'We have wasted time, Prince Mohammed. So you prefer to defy both France and England. You set yourself up against the two greatest powers in the world – you, a small backward country without weapons, without any army, without military training.'

Mario shook his head. 'I did not say that we would defy France and England. I said that we would give, but you implied that you would take. Would it not be better if you were to listen to our offer?'

'I am listening.'

'Know you Casablanca?'

Napoleon pursed his lips in concentration. 'A seaport.'

'Strategically located on the Atlantic. Ships based there could control the entrance to the Mediterranean. And, in addition to Casablanca, we would allow you to patrol the shore from Casablanca to Rabat and on to Tangiers.'

'Then you offer me a naval base at Casablanca?'

'There is a fine harbour.'

'And troop movements along the coast?'

'For a distance of two miles inland. However, I warn you, if one soldier should stray over that line. . . .'

'I know . . . in his mouth.'

'Yes.'

Napoleon stood up, pulled at his tight white trousers, which were already damp with sweat, and sat down again.

'My compliments to His Magnificence, the Sultan. We

accept his terms. We'll take the niggardly two miles of coastline and we'll occupy your stinking village of Casablanca. But you're not fooling me, young man. I know exactly what your game is. You're letting the French protect you against the English.'

Mario smiled in mute acceptance of Napoleon's statement, then added, 'But if you are unwilling, perhaps the English will be glad to protect us from the French.'

'*Mon Dieu*, no! We accept your terms.' The Emperor reached inside his coat and drew forth a formidable-looking parchment. 'This was the treaty I would have had you sign. It's valueless now. We'll write another.'

'One in French and one in Arabic.'

'Agreed, but in the name of God, let us get off these goddamned chairs and go somewhere where we can at least sit in comfort and where my feet can touch the floor.' Napoleon stood up and Mario followed him. Together they walked down the loggia in front of the soldiers to the entrance of a small room.

'Know you the story of this room, Your Majesty?' Mario held back the silken hanging for Napoleon to enter.

'No. Has it a story?'

'Oh, a most interesting one. It was here that the entire family of a great Moorish prince was murdered by Boabdil, the last Moorish ruler of Spain. He invited them here to dinner, every male in that family. Behind each man stood one of Boadbil's slaves. During the dinner, instead of serving food, each slave placed a bowstring quietly around the neck of the guest in front of him.' Mario's hands, clenched as though holding a string, jerked apart suddenly. 'It was all over in a moment, very quietly. You see, one of the men of that family had happened to see Boabdil's favourite wife walking in the garden.'

'And for that he murdered them all?'

'I thought it might help you understand the Moorish character, Your Majesty.'

As Napoleon seated himself, he looked behind his chair. Mario caught the furtive look, drew the dagger from his belt and flung it on the table, where it spun in circles.

'I am not Boabdil,' he said. 'And now, Your Majesty, with your permission.' He called Juanele to him and sent him off for scribes, parchment, ink and quills. When a smart young officer and an aged Moor had arrived and settled themselves before another table, Napoleon started to dictate. His French was rapid but the old Iman understood it and wrote his cursive Arabic as quickly as the young lieutenant did his French. When Napoleon had finished they both signed and witnesses were called in who read over the documents and signed below them. It was all over.

Once more Mario held back the silken hanging for Napoleon to pass. Again they walked the length of the loggia, passing the gaudy thrones, around the far side of the courtyard. Napoleon stopped, shielded his eyes from the sun and looked out over the court.

'The Moors built well, young Prince.' His eyes lifted to the chiselled stone and plaster. 'They ruled Spain for eight hundred years, and today Spain is as much Moorish as it is European. A Spaniard is nothing more than a Christianized Moor.'

'And a Moor is nothing more than an Islamized Spaniard,' Mario added.

For a moment, Napoleon stopped being an emperor. He regarded Mario, standing in a shaft of sunlight. A slow smile spread across his tense face. 'Your father is the powerful Emir of Marrakech, I believe.'

Mario bowed.

'Will you take a message to your father from me?'

Again Mario bowed.

'Tell him that Napoleon greets him, but greets him with envy.'

'And why, Your Majesty.'

'Because he has a son like you. I have no son, Prince Mohammed. I have all of Europe in my hand, but I have no son. That is why I envy your father.'

'I am not worthy to carry such a message, Your Majesty.'

'Then I shall write it and send it to your father. It will arrive tomorrow at your headquarters in Malaga. Now I am going to ask a favour of you, Prince Mohammed.'

'That which I have is yours, Your Majesty.'

Napoleon held up his hand in warning. 'Not too fast. I have been told that a Moslem will not touch the hand of a Christian.'

'It is not our custom.'

'Then if I were to offer you my hand, you would refuse it?'

'No, Your Majesty, I would be very proud.' The sleeve of the *djellabah* fell back from Mario's hand as he extended it.

Napoleon took it and shook it heartily. He relinquished it to fumble with the clasp of the decoration on his coat, removed it and pinned it through the stiff silk of Mario's *djellabah*. The star of the Legion of Honour gleamed whitely against the stiff white taffeta.

'Your *aide de camp*?' Napoleon questioned, as he regarded Juanele.

'My most trusted lieutenant,' Mario answered.

With a quick motion of his hand, Napoleon beckoned one of his officers to him, flipped the various gaudy stars on his chest until he found another Legion cross, unpinned it, and fastened it to Juanele's robe. Without another word, he turned and passed through the doorway. Mario waited until the last French uniform had left. He walked slowly back to the dais with the two thrones and regarded them. He eyed them with satisfaction.

'Juanele, see that these chairs are transported back to Marrakech. Two men sat on them today. One started out in Corsica and became the greatest man in Europe. Another started out in the slums of Havana and sat beside the first as his equal. Surely the seats of two such hypocrites should be preserved for posterity.'

Chapter Fifty-one

THE RETURN to Malaga with its Spanish streets, its Spanish palace and its Spanish rooms was like arriving anew in Spain after the few days spent in the Moorish Alhambra. Mario found himself impatient to return to Morocco itself.

He had feared this journey to Europe more than he had wanted to admit. Perhaps when he saw Spain again, returned to the life he had once known, a certain nostalgia would grip him and he would want to remain. Now he realized that whatever fears he had had were groundless. Spain awoke no answering chord within him. He felt confined, confused and insecure.

Yes, he was glad to be on his way back to Marrakech. His nerves had been too tightly drawn in Granada. He had dreaded the meeting with Napoleon, felt somewhat incapable of handling the delicate situation, and was apprehensive about the results. Now that it was over, he needed something to relieve the strain, smooth out the shattered tensions and relieve the pent-up frustrations. He knew exactly what one thing would accomplish all these desired results. Not so much what but who! He pondered the four slaves of his *hareem* and it was difficult to decide just which one he would ultimately choose.

Once the stairs had been ascended and the sweaty robes dropped to the floor, he had no difficulty in making up his mind. He merely had Juanele summon all four of his women and, with their help, he soon slid the thick, hard mattress, from the heavy, draped contraption that the Spaniards called a bed, down on to the floor. Although it was neither as yielding nor as comfortable as his own divan at home, he nevertheless found it an improvement over the high rigid bed.

Later he awoke in the dark, conscious of the perfumed softness of the sleeping bodies near him, shook them all into wakefulness and sent them away to their own quarters. Their words of endearment and their attempts to revive his fire of the past hour were of no avail. They had served his purpose. Now he wanted cool water for his heated body, food for his empty stomach and . . . yes, he wanted hot coffee, steaming, bitter, strong and acrid, such as he had formerly tasted in Havana.

He shifted lazily to his stomach, found a dry spot on the pillow and, in spite of hunger, sought sleep again. But the sudden image of Zaydah banished sleep. The more he thought about her the more he was tempted to summon the four slaves back again. But he realized that neither individually nor collectively would they be able to satisfy him nor stop his thoughts from returning again and again to Zaydah. There was only one immediate solution – a bath and supper, with Juanele to talk to him. He jumped up, strode across the floor, opened the door and was about to clap his hands when Juanele appeared, running up the corridor.

'You were coming?' Mario allowed the quickening steps of the boy to reach him. 'You were coming although I had not summoned you?'

Juanele grinned. 'I could say that, as a faithful slave, I had already known of my master's desires, but that would be a lie – *que mentira*! No, my Mario, I did not anticipate your summons. Instead I came to awaken you, to tell you that there is somebody below to see you.'

'Who? Napoleon again?'

'No, it is not Napoleon.' Juanele laughed. 'This man came alone. He is an old man, and he asked to see Prince Mohammed, the Moorish ambassador. I told him Your Highness was sleeping, and he seemed much disappointed. Then I told him I would see if you were awake, and he thanked me. So I came to rap on your door. His name is Frontera Baja.'

'What?' Mario grabbed the boy's shoulders and shook him. 'Frontera Baja.'

'*Dios mio*, Juanele! That's my father.'

'You mean your real father.'

'I do.'

Juanele studied Mario's face carefully. 'Yes, my Mario, he is your father. Now I see it. You look exactly like him.'

'You say he merely wanted to see the ambassador?'

'Yes.'

Mario glanced around the room. He dimly remembered seeing a screen somewhere among the furnishings. Yes, there it was – a bulky affair of dull brocade with a carved and mirrored top. With a motion of his head, he directed Juanele to bring it out into the centre of the room and open it up. The four leaves spread into a wide semicircle. Mario stepped behind it and applied his eye to one of the cracks. He could see clearly enough anyone who might be standing on the other side.

'Get me some clothes, Juanele. Then go below. Tell Frontera Baja that the ambassador will see him. Say to him that Prince Mohammed has been sleeping and that he is dressing to go out, but, if the interview is important, he will grant it while he is dressing. Bring my father up here, but do not mention my real name. I will stay behind the screen, and he will not be able to see me.'

'Nor can he harm you, Mario. This time you are not alone in Spain. You have a hundred Moorish soldiers right here in the palace with you.'

'And the last time I was in Spain, I was the Conde de San Mateo, but that didn't do me much good. Bring him up, Juanele. Let us hear what he wants. I might have loved the man if I could have known him long enough to trust him.' He listened to Juanele's footsteps go down the hall and then sought the sanctuary of the screen.

The soft footsteps of Juanele, followed by the harsh sounds of leather boots, came up the hall. Slowly the door to Mario's room opened. He saw Juanele stop on the threshold.

'Your Highness' – Juanele was speaking in Spanish – 'there is a man here to see you.'

'And who is that man?' Mario answered in Spanish.

'He says that he is the Marques de la Frontera Baja, and that he will require only a moment of Your Highness' time. He has a question he would like to ask you.'

'Bid him come in and be seated, Juanele.' Mario saw the figure in the door behind Juanele. Yes, it was his father, but how different from the man he had left behind in Havana! That man had been prosperous, assured. This man, in spite of the cleanness of his threadbare clothes, looked crushed – as though he had lost everything.

Frontera Baja lifted his head to look at the blank, brocaded screen, hesitated only a moment, and then spoke.

'Your Highness?' his voice questioned.

'Your Excellency.' Mario's voice was clear and without emotion, at least he tried to make it sound so.

'You will pardon me, I hope, for this intrusion. I would not have entered your bedroom without the assurance of your major domo that it was acceptable to you.'

'It is quite all right, Your Excellency.'

'You call me "Excellency"?'

'Even in Morocco we have heard of the Marques de la Frontera Baja.'

Mario could see his father reach for a chair and sit down in it, still staring at the blank panels of the screen.

'Thank you, Prince Mohammed. Have I your name correctly?'

'Quite right. My name is Mohammed ibn. . . .' Mario hesitated. 'As you probably know, our Moorish word *ibn* means "son of". My full name is Mohammed ibn. . . .' Again he hesitated. 'Mohammed ibn Mario.'

'Did you say "Mario", Your Highness?'

'Yes.'

'Strange. That is a Christian name. It is also my name, and the name about which I have come to inquire. I had a son named Mario, and it is about him that I seek information.'

'Proceed, Your Excellency.'

'My son was in Spain while I was attending to some business in the colonies. While he was here, he was taken prisoner. I understand that he was sold into captivity in Morocco. That is why I have come to you – to ask if you would interest yourself in my son's case and try to locate him for me.'

'A Christian slave, by the name of Mario, sold in Morocco? Can you tell me more about him? I can well understand, if he is your son, that you are anxious.'

'More than I can tell you, Prince Mohammed. There are many things I want to explain to him, and naturally a father's heart aches for his son.'

'As my father's would ache for me, were I not to return,' Mario added.

'But perhaps his not as much as mine. You see, your father has had you since you were a child. You have always been secure in his love and affection. I but found my son, only to have him taken away from me. I was never able to let him know that I cared about him.'

'Then you must have been a careless father, Your Excellency.' Mario peered through the crack to see the expression on his father's face, but Frontera Baja's head had dropped to his chest.

'I was, Your Highness, and now I regret it. There was a time when I gave very little thought to such matters as the welfare of my son. Even in the few brief moments I knew him, I was not aware that I cared about him. But now I would make it up to him if I could ever find him again.'

'Then what would you that I do?'

'If you could locate him in Morocco, you could tell him that his father in Spain was asking for him. Unfortunately I do not have the means now to ransom him.'

'I would be glad to convey your message, but who shall I ask for?'

'His name is Mario, Count of San Mateo.'

'That Mario! Are you sure?'

The man looked at the screen with surprise. 'Why of course I'm sure. I know my son's name.'

'Could he perhaps have been called Mario El Rubio?' Mario saw his father jump from the chair, walk the few paces to the screen and stand there expectantly.

'You know him, Prince Mohammed? You know him?'

'He is tall, with a head of blond hair that curls? Well-built, but of a surly, ungovernable temper?'

'Well-built, yes, but not surly unless he has been made so. Brave, yes! Strong, yes! And, Prince Mohammed, that Mario is my son, I am proud of him, wherever he is or whatever he is.'

'Your words move me, Your Excellency. I do know the man of whom you speak. He has caused us more trouble than any other slave. He killed an overseer on the walls of Marrakech and was sentenced to be crucified. But, when I passed as they were raising him to the cross, I stopped the execution.'

'Thank God. But why, Your Highness?'

'Because the man had been crucified once before.' Mario saw his father step backward, sink into the chair. The Marques was weeping and had difficulty in speaking.

'Yes, yes, I know. I know what happened to him, but, as God is my witness, I have revenged him.'

Mario pulled the *djellabah* from the top of the screen and slipped it on. He was completely dressed now.

'And how did you revenge him, Your Excellency?'

'With these hands.' The Marques held up his hands, which were trembling. 'I killed my brother – the one who tortured him.' He sank back into the chair.

Mario wound the white turban around his head, then changed his mind and threw it to the floor. He stepped from behind the screen, his light slippers making no sound on the polished tiles. His father had not heard him and sat, his elbows on the chair, his head low, held in his hands. A few steps carried Mario to his father and he laid his hand gently on the man's shoulder.

'Do not let it grieve you. Your brother was an evil man. He deserved to die.'

Slowly Frontera raised his head, aware of the hand on his shoulder and the white drapery of the sleeve that hung down from it. 'Perhaps I can borrow the money for the ransom. Your Highness. Name your figure.'

Mario walked around in front of the chair. Frontera Baja looked up at him. His pale eyes scanned Mario's face carefully. Then he closed his eyes and shook his head. 'It cannot be! It cannot be.'

'But it is,' Mario answered. 'Yes, *padre mio*, I am Mario.'

Frontera Baja opened his eyes slowly. His hands reached out and his trembling fingers touched Mario's arms. Slowly, his weight heavy on Mario, he stood up until his eyes were on a level with Mario's. One hand slowly released its grip on Mario's arm and clutched at the thin silk of the *kaftan*. It gave way and revealed Mario's chest. Frontera Baja took one look at the cruel outlines of the cross and collapsed in Mario's arms.

Chapter Fifty-two

THE PALACE, temporarily under the jurisdiction of Islam, had neither wine nor brandy, but a word to Juanele sent him scurrying to the nearest *bodega* for a bottle of cognac. When he came running back up the stairs and had managed to get the cork out of the bottle and a few drops between Frontera Baja's lips, Mario saw his father's eyelids flutter, then open.

They raised him to a sitting position, propped pillows behind him on the floor and waited for the colour to return to his cheeks. When he could safely be lifted to a chair and after he had taken a few more sips of brandy, he was able to talk. At first his words came haltingly, but they were a revelation to Mario. The bond that had been established between them that day in Havana was stronger than Mario had ever supposed.

Frontera Baja had been proud of his son, proud of the appearance he had made as he walked across the hotel lobby in Havana. What had started out to be a callous sacrifice on the altar of his own selfishness and safety had struck a far deeper and more responsive chord in the older man's heart. As soon as he had put Mario on the ship, he regretted his son's departure. He wished that he had kept him in Havana, although after the public execution of El Rubio that would have been wellnigh impossible.

Then he wished that he had gone to Spain with Mario, but unfortunately his business detained him in Cuba. He had, however, terminated his business on the island as soon as possible. Mindful of the months that had passed since he dispatched Mario, he sailed for Spain, his destination the house of Don Baltazar in Cadiz. His arrival there, with full expectation of greeting Mario, had been a disappointment, but he learned from Don Baltazar of Mario's capture and saw the importance of Camporeal's visit which preceded Mario's arrest.

From Cadiz, Frontera Baja departed in search of Camporeal, finally located him at Jerez and gave his brother a taste of the Frontera dungeons. By a sparse diet of one loaf of bread and one jug of water a week, he had finally starved the truth out of Camporeal. At his discovery of all that had happened to

Mario, he clasped his hands around his brother's throat and choked what little life still existed out of his emaciated body.

Frontera Baja had even considered a voyage to Fez, something quite unheard of under conditions that existed between Spain and Morocco, but in this he had been dissuaded by Don Baltazar, who had volunteered to have an undercover search made for Mario in Morocco. Don Baltazar's agents had had little luck. They had learned in Tangiers that two slaves answering the description of Mario and Ramon had been landed there and sent on to Fez, but there the trail ended. Discreet inquiries in Fez had elicited no further information.

Rumour had told Don Baltazar's agents that a tall blond *N'zrani* had been killed as the leader of a slave riot in Marrakech. The meagre description seemed to tally with Mario, to the end that both Don Baltazar and Frontera Baja had almost accepted the fact of his death; but without definite proof, Frontera had been loath to believe Mario dead. Although Frontera knew that Mario would probably have been one of the ringleaders of any insurrection, somehow he could never bring himself to believe that Mario was the tall blond who had died in Marrakech.

As Frontera, along with Almendares, had been high in favour at court, the downfall of Their Majesties of Spain, along with the Prince of the Peace, had also been the downfall of Frontera Baja. His once-prosperous estates and his large holdings in the colonies were all forfeit to the new regime. The Frontera properties passed from his hands to be distributed as favours to those who upheld the French, and to buy support for Napoleon's brother Joseph, whose position as King of Spain was far from secure.

As the Marques de Frontera Baja, with unlimited means at his disposal, his search for Mario might have been possible, but as the Marques de Frontera Baja, penniless in Spain, there was little that he could do. He remained on, living on the proceeds of the few jewels he had managed to save, hoping that the Bonaparte regime would fall and that he would regain his properties and, with them, be able to get some word of Mario.

The arrival of the Moorish ambassador had been an opportunity too good to overlook, and Frontera Baja had made the long journey from the little house in Jerez – his only remaining property – to Granada, only to arrive too late and find that the ambassador had left for Malaga.

A friend of earlier days in Granada had lent him a horse and he had made the trip to Malaga, arriving only an hour or so after Mario. He had called at the palace, had been admitted, had addressed the blankness of the brocaded screen and heard the voice that issued from behind it, but never, no never, had he even imagined that the illustrious Prince of Marrakech who represented the Shereefian Sultan might be the object of his search – his own son, Mario.

Even now, with Mario beside him and the indisputable evidence of Camporeal's decoration on Mario's chest, it was hard to believe, and he must listen to Mario's long tale with wonderment and many shakes of his head. Yes, he had known about the presence of Adan in Cadiz. He had known that he and Mario were friends. This much Don Baltazar had told him. He had of course known of Mario's torture and his departure from Spain. From there on, he could only listen and marvel until Mario had finished. Frontera Baja sat still, shaking his head in wonderment. His hand reached across the table for the bottle of cognac, poured out a full wine glass and offered it to Mario.

Mario shook his head. 'Strange as it may seem, Father, my allegiance to Islam is more than merely tongue service. I am a Moslem now and I follow the laws of the Quoran. Therefore I do not drink spirits.'

Frontera downed the contents of the wine glass in one gulp. 'Then you intend to return to Morocco, my son.'

Mario did not answer.

'Am I to find you, only to lose you?' Frontera persisted. There was a note of desperation in his voice.

'You force a hard decision, my father.'

'But remember that I *am* your father, Mario.'

'Are you? Was it love for the poor woman who was my mother that prompted you to plant your seed in her? Was it love for me that caused you to neglect me for so many years until it served your purpose to recognize me? Was it the action of a father to send me to Spain to receive the vengeance of Camporeal?' He hesitated and looked at the eager face of the man in front of him. 'And yet, I suppose you are my father.'

'I am.'

'But only by accident. Because you once slept with a woman and used her body for your own pleasure, I am the result. Therefore you claim me as your son. But I have a father who claims me, not by mere accident, but because he loves me. And although I do not know the meaning of the word "love" between a father and son, I think I love him. At least I honour him, I respect him and, yes, by my faith in Allah, I love him. Perhaps I could have had the same feeling for you. I believe I felt a stirring of it the last time I saw you. I was proud to claim you, the Marques of Frontera Baja, as my father. But' – he pointed his finger at the old man – 'you didn't want me then.'

Frontera Baja bit his lips and looked up at Mario, but he did not answer.

'I'll answer for you,' Mario continued. 'You did not. You were willing to ship me to Spain so that, if Camporeal wanted to plunge a dagger into someone, it would not be your precious skin that it would puncture. *Verdad?*'

'You are right, Mario.'

'But instead of a dagger, my fond uncle did this.' Mario ripped open his *kaftan* to the waist. 'This! This is what I have to thank you for.'

'It has been revenged.'

'It can never be revenged. As long as I live I must carry this hateful picture, must shun the gaze of True Believers in my home, must go to the *hamman* alone and unattended except by Ramon, the slave you gave me, or Juanele, the slave I acquired. Even my father, the Emir, would not let his eyes dwell on this, my disgrace.'

'But if you were in Cuba or Spain, my son, it would be nothing to be ashamed of.'

'I was executed in Cuba, shot by a squad of soldiers who thought no more of killing El Rubio than I would a male slave who tried to enter my *hareem*. There is only one thing that would ever draw me back to Cuba.'

Frontera looked up hopefully. 'One thing, my son? If there is anything – anything – that would draw you to Cuba, let me know.'

Mario held up his hand to stem the hopefulness of the other's words. 'Not so fast! I said there was only one thing, and that is the memory of the woman who raised me, little Ana. You took me from her.'

'And today she is well provided for.' Frontera smiled. 'I arranged it all before I left Havana. It's the one thing you can give me credit for, Mario. She has a decent home, or at least she had when I left, but now I do not know. My Cuban estates have been confiscated and the settlement I made on her has probably been wiped away.'

Mario looked at his father with disbelief. Surely the man had changed. That he had provided for Ana merely because of her association with Mario was a strong point in his favour. Suddenly the barrier between them dissolved. Mario reached his hand across to the other and took his father's hand in his own.

'You did that for Ana?' Once more he felt the warmth of her love. Once more he realized all the little sacrifices she had made for him and the patient devotion she had lavished on him.

Frontera nodded his head.

'Then let us start all over again, Father. Let us forget all that is past and become friends. No, friends is not the word. Let us become father and son once more.'

'Then you will go with me to Cuba?'

'No, but you will go. I have great obligations in Marrakech – obligations that transcend even the duty a son owes his father. Remember, in Marrakech I have another father to whom I owe much, and I have the son of Adan whom I must guard, and that, *padre mio*, is a sacred trust. I have these two obligations; and, even more than that, I have a duty to myself.'

'To yourself?'

'Yes. I have gone through life without knowing love. Many women have enjoyed my body and my body has enjoyed many women.' He laughed. 'They even wanted the harridan Queen of Spain to slobber over it. But I have never known love. Now for the first time in my life I do know it, and I owe it to myself to discover more about it.'

'And she is in Marrakech?'

'She is.'

Frontera's hand slowly disengaged itself from Mario's. 'I understand. The love of a man for a woman exceeds the love of a son for his father. I cannot quarrel with you, Mario, but let me go with you to Marrakech.'

Mario laughed again. 'I cannot see the Marques de la Frontera Baja as a Christian slave of the Emir.'

'As the father of the Emir's son, need I be a slave?'

'You are a Christian, my father. Would you embrace Islam?' Mario shook his head. 'It is painful, my father, and I doubt, at your age, if you would survive the operation.'

'*Dios mio*, what operation?'

'Circumcision is an Islamic rite.'

'Heavens, no!'

'But as a Christian you cannot live in Marrakech unless you are a slave – not even you, the father of the Emir's son. No, it saddens me, but we meet only to part. But I will see that you get to Havana.'

'I have no money, Mario.'

'And I have enough gold to buy the proudest ship in Spain and send you back a lone passenger.'

Frontera rose slowly from his chair. 'You would send me away, Mario?'

'No, Father. We separate, that is all. This time it is different. We separate as father and son and there is a great bond between us. Know you that wherever you go, I shall always think of you as my father and, wherever I may be, I shall be your son. We shall write to each other through the good offices of Don Baltazar. We shall never lose track of each other again. I shall support you as long as you live, in the state to which a marques of Spain is entitled.' Mario stopped and his eyes scanned his father's face carefully. 'But I shall do this on one condition.'

'Ask what you will, my son. If it is within my means, I shall grant it.'

'No, promise me not too hastily. Perhaps the condition I impose will be impossible.'

'Try me and see.'

'You are growing old, my father. And old age brings loneliness. That very loneliness has impelled you to me, right?'

Frontera agreed.

'Then, when you get to Havana, you will find more loneliness. You will live alone, waited on impersonally by servants, but there will be nobody to wake in the night if you cough or minister to you if you are sick or to spend the quiet days of old age with you.'

'I had hoped. . . .'

'But even a son does not sit with his father and watch the world go by. You need a wife, Father.'

'Bah! I have seen enough of women. I can buy all I want with *pesetas*.'

'But *pesetas* will not buy the companionship of one sitting on the balcony with you watching the *paseo* go by. *Pesetas* will not impel one to tuck the rug more warmly about your legs if you feel a draught. *Pesetas* will not pay one to sit beside your bed if you are ill. Yet there is one who would.'

'You mean?'

'Ana.'

'Good God, should I make a whorehouse doxie into the Marquesa de la Frontera Baja?'

'And why not? She is the only mother I have ever known, and you are my father. Ana is good, and she would be devoted to you. Together you would find great happiness, for I know her and I know what she is. A whorehouse doxie, you say? Yes, but she became one to support me. Think, Father. Through the miles that separate Havana from Marrakech, I could think of you and Ana, the two whom I love, together.'

'This would please you, Mario?' Frontera stood up.

'More than anything else you could possibly do for me.'

Frontera hesitated for a moment as he reached for his hat and cane.

'You know, in decent clothes, Ana is a very presentable woman. Nobody would know she is a mulatto, and as the Marquesa de la Frontera Baja nobody would dare to say so.'

Mario took the hat and cane from his father and laid them back on the table. 'I do not leave until tomorrow. Tonight you are the guest of the Sultan Suleiman of Morocco and his ambassador Prince Mohammed. Your son also invites you to stay. This night we shall spend in talk. On the morrow you will leave Malaga in your own coach, en route to Cuba, stopping at Cadiz on the way. I shall board my ship for Morocco.' Mario reached for the bottle of cognac. 'This once, I shall break the law of Islam.' He poured two glasses and handed one to his father. He raised his glass and heard the clink of crystal as it touched Frontera's.

'I drink to a wedding in Havana, *padre mio*, to you and to my mother, the Marquesa de la Frontera Baja.'

They drank and, although the fiery liquor choked in Mario's throat, he swallowed it manfully, then sent his glass crashing to the tiles. Frontera's glass followed it. Juanele, outside the room, heard the noise and opened the door.

'It's all right, Juanele,' Mario assured him. 'The Marques de la Frontera Baja dines tonight with me. Tell the kitchen to pay special attention to the *couscous*. It is seldom that we have so distinguished a guest.'

Chapter Fifty-three

THE RAM'S horn of the Iman who travelled with Mario's suite sounded the call to morning prayers, and still Mario and his father talked. As the unmusical blast echoed through the sleeping corridors of the Spanish palace, Mario pressed his fingers to his lips as a signal to his father to be quiet, spread his robe on the floor and abased himself in the direction of Holy Mecca. When he had finished his prayers, he ignored the look of surprised wonderment on his father's face and continued on with their conversation as though nothing unusual had happened.

When breakfast was over and Juanele came to remove the trays of food, he whispered in Mario's ear. Mario's hand on his father's arm led the older man to the windows, and they stepped out on to the balcony. Below, in the courtyard of the palace, a glistening coach with liveried coachmen and outriders was standing, with the horses nervously pawing the ground. How easily, Mario thought, miracles can appear when one's pockets are lined with gold! Gold! That reminded him, and he directed Juanele to open one of the cedar chests. He selected two of the heavy goatskin bags and handed them to his father. There was enough in them for Frontera Baja to charter his own boat to carry him to Havana.

Their parting was brief. Both had many words they might have said but there was no need for them now. Twice in their lifetime they had met, only to be parted. Mario felt he would never see his father again.

All through the night, as Mario and his father talked, Mario's slaves had been moving his belongings to the ship, and now, his father having been sped on his way, Mario's women and his other chattels were carried on board. He and Juanele, accompanied by the *alcalde* of Malaga and a delegation of French soldiers, rode through the streets to the quay, which was lined with *Malagueños*, curious to see the Moorish prince depart.

Mario spent the first day in his cabin, regaining the sleep he had lost the night before – or as much sleep as was possible between the welcome ministrations of his four charmers. Now that the journey was nearing an end, they were fearful that they would be sent back to Fez. Consequently they doubled their attentions to him, pleading and importuning between their kisses that he take them with him to Marrakech. For, as one of them informed him – which opinion was echoed by the other three – having slept with Mario no other man could possibly take his place. Fortunately Mario had become sufficiently Moslem merely to smile his reply at them and whisper '*In'sha'allah*'. As Allah wills was a most convenient answer, as it relieved him of all obligations – although he could see that it was hardly a favourable answer to any one of the four.

Mario had sent messengers directly from the Alhambra, at the conclusion of his meeting with Napoleon, to the Grand Vizier in Tangiers, so the elderly statesman was fully acquainted with Mario's success. But even this knowledge could not prepare Mario for the almost regal reception which Morocco gave him. All of Tangiers was in a holiday mood. Banners of varicoloured silks with cursive Arabic characters proclaimed Mario as the Saviour of His Country, the Protecting Arm of Allah, the Eagle of Marrakech, and the Shadow of the Sublime Sultan. These greeted him as his small boat, rowed by stalwart Moors, arrived at the stone quay of Tangiers.

An enormous white umbrella fringed with gold appeared above the maze of *djellabahs*. Under it, walking in solemn dignity, was the Grand Vizier himself. He advanced to Mario, took him by the arm and led him to a horse, then mounted his own beside him. The sea of *djellabahs* parted and they rode side by side through the narrow streets. As they advanced, the standing Moors knelt in the gutters at their approach and their backs, bending in unison, looked like a field of grain under a strong wind.

The Tangiers palace was filled with the nobles of Morocco, and they too bowed their proud backs as Mario and the Grand Vizier entered. Only when they were finally alone in the same little room, seated on the same divan with glasses of steaming mint tea, did the Grand Vizier speak. Then he requested a full verbal report of Mario's visit and his talk with Napoleon.

His thin lips parted in a wry smile at Mario's account of the ornate thrones and the uncomfortable figure of the little emperor in his sweat-stained breeches perched upon one of them, dangling his feet in the air. He applauded Mario's diplomacy, seemed relieved at the ease with which the question was settled, and gave his complete approval of the concessions which Mario had made. Now Morocco would not suffer the fate of her sister, Egypt. Napoleon had looked on the Pyramids, but he would never see the Bab Mansour of Fez nor the Koutoubia of Marrakech. Morocco was saved.

Now came the presents from the Sultan, and the honours. There were robes of heavy silk shot through with gold, a jewelled blade whose hilt flashed with myriad-coloured gems; the title of Emir of Abda, which placed Mario equal in rank with his father the Emir, if not equal in importance. And last, the Grand Vizier presented Mario with the four charming companions of the voyage. These things the Vizier conferred in the name of the Sultan. But when he had finished with the munificence of Suleiman, even more cherished than all the tinselled baubles to Mario was the coolness of the thin-veined hand of the Vizier, placed over Mario's, and the words of the man.

'We owe much to you, *N'zrani* born. We shall not forget. Now, go to your father in Marrakech. The sight of you will do much to comfort him for the loss of Prince Adan, and he can well assuage his grief over the son that has passed into Paradise by the son who returns to him.' He stood up and accompanied Mario to the door. His farewell was only a slow smile and the pressure of a hand on Mario's arm, but Mario knew that he had made an important friend. Surely Allah, in his all-knowing wisdom, had been good.

Mario was anxious to start for home. Weeks of protocol and stiff-backed ceremonies had made him anxious for the freedom of his own tent, for the long days on his horse, for the cool shadows of his own palace in Marrakech, for the boy Mohammed, for Ramon and – now he could admit it to himself – for the same air that Zaydah breathed.

Now at least he could think of her. Now he could hope. Now he could close his eyes and see her bending over him as he had lain stretched in the tepid water of his bath. Now he could relive that one moment of ecstasy, that one kiss that had so stirred his passions. Perhaps now, after these years of waiting, it could be repeated.

Chapter Fifty-four

JUANELE COULD still feel the pressure of Mario's arm on his shoulder as they lifted the flap of the tent and entered into the softly lighted interior. Once inside, Juanele turned to Mario, helped him pull the heavy woollen robe up over his head, and then asked almost too casually, 'Which one of the girls shall I summon for tonight?'

Mario regarded the boy with indulgence and smiled. 'Tonight, *chico hombre*, I shall dispense with all my *houris*. I am not sleepy, but still I am tired, too exhausted to respond to any of them. Perhaps my thoughts are too much with Adan this evening. Perhaps I have too many regrets – things I should have done and never did.'

'There is water heated for your bath, Mario.' Juanele pointed to the curtain that divided the tent. 'Shall I bring it in and bathe you?'

'What matters a bath if I sleep alone?'

'No bedmate, no bath?' Juanele shook his head in disbelief as he watched Mario take off his *djellabah*, kick off the *babouches* and strip himself of the white linen trousers. As his master stood naked in the flickering light of the oil lamps, Juanele regarded him, then suddenly lowered his head so that Mario might not read what was in his eyes. Slowly he crossed the soft rugs, picked up Mario's trousers, refolded the length of silk that made up the turban, straightened the *babouches* so that they stood side by side.

Then, trying hard to control his voice, he asked hesitantly, 'Tonight may I move my mattress to where it rightfully belongs – to the foot of your bed?'

Mario stretched out on the divan, drew a soft blanket over his knees and grinned at the boy.

'That would make you happy, Juanele?'

'Yes, my master.'

'Why do you call me *master* tonight?'

'Because I do not forget I am still your slave.'

'Then bring your mattress in here, if you will. But I do not intend to sleep for a while. See?' He pointed to the thick book of vellum sheets on the tabouret. 'I would learn some of the arts of making love from the Persian poets.'

'Then while you read, I shall use the water you do not want to bathe myself.' Juanele lifted the curtain to pass to the other part of the tent. Mario did not reply, so Juanele ducked under and went into the other side.

Sidi Mokar had used Juanele for many tasks, often abused him, sometimes neglected him, and even at times ignored him. The youth had been his body servant and valet, his bath-boy and masseur, his cook and table servant, his messenger and orderly, his page and cupbearer, his flunky and sycophant, his bedfellow and his beloved. Mokar had never been deliberately cruel to Juanele, nor did the boy resent the treatment he had received. Both knew that a slave was a thing, not a person – a thing to be used as long as it was serviceable, and then discarded.

And yet, Mokar had had a deep affection for the boy, a real affection such as a man develops for a faithful dog. When the boy knelt to kiss his feet, which the master insisted that he do at least twice a day, Mokar would often reach down to take him up in his arms. The master was as faithful to the slave as the slave was to his owner. Mokar, who was constantly travelling on the Sultan's business, maintained no *hareem* and kept no women. There was only Juanele, who was always with him, always ready to supply all his master's wants.

Now, with Mokar dead, Juanele was bereft. He was desolate and desolated. True, his ownership had been transferred to Mario, and now he was Mario's slave, but he was still unable to forget his former owner and the joy he had derived from serving him. But, perhaps most of all, he missed the love he had enjoyed in the intimacy of Mokar's bed. And now he was not only lonely – he was young and anxious to expend his youth while it was still desirable. Sleeping on the mattress at the foot of Mario's bed, where he could see and hear his master, was better than being alone in the other part of the tent, but it was not what Juanele really desired.

The boy had transferred both his affection and his desire for Mokar to Mario, though he had so far received no evidence of Mario's acceptance of these gifts. Mario liked Juanele, imposed few duties on him, and felt close to him because of their common Spanish birthright. He would have freed Juanele in a moment, had it been possible. As it was, he demanded just token service and companionship. The boy's only duties were to serve him, sleep on the floor at the foot of his bed, and accompany him to the *hamman* and wait upon him there, if Ramon was otherwise occupied. Juanele knew the secret of the tattoo, Juanele spoke Spanish, and Juanele was a comfortable person to have around – he was always good-natured, smiling, gaily mischievous and entertaining.

Mario considered the boy as he did his palace eunuchs – sexless. Juanele knew all the secrets of Mario's bedchamber, and Mario never sensed the boy's agony as he listened in the night to the noises of pleasure that came from the various women who shared Mario's bed.

The sight of Mario, naked in the lamplight, had aroused Juanele's desires, and he felt sure that if once he were able to express his love for Mario, Mario would at least accept it as a substitute for his *hareem* women, when they were not in evidence, or when Mario did not desire them, as tonight. And now the two of them were alone in the tent and the tent was isolated from the rest of the camp.

Juanele smiled to himself as he poured the water from the big kettle into a shallow pan and sat down in it to lather his body with the bland olive oil soap from Castile. After he had soaped himself thoroughly, he unwound the braids from his head, unbraided them and washed his hair, then dried his body and his hair until the hair fell in soft ripples down over his shoulders. He had no beard, so it was not necessary for him to shave, but he plucked out the few hairs that grew on his chest, combed and pomaded the hair on his body and pared his nails.

In one of his bundles he found a little cedar box. This he opened, and he took out of it an assortment of cosmetics which Mokar had given him and applied them to his body. Then he found a bottle of perfume which he had teased away from the chief eunuch of the Sultan's *hareem*. It had always had the effect of stimulating Mokar's passion, perhaps it would do as much for Mario. Besides jasmine and other pungent Levantine oils, there was a trace, just a hint, of that malodorous musk which in its attenuation excites lubricity in whoever inhales it. Juanele felt that now, if ever, he could gain some recognition from Mario. He was clean, he smelled sweet, and he knew that his body was as smooth, as soft and as seductively curved as any woman's.

Slowly, so as not to disturb Mario, he raised the curtain that divided the tent and stepped into Mario's apartment. Mario was lying back on the pillows, his eyes closed, the blanket tossed on the floor and the book of erotic verse dropped from his hand. The light of the oil lamps cast a flickering yellow light on his body. As Juanele approached the divan, Mario stirred, opened his eyes and regarded the boy with amazement.

'You, Juanele? *Dios mio*, I thought at first it was one of my girls, but I doubt if even one of them looks as beautiful as you tonight. I've never seen you with your hair unbraided. If you had on *hareem* trousers instead of being naked, you'd fetch a goodly price on the slave market.' He raised himself up on one elbow. 'By all the *djinns* of the desert, boy, you look good enough to —'

'To what, my master?'

'To wiggle your pretty little behind out and heat me some water for tea. That's all.'

'The water is heated. But I wonder if you want tea tonight.'

'And why wouldn't I want tea tonight?'

'Because I have a surprise for you.'

'Yes?'

'Yes, Mario. Something that will take you back many miles in your memories. Here.' He withdrew a hand from behind his back and brought forth a bottle, which he placed in Mario's hands. Mario looked at the bottle and smiled.

'It's been a long time since I saw a bottle of real Cuban rum.' He placed it regretfully on the tabouret side of the divan. 'Where did you get it?'

'In Malaga.'

'And what do you propose to do with it?'

'To give it to you.'

'But I don't drink rum now, Juanele. You forget, I am a Moslem, and according to the law of the Prophet. . . .'

'Bah! According to the law of the Prophet! Forget it this one night. There's many a long-faced Moslem in Tangiers who has a cellar well-stocked with wines from Spain and Portugal. Drinking rum in Havana never hurt your soul. How can it harm you now? There's nobody here but you and me, and, in spite of everything you say, Mario, you're no Moor. You're as Spanish as I am. Come, Mario, let me pour out two glasses and we'll drink together.'

Mario regarded the bottle, reached for it and tested the

cork. He could not remove it, and he shook his head and returned the bottle to Juanele.

'You see, we cannot remove the cork, so we cannot drink. And I'm damn sure of one thing, boy. In all our baggage there is no such a thing as a corkscrew. Therefore it's a sign from Allah that we should not drink the forbidden liquor.'

Juanele cracked the neck of the bottle so expertly on the tent pole that scarcely a drop was lost. He nodded knowingly as he poured out two cupfuls and handed one to Mario.

'Look, Mario,' he said, 'you have never seen me dance. Tonight, while you sip your rum, I shall dance for you as I did for Sidi Mokar. There is no music, but I can hum the tune.' Juanele finished his drink in one gulp and backed a few feet away from the couch, taking care to place the rum bottle within easy reach of Mario's hand.

He took a posture, feet together, head high, and began to sway, humming a plaintive yet seductive strain. Slowly his arms and hands began to move in a gesture of supplication. The muscles of his neck grew tense as his face assumed an expression of complete dejection. Although his feet did not move the muscles of his calves and thighs twitched with tension. It was a completely expressed longing; the downcast eyes betokened unsatisfied desire, the moving hands showed his frustration.

Gradually his eyes lifted to stare at Mario, the tempo of his voice increased until it suddenly became joyful, and the action of the dance grew more abandoned. The longing had ceased, the lover had been found and now there was no more unhappiness, only a wild desire to court, to please, to win, to conquer. Although he did not move his feet, the dance became wilder and the gyrations of his stomach more violent. It seemed that the frantic thrusts would tear the boy apart. Every muscle was strained, every sinew stretched. His face contorted into a bestial mask and instead of music his breath came in short, animal gasps. Then, with one last ebullient thrust, he expended himself and sank to the floor, exhausted.

Throughout the performance, Mario's eyes had been fixed on Juanele, hypnotized by the boy's grace, and obscene exhibitionism. And, he had to admit, he had been attracted by the boy's beauty. Now he held out his hand to Juanele, who crawled on his knees to the bed and prostrated himself before Mario.

'Let me warm myself beside you, Mario.' Without waiting for further invitation, Juanele turned and laid his head on the pillow beside Mario's. He waited for the words he feared might follow his action. Then, throwing caution to the winds, he brought his lips to Mario's.

Suddenly Mario came to himself. 'So that was your game?' he cried, pushing Juanele away. 'That was the reason for the rum, the perfume, the dancing and all the other arts. Well, let me remind you of one thing. I'm no Sidi Mokar. I'm no Moor who seeks the kisses of a perfumed boy. I don't want them from you or anyone else. And furthermore, you happen to be my slave – even though I've never treated you as such.'

He bounded out of bed and stepped across the prostrate figure on the floor. Two steps carried him to the wall of the tent, where he snatched down one of the whips of plaited silk which he kept for his women. Although they were capable of inflicting severe pain in their application, they were not designed to lacerate the flesh.

Juanele gazed in wild-eyed fear as Mario advanced towards him, he raised the whip and brought it down on the boy. Juanele strove to get up and escape the lash, but Mario was too quick for him. He grabbed at the boy and flung him back on the floor. Once again Juanele slithered along the carpets but Mario reached out, grabbed him by the ankle, and pulled him back. Still holding him with one hand, he reached towards the tabouret, grabbed at the length of silk which formed his turban, and tied one end around the boy's ankle, then secured the other end to his own.

As Juanele struggled to free himself, Mario took the bottle of rum and poured it over the struggling boy. Then his whip upraised, he let it descend. Time and time and time again it swished through the air and found its mark on the body that squirmed and floundered on the rugs. Red welts appeared and crisscrossed themselves over the smooth body – but during it, in spite of the pain, Juanele never screamed. His low moans and whimpers betokened his suffering, but he had presence of mind enough not to wake the sleeping camp.

He lifted his head to Mario, but a sweep of the lash cut him across the face, drawing blood for the first time. Mutely he stared up at Mario, trying to gain some recognition in the frenzied eyes of the man whom he loved as his master and friend and whom he had hoped to love even more. But Mario was beyond caring. The unaccustomed rum, the distaste for Juanele's action, and his own frustration, had deprived him of all reason.

Still staring up at him, Juanele crept forward, grabbed Mario's ankles, lowered his head and kissed Mario's feet. For the first time, he gasped out words.

'Kill me, Mario. Kill me, if you wish. But as you do, remember this: my only crime was loving you as Adan did.'

The frenzy disappeared from Mario's eyes. His upraised hand fell to his side and the whip slipped to the floor. He shook his head as if in disbelief at his own actions, and gazed down at the boy in a trance, bewildered and awe-struck. Painfully and with effort, Juanele hoisted himself to his feet, swayed and would have collapsed had not Mario put out a hand to steady him.

'Why don't you finish the job, Mario? Why don't you kill me? Whip me to death!'

Mario gazed at him, stupefied and dumb.

'I'm waiting, Mario. But instead of the whip, the knife would be quicker. Here.' He reached down to the tabouret and took Mario's silver dagger, unsheathed it and handed it to Mario. Mario reached for it instinctively without seeing it, then let it fall to the floor.

'Juanele —'

'Yes, my master.'

'Juanele, did I do this to you?'

'Yes, my master.'

'Stop calling me master. You are as freeborn as I.'

'But only a master beats a slave.'

Mario hung his head. 'Little Juanele! The first one to speak a kind word to me in Morocco. Little Juanele, who tried to protect me. Little Juanele, who has suffered as much as I have.' He relinquished his hold on the boy and regarded him intently. 'Good God, boy, what have I done to you?' His hand came up and tenderly touched the blood on Juanele's face.

'It's not what you did to me, Mario. It's what I did to you.'

Mario nodded in humble agreement, stepped towards the divan, but tripped on the hobble that tied him to Juanele and fell, sprawling on the rugs. He made no attempt to get up, although Juanele came towards him and knelt beside him, his arms outstretched to raise him.

'Keep away from me, boy, don't touch me,' Mario Commanded. 'Do you hear? Don't touch me.'

'Yes, my master.'

'Be quiet! Let me speak. Oh, Juanele, what is there about me that makes people want me? Tell me! Tell me, Juanele. Why do a rough sailor, a cheap whore, a Spanish duchess, a Moorish prince, and even you, want me? *Dio mio!* All my life it has been this way. I've enjoyed it, yes, but it's been my damnation. Even the Queen of Spain wanted me and, because I did not want her, see what happened to me. It's been "Mario, kiss me, Mario, fondle me, Mario, pleasure me, Mario, sleep with me, straddle me as you would a horse, ride me, whip me, play with me, hurt me, love me, drown me in a whirlpool of love!" Why, Juanele? Why, oh good God, why?'

'Because you are you, Mario. There's something about you that, when a woman looks at you, rouses her desire. And not only women; men too. It's common gossip in the palaces of Marrakech that half the men there want you.'

'But why, Juanele, why?'

'I know, but I cannot explain. Maybe it's your eyes, your body – I don't know. But I do know this. They look at you, men and women both, and they are not content until they solve the riddle of that which is hidden, and experience the supreme gratification which they feel that only you can give them. Yes, Mario, I tried it tonight. Had you given me what I wanted, I could have died happily. But I was wrong, and I failed. Now you have punished me. But please do not hold it against me, Mario. Let me go on being your slave.'

'And so you shall. But in being my slave, you shall do as I order. Pick up the whip.'

Juanele stooped and took hold of it, then started to walk to the other side of the tent to replace it on the wall. But the silk that bound him to Mario held him. He bent to loosen the knot, but Mario stopped him.

'Wait, do not untie it. You are to use the whip. On me. I would humiliate this flesh that has caused me so much trouble.'

'Oh no, Mario. Not on you!'

'Yes, I have need of it. I must remember this night. I must remember it always, and no longer rely on the enticements of my body to gain my desires. I must remember how I whipped you, Juanele, and repaid your goodness to me with pain. I must remember how I traded on this body to get what I wanted from Adan, and yet denied him that which he wanted but never asked for. I must never forget how I have gone through life, accepting the things which came to me because I was fortunate enough to possess this body, which it seems all the world desires. Is there nothing to Mario but this flesh? Has he only a body, a face, and the equipment of a man? Is that true, Juanele?' He pointed to his loins. 'Is this all of Mario that matters? Tell me the truth, Juanele.'

'No, no, Mario! You are something more than a face and a body. You are Mario.'

'Then let me taste the whip. If there is a Mario, he will not suffer from what the whip does to the body. If there is only a body, then let there be pain!'

'I can't, Mario, I can't!' Juanele was sobbing.

'Can't? Do you disobey me? You are my slave. Obey!'

'No, Mario —'

'I command it! Start, Juanele! If not, I swear to you, tomorrow I'll sell you to some Berber *caid* who lives beyond the High Atlas, so that I'll never have to look at you again. I warn you.'

Juanele knew that Mario meant his words. Slowly he raised his arm and let the lash fall leniently on Mario. It met his flesh with a slow, snake-like writhing, coiling around his thighs.

Mario sat up, grabbed the whip from the boy's hands and gave him a vicious lash. 'Like that! I am no weakling. Now begin.' He forced the whip back into Juanele's hand.

Juanele obeyed. He brought the lash down with all his force and winced as he saw the red line appear across Mario's breech. Mario flinched, but did not move. As the whip descended again and again, Mario struggled to free himself from the length of silk, rolling sideways on the floor to avoid the lash. But time after time it cut into him, until a spurt of blood caused Juanele to throw down the whip and sink on the rugs beside Mario.

'I can't. No more, no more.'

Mario struggled to his feet and sank down on the divan. He motioned to the mattress at the foot of his bed and then to the knot on his ankle. His voice was hoarse and rasping. 'Untie this. Then go to sleep. Tomorrow, if Allah is willing, we ride early for Marrakech. I've learned a lesson tonight, Juanele.

Perhaps you've learned one too. And I have a promise to make to you.'

'That I shall not be sold to a *caid* beyond the High Atlas?'

'Of course not – but that is not what I had in mind.' Mario groaned and pulled the robe of camel hair over him while he listened to Juanele bedding himself down on the mattress.

'Then what, Mario?'

'This. No man can go through life without love. You need it as much as I do. I have my *hareem*. So shall you have yours. When you arrive in Marrakech I shall buy you the prettiest boy in the slave market. He shall be yours – your *hareem*.'

Juanele sat up on his mattress to extinguish the last burning lamp. For the first time he laughed. 'Mario, Mario? Think you that I want a dainty, long-haired boy? How little you know me. I'd hate him and he'd hate me. After one day we would be quarrelling about which one of us was the prettier. He'd steal my perfumes and be making eyes at other men, and I'd probably end up by beating the little *marico*. No, I want no girlish boy tagging around after me.'

'Then I'll buy you some Hamite warrior – some tall, hawk-nosed stallion with a chest like a barrel, if you desire a husband instead of a wife.'

'That would be more to my liking.' Juanele laughed in the darkness. 'But save your money. There is already one who wants me, and now that I know I cannot have you, it is he that I would desire.'

'Then who?'

'Ramon.'

'Ramon? He does not care for boys.'

'How do you know? Have you ever asked him? Have you ever stopped to think that Ramon is a man with desires?'

Mario pondered a moment. Ramon had always seemed as sexless as Juanele. 'Then, Ramon. . . .'

'Have you ever known him to seek a woman?'

'No.'

'I know that Ramon likes me. He would not say so, out of loyalty to you, but I know.'

Mario turned in his bed, trying to find a spot where the pressure of his body on the cushions did not pain him. Suddenly he laughed. 'Then, Juanele, Ramon you shall have – with my blessing on you both.'

Chapter Fifty-five

NEWS TRAVELLED fast in Morocco. It was borne over the rolling hills and the level wastelands between Tangiers and Marrakech by riders who spared neither themselves nor their horses in order that the Emir might know of the honours his son had received from the hand of the Sultan. So, when Mario arrived after his more leisurely journey, the gala reception which had been staged in Tangiers was duplicated in Marrakech. As his travel-worn caravan drew up to the palace, the Emir was waiting for him. Mario dismounted and was about to bend his knee, when a restraining hand stopped him.

'The Emir of Abda does not kneel before the Emir of Marrakech,' the old man said.

'But the son of the Emir of Marrakech kneels to honour his illustrious father.' Mario completed the obeisance only to be brought to his feet and enfolded in his father's arms. Together they walked up the steps of the palace, and now there was a new, fierce pride in the Emir's glance, a new bearing as he escorted Mario before the assembled nobles of his realm. His grief over Adan had been temporarily lulled by the honours awarded to his adopted son.

Pride in his son Mohammed was an emotion he could well afford. He looked upon Mario, who loomed a head taller than himself. This, then, was a man of his own creating. This he had rescued from the sweating slaves who toiled on his walls. This he had converted to Islam. This he had sent to serve his country and, by a few words, this one-time infidel slave had gained more peace and security for Morocco than all the petty wars and tribal killings of the assembled nobles.

Again he looked up, and caught Mario's eyes looking down at him. They were not the dark eyes fringed with black lashes of his own son, but, although they shone with a strange blue in the tanned face, they looked at him with the same respect and love that Adan's had.

Together they reached the top of the stairs and started down the long corridor to the Presence Room. On entering, Mario smiled to see the two ornate thrones which he had sent on from the Alhambra, sitting at equal heights on a raised dais, instead of the divan which had always served the Emir for his audiences. This time the Emir occupied Mario's chair and Mario occupied the one Napoleon had sat in.

The reception started, and as the huge black slave from Senegal called out their names, one noble after another, rich in embroidered *kaftan*, snowy white *djellabah* and carefully folded turban, made his way up the carpeted aisle and bowed first to the Emir and then to Mario, muttered a few flowery compliments in stilted Arabic and backed away. The procession seemed interminable but nobody, down to the least important *caid*, could be slighted, and each was jealous of his prerogative – to walk to the twin thrones, bow before the two Emirs and walk away.

Finally, the last *sidi* made his way backwards down the rugs, and the wearisome ritual ended. Then the feast began and the huge copper platters with roast kids and lambs, the big tented bowls of *couscous*, the honey cakes and almond pastries were spread out on the floor. Before Mario and the Emir, sitting on the thrones, two tables were placed, and for the first time in Morocco Mario ate his food sitting in a chair instead of on the floor. He found, much to his surprise, that he was now too Moorish for it to be comfortable.

At length the feasting was over, the Sultan's gifts had been displayed and admired, and the last lingering guest had departed. Mario and the Emir were left alone, and it was with relief that they quitted the hard upholstery of the gilded thrones for the softness of a divan in the Emir's room. Both of them felt at a loss to know where to begin. They sat silently, looking at each other in the flickering light of the argon lamps, watching the smoke curl in spirals to the ceiling. They were contented, replete with food and drink, yet happy in the knowledge of each other's presence.

It was the Emir who finally broke the silence.

'You have done well, my Mohammed.'

'Whatever I have done my father, has only been because of you and as a tribute to Adan. Remember – were it not for him and for you, my poor carcase would long ago have rotted on a wooden cross in the Djmaa el Fna.'

'And Morocco would have been the poorer. We lost a slave, but we gained a man.'

'You are kind, my father.'

The old man fingered the fat smooth beads of amber in his hands, clicking the beads together as he pushed them, one after another, along the string. 'Let us talk, Mohammed.' He spaced the words evenly, one between each bead. 'Let us talk tonight and settle many things, for since my son Adan left us so suddenly I have been thinking much of death.'

Mario shook his head as he regarded the other. 'But why think of death when you are still alive, strong and healthy as the stallion who fills his nostrils with the desert wind?'

A rueful smile crept over the Emir's face. 'Thank you for the comparison. Many years ago I was a stallion and I rode my mares well. There are many bastard princes here in my palace, and it is of these that I want to talk to you, Mohammed. As long as I live, I control them; they do not dare to act against my will. Each one knows that my sword is sharp and my anger quick, and that I would as soon kill him as scotch a serpent. I have no affection for these sons of concubines. All my love was centred on Adan. He was the only one I cherished. Now that he has gone, these others mean nothing to me. Neither they nor you can legitimately inherit my reign, but, Mohammed, legitimate or not, they would seize the power if they dared. Nothing stands between them and the Emirate of Marrakech but a small boy, and that boy Mohammed must succeed me.'

'And I agree with you. Adan's son must take your place when the sad day comes that you are no longer here.'

The Emir smiled. 'Even you, Mohammed, admit the possibility of my death.'

'It may not be for many years.'

'But it will come, as Allah wills, and that is what we must talk about. You are the only one I can trust. Your loyalty has been proved. Yours will be the responsibility, yours the burden. Can you, born a *N'zrani*, raised in Spanish ways, combat the evil influence of oriental palace politics? Know you that even now, without any doubt, some one of my bastard sons is probably plotting how he can overthrow me, slip a bowstring around the boy Mohammed's neck, and throw you over the walls tomorrow, so that he can sit on the divan himself? Yet, when he meets me tomorrow, he will be all fawning smiles and affected loyalty to me. How do I know which one it is, or how many of them are involved? I cannot know – nor can I tell you how you shall know – when a plot is hatching.'

'A *hareem* serves a man well, my father, but its fruit is

poisonous. There are too many useless sons with nothing to do but plot mischief. Perhaps it would be better to strangle the sons and let the daughters live.'

'These sons are the curse of Islam, Mohammed – idle and useless, but cunning. Mistrust them all. Watch them like a mother hen watches the hawk circling in the sky. Build up your own circle of retainers in the palace. Many will flock to you now when they see the favours I heap upon you. Be careful with your trusts. Set up a system of espionage so that every man will tattle on his neighbour. And above all, trust none of the women of your own or Adan's *hareem*.'

Mario looked up in surprise. 'What do you mean by saying "Adan's *hareem*"?'

'Because, according to the will which he left behind, everything that he possessed now belongs to you. Of course that includes the women of his *hareem*, as well as his palace, his horses, and everything else that he owned.'

Mario was silent for a moment, carefully considering his words. The next step was dangerous ground. He hesitated to approach it, for one false step might send all his dreams tumbling into nothingness. He swallowed, the muscles of his throat contracting; the dryness of his lips made speaking difficult.

'Everything, my father?'

'Yes,' the Emir nodded.

'But there is one thing he could not leave me.' Mario tried to keep the edge of anxiety from his voice.

'What single thing would you except from my son's estate?'

'The Lady Zaydah, the mother of the boy.'

'The Lady Zaydah is not a chattel, Mohammed. Adan could not give her to you.'

'But Adan did!'

'What do you mean?' The beads dropped from the Emir's hands and clattered to the floor. 'Explain your words, Mohammed, for they are words I do not understand. Adan could not give you his wife – not when he was alive – and he had no forewarning that he might die.'

Mario swallowed again, wet his lips with the tip of his tongue. His whole world depended on his choice of the next few words. 'Adan did not give me his wife, of that you can be sure, my father. Adan's wife was precious to him.'

'Was she?' The old man leaned anxiously forward. 'I hope she was, for at times I had doubts of my son's manhood.'

'Then never doubt it again.' Once more Mario swallowed hard. A little prayer raced across his mind. Let Allah forgive him for the falsehood he might say, for he was saying them not alone through selfishness but out of kindness to the man who sat beside him. 'From the first time I met Adan in the house of Don Baltazar, he had nothing but the thought of Zaydah on his mind. I still bear the scar of his jealous knife.'

'I rejoice to hear it. Not the scar that you bear, but about Adan.' His eyes questioned Mario. 'But, welcome as your words are, they do not explain Adan's gift of his wife to you.'

'On the night that Mohammed was born, Adan came to my palace. Would that I could describe his face! Even when he entered the portals of Paradise, he could not have been more joyful. He bade me dress and follow him. We crossed the courtyard to his palace and entered his *hareem*.'

'You, Mohammed? You entered the *hareem* of Adan?'

'At his invitation and on his insistence.'

'And then. . . .'

'He took me to the bed of the Lady Zaydah, pulled back the coverlet that covered his son, and showed him to me.'

'And you saw his mother?'

'Only the veil across her face.'

The old man sighed in relief.

Mario was on firmer ground now. The words came more easily. 'Together Adan and I knelt before the bed, and there Adan made me swear that not only would I give my life for the young prince, but that I would guard and protect his mother too.'

'Then indeed he did give her to you, and your words were true.'

Mario hesitated only a moment. This was the important question. 'Do you approve then that I should marry the Lady Zaydah and become in truth the father, if only the stepfather of your grandson?'

The minutes that the Emir delayed in answering stretched like leaden centuries for Mario. He hardly dared to breathe, for he did not even want the sound of his breath to change the course of the Emir's thoughts.

The old man looked up. His fingers fumbled at the collar of his *kaftan*, drawing it together as though a chill wind had blown into the room. Gradually the heavy lines that channelled his face from nostril to chin relaxed. He nodded his head slowly.

'It is fitting, Mohammed. I can see that it was the wish of Adan. And as the boy's father, the husband of his mother, you can protect him better. Now there can be one establishment instead of two. Now you can keep him under your eyes waking and sleeping. Yes, Mohammed, you shall take the Lady Zaydah for your wife.'

Mario uncurled one foot and stretched it to the floor.

'Are you leaving?' the Emir asked.

'I would send a messenger to the lady to acquaint her with the facts of her betrothal.'

'You'll do nothing of the kind, my son. She will be informed in the proper manner. And think you not that you shall see her until you find her beside you in the marriage bed, for this marriage will be made in due accordance with the accepted rites.'

'And when will it take place?' Mario tried hard to keep his voice normal.

'The month after Ramadan.'

Mario counted on his fingers. 'Three months. It is well.'

'Those will be three busy months for you, my son.'

'Any occupation will be welcome – twice welcome if it is your pleasure.'

'Ah, you agree before you know what lies before you?'

'Then tell me, Father.'

'From now on, Mohammed, you are my shadow. We meet at the first call of the *muezzin* and we stay together until the last. There is much for you to learn, much that Adan had no interest in learning. He was not a statesman. For him the horses, the hawks, the carefree life! But that is not so for you. You must learn every detail of my government. You must learn how to judge, how to rule, how to reward and punish. You must become acquainted with my own thoughts and the way I think them, that they may become your thoughts. Together we shall preserve all this for the son of Adan.' He waved his hand as if to encircle the whole city of Marrakech. 'Although you can never be Emir, you, with the help of those two who are faithful to you, will see that my grandson someday sits on my divan.'

'You spoke of those who are faithful to me?'

'You have the ability to engender loyalty in the hearts of those who love you. I speak of the faithful black and the boy who belonged to Sidi Mokar. One is a Negro, the other a

Christian slave, but their hearts are yours. They are loyal and they will serve you well. I think either of them would die for you. Allah's ways are beyond the understanding of humans, but it seems that he entrusts my dynasty to three *N'zrani*-born – a Spanish count, a Negro slave, and an Andalusian beggar.'

Mario brought his foot back up on the divan. He noticed that the Emir was smiling.

'There is little that goes on in my realm that I do not know, Mohammed. I knew about your midnight visit with Adan to his *hareem*, but I was testing you. I am pleased with you, my son. Adan's honour is safe in your hands. Now it draws on to morning. Seek your divan in your own palace, and may Allah give you pleasant dreams!'

As Mario rose to go, the Emir plucked at his sleeve.

'A word of advice, my son.'

'Yes, Father.'

'The four slaves that the Sultan gave you – those which accompanied you to Spain.'

'Yes?' Mario questioned with his eyes.

'They have worked hard, so I have been informed. Do let them rest tonight. Choose other fillies from your plenteous stable, and if you do not find any to your liking there, summon the eunuch of Adan's *hareem* and choose from among those. I think each of the Sultan's four deserves a rest. They have been ridden hard, all the way to Spain and back.'

Mario bowed in mock obeisance. 'As usual, my father, your advice is excellent and your sources of information most trustworthy.' He winked at the old man as he left the room and the slowly lowered eyelid of the Emir winked back at him.

Chapter Fifty-six

MARIO LEARNED in the months that passed before Ramadan that the government of a province as large and as rich as that of Marrakech was no sinecure. It was certainly not accomplished by the long, lazy days he had enjoyed with Adan, riding, hunting, hawking and whoring. Instead, it was hard work – work which required all his energy and left him exhausted at the end of the day.

The Emir had never demanded such service of Adan; possibly he had realized his own son's ineptitude for government. But where he had been lenient with Adan, he was strict with Mario. Mario must learn every detail, learn it well and learn it quickly. He must be judge and jury, treasurer and ruler, the host of Morocco, the chief supporter of the Faith, the guardian of the successor of the Emir. All of these responsible posts must be learned in breathless haste. Mario did not realize until a few weeks had passed that the Emir's unusual burst of energy had been planned deliberately by the old man in part to banish Adan's image from the thoughts of both of them.

From the *muezzin's* first call to his last, they were both running to catch up with their shadows. Things which had been neglected for years were unearthed, settled, and dispatched. A vast building programme was inaugurated in the city of Marrakech, which spread to the outlying *casbahs* in the mountains. Crumbling walls in the mountain *casbahs* were rebuilt. Marrakech was more securely fortified, and Adan's palace was enlarged for Mario, to accommodate the double *hareem*.

The slave caravans from the south came through with stalwart Africans. The slave caravans from Fez arrived with perishing Christians – and still they came, their numbers swallowed up in the maws of new walls, new fortifications, new buildings, new wells, waterways, irrigation, canals, pools and date orchards. The architects of Marrakech spent long hours submitting new sketches to the Emir, who examined them without comment before handing them over to Mario for his approval or disapproval. In most decisions, Mario's word was final.

But the surge in building activity was only a part of the whole. No longer did Mario wonder where the money came from to support him and his household. Now he knew. He spent part of each day in the dusty, cedar-lined office of the chief treasurer. He knew the tax rates of all the *caids* – how much they had to pay, when they could be expected to pay it, and exactly what should be done when the levies were not forthcoming.

That meant they were to dispatch a company of the Emir's mounted troops to whatever outlying *casbah* had fallen behind in its payments. Although their arrival might betoken bribes to the captain in charge, fervent protestations of the *caid's* inability to pay the levy, or absolute refusal, the soldiers always returned with panniered mules carrying heavy chests filled with gold.

Sometimes they brought the reluctant *caid* back with them. Uusually a day spent hanging by the thumb of one hand, so that his toes barely touched the ground, was sufficient to send him back to his *casbah* willing to co-operate in the matter of future taxes. Then, of course, it was the turn of the *caid* to wring more money out of his already starving population.

But the tax monies were paid, the money was received in Marrakech, and every new pair of gold-embroidered *babouches* that Mario wore was paid for by some poor wretch who had been forced to see his family starve, while the millet that would have fed them went to pay for Mario's shoes. Better, however, for the peasants to starve than for the Emir's son to go barefooted.

The mornings were allotted to the dispensation of justice in the Presence Chamber. Now Mario sat beside the Emir on the divan – the thrones were found to be too uncomfortable for any prolonged session – and heard the pleas of those who sued for justice and the vehement denials of those who were sued. Trials that formerly ran into weeks of oratorical outbursts were now settled in an hour. The Emir's justice was swift, and – so Mario felt – not always just. But once the Emir had made up his mind as to the guilt or innocence of a party, his decision was immediately forthcoming and was final.

'You can tell when they are lying, my son,' the Emir warned Mario, 'by looking at their eyes. Close your ears if you must, but look at their eyes. The man who has a just cause lowers his eyes as he pleads his case. He is devoid of arrogance. He sues with the simple conviction that he is right. The man with a false case assumes a borrowed air of confidence. He looks you straight in the eye and his words come readily; he has rehearsed his lies over and over in his mind. The glib ones are the guilty ones.'

And as Mario sat on the bed of justice, he came to realize the truth of the old man's advice. The honest cause was pleaded, slowly, with downcast eyes. The rascal spread his feet apart, looked directly at the Emir and launched into a carefully planned speech in which the words were far more forceful than necessary. So Mario learned justice as he learned finance.

There still remained, however, one most important facet of government, and certainly the most difficult for him to learn – palace politics. It was here that both Ramon and Juanele were invaluable. Now both of them could reach in the sleeves of their *djellabahs* and feel the hardness of gold in a smooth leather bag. This gold could pass stealthily from their hands to another's and, in return, it would bring valuable information.

Thus Mario learned that Ibrahim, the second son of the Emir by his Persian concubine, was planning to poison him. Not directly, of course. No! Ibrahim was presenting his brother Mohammed with a new slave girl for his *hareem*, one Ibrahim had sent to Egypt to acquire. Ibrahim had heard that this one had been trained in certain oriental arts that prolonged a man's ecstasy indefinitely. She achieved this prolongation of pleasure by a special nougat which she alone knew how to prepare, of candied rose leaves and some exotic Arabian drug. Mario had only to eat the nougat and he would enter an earthly paradise which few men had ever experienced. It was Juanele's gold, however, which found out from the chief eunuch that the so-called aphrodisiac was a fatal poison which would dispatch Mario to a paradise other than earthly.

And so it went, the constant intrigue that centred around Mario. That he was able to trust Ramon and Juanele saved his life on many occasions and, gradually, through them and through his own personality, he built up a faction in the palace which derived their strength from him and realized that his power was their power.

The weeks passed slowly before Ramadan, and although the holy month of fasting brought some cessation to their work, it did not renew their energy. It was a difficult time – the month when tempers were strained to a fine wire which would snap at the slightest touch. Enforced fasting during the day, when food and water were denied to True Believers, made enemies of friends, and the short nights, filled with feasting and caresses, did little to prepare them for the next day of fasting. Ordinary business came to a standstill; only the Christian slaves toiled on, targets for the increased abuse of their masters.

The slaves and concubines in Mario's *hareem* saw little of him, and the handkerchief fluttered from the balcony after the horns sounded, more often than not. As the day when he might claim Zaydah approached, he felt less need of the ministrations of his *hareem*.

Zaydah's name had not again been mentioned between Mario and the Emir. Although the boy Mohammed was brought to Mario daily, he had received no word or sign from Zaydah. Through the devious grapevine of palace gossip, relayed to him by either Ramon or Juanele, he knew that she was well; but he was unable to find out whether or not she had been informed of her coming marriage to him. Nor was he too sure about the marriage himself. He did not wish to bring up the subject with the Emir a second time, and the old man never mentioned it – until one day when the long, nervous month of Ramadan had nearly ended and he called Mario into the little room which they used for their most private discussions.

'The month of Ramadan is nearly ended, my son.' The Emir plumped a pillow behind his back and settled down, his quick glance noting in Mario's face the tense lines which the month of Ramadan had brought.

'Praise be to Allah,' Mario sighed.

'Yes, it is an ordeal of the flesh,' the Emir agreed, 'but it glorifies the All-Knowing One. It is good that we deprive ourselves for a period and let our thoughts dwell on the All High.'

'But do they, my father?' Mario's doubt was evident in his voice. 'Do not the ears of men listen for the horns of Ramadan when they sound at night, so that they may break their fast and tumble into bed with their women?'

'Unfortunately yes, my son. They do. But the discipline of going without during the hours of the day is good for them. Their hands do not reach to roll the *couscous* into a ball, stretch for a glass of tea, or cup the breasts of their women whenever they will. At least they restrain themselves, if only for hours. In the end they reap and benefit. But, as I was saying, the month of Ramadan nears its close and I have not forgotten the promise I made you. You shall take the Lady Zaydah to wife, and tonight we shall set the date. If agreeable to you, we shall make it one week from tonight.'

Mario clenched his fists tightly under the folds of his robe. A week from tonight, he thought. At last it was settled. Now he could hope with certainty. Now the promise given him long ago in the bath at Don Baltazar's house was about to be realized. A week from tonight! He looked up at the Emir, his eyes swimming with gratitude.

'Thank you, my father. It is agreeable to me. But let me ask you one question. Will it be agreeable to the Lady Zaydah?'

The Emir belched slightly and patted his stomach. 'The lamb tonight was ill-prepared. What did you say, my son? Oh yes, the Lady Zaydah! We do not have to consider whether or not it is agreeable to her. If I say so, it must be. She has no choice in the matter.'

'But does she know?'

'She does.'

'And has she expressed any opinion about being married to me?'

The Emir shook his head. 'When I informed her, she merely bowed her head and said "*In'sha'allah*", as any dutiful woman would do.' He looked straight at Mario. 'I think, my son, she will appreciate her new master, for despite your kind words I have always doubted just how proficient my son Adan was when it came to bedding a wife. We spoiled Adan, Mohammed. Let it be a lesson to you in regard to the young Mohammed, and do not make the mistake I made with Adan. When Adan was but a boy of twelve, I sent a female slave to bed with him. By the time he was fourteen, he had his own *hareem* of concubines, and by the time he was sixteen, he was drained of energy and desire. Do not make the same mistake I made with Adan with the young Mohammed. Keep him from the softness of the *hareem*. Put him in the barracks if necessary, but do not let him be spoiled by the indulgent caresses of women while he is still too young to appreciate them. And now. . . .' The Emir rose slowly, walked across to the fretted window and looked out on the moonlit paleness of the Koutoubia tower. 'The *muezzin* mounts the tower, my son. Soon we shall hear the horns of Ramadan and we shall rush through the corridors to our *hareems* and to our feasts. May Allah go with you, Mohammed.'

'And protect you, my father.'

'Now go, my son. Tonight your mind is settled and you are at peace. I could ask no more from a son than I have found in you. I have tested you, Mohammed, during these last few months. I have nearly killed myself doing it, but I had to know the extent of your ability to act for my grandson. In all my years of ruling Marrakech, I have never worked so hard, put in such gruelling hours, or made such a slave of myself as I have these last few months. But I have found out much. You are a man, my son – a man who can lead other men. If, forty days ago, the Angel Gabriel had written my name in his book, foretelling my death on this very night, I could accept the will of Allah, for I would know that I was leaving you behind.'

As he opened the door for Mario to pass through, his thin, veined hand rested for a second on Mario's arm. Mario placed his over it, hesitated for a moment in the doorway as he looked up at the man he had come to know as his father, pressed the hand with firmness, and left. As the door closed behind him, Juanele, who had been sitting on the floor, rose and followed him down the hall.

Chapter Fifty-seven

ALL OF the colour, excitement, and riotous entertainment of a Moorish wedding were missing from the nuptials of Mario and Zaydah. No caravans of dashing horsemen arrived from the distant *casbahs*, no panniered mules laden with gifts were driven through the gates, no tents of visiting *caids* and *sheiks* encircled the city. The days were without dashing sorties, and the nights were devoid of feasting and revelling. Owing to Adan's recent death it was a quiet, almost sombre, affair – a *fait accompli* before even the Emir's own Court knew about it.

On the evening of the wedding day, the Emir walked alone across the courtyard that separated his palace from Mario's, and sat on the divan in Mario's bedroom while Mario finished dressing. For this, the most important night in his life, Mario wore only a plain white *djellabah*. Then the two of them, followed by Ramon and Juanele, recrossed the courtyard and entered the shadowy gates of Adan's palace.

It was the first time Mario had entered it since Adan's death, and he half thought he could see Adan welcoming him from the top of the stairs, catch the tone of his voice as he called from the upper rooms, or hear the soft slap of his slippers on the marble floors. But, although he convinced himself that he was only daydreaming, he nevertheless sensed Adan's presence, and somehow Mario felt that Adan's mood was strangely sad, yet happy too.

The four of them ascended the stairs and passed down the corridor to the double doors of intricately carved cedar which led to Adan's room. They were tightly closed. The Emir, with a gesture of dismissal, bade Ramon and Juanele wait outside, then lifted one hand and rapped lightly on the door. One of the pair swung slowly, quietly, inward, and Mario followed his father inside. European candles had replaced the lamps of argon oil, but their flickering flames did little to illuminate the vast room.

As Mario's eyes became accustomed to the half darkness, he saw, sitting on the divan, a figure dressed in stiff cloth-of-gold, with a heavy veil covering the entire face. Not even the eyes were visible. He had no way of knowing who it was; the stiff costume hid all bodily contours as the veil hid the face. He guessed that it must be Zaydah, although the figure gave no sign of recognition. Not even a fold of the dress or draperies moved.

The Emir seated himself on another divan, facing the one with the veiled figure, and motioned to Mario to sit beside him. Evidently their movements had been observed for no sooner were they seated than a figure emerged from the shadows of the walls and advanced to the centre of the room. It was the Iman from the mosque – the same learned old man who had instructed Mario in religion when he had first arrived in Marrakech. He advanced slowly, sank to the floor, before the Emir, then arose and made a lesser obeisance in front of Mario.

The ceremony was brief and took only a few moments. After it was over the Iman bowed his way out of the room. When he had gone, the Emir clapped his hands. An unveiled female slave appeared and the Emir ordered more candles. When these were brought and lighted, Mario saw the outlines of a bed – high pillars which surrounded a divan – the whole draped from the ceiling in red silk. The Emir rose, extended his hand to Mario, and led him over to the facing divan, found a slender hand among the welter of gold cloth and placed it in Mario's.

The Emir's voice was without a quaver, although Mario was certain there were tears in the old man's eyes.

'Mohammed, my son, tonight I entrust you with my most cherished possession – my grandson. You are now his father, the husband of his mother. Guard my grandson, Mohammed ibn Ibrahim, and, if Allah wills, he will someday sit in my seat and govern this city. Let his life be your life, and treat him as you would a son of your own, for, as the blood of my son still flows in your veins, so must your blood be in Adan's son. I leave you now, Mohammed.' Without addressing Zaydah, he turned, walked the few steps to the door without turning around, and went out. The door closed silently behind him.

They were alone. Zaydah, who had not moved since Mario's entrance, except to allow her hand to be placed in his, slowly raised her other hand and unhooked the clasp that held her veil over her face. She did not lower it all at once. First she uncovered her eyes, and Mario found them looking straight into his. The veil dropped and he saw her cheeks, her lips and her chin. Then it fell to the floor and for the first time since that long-ago night in Cadiz, he beheld her face. She stood up, an awkward bundle of gold tissue.

He held her at arm's length, studying every contour of her face, like a starving man who is suddenly confronted with a table full of food. His desire was overpowering, but he did not know how to begin. Her eyes fascinated him, her mouth bewitched him, the curve of her cheek begged for the stroke of his fingers, the tendrils of her hair cried out to be touched. He lowered his arms, which had held her at a distance, and she took a single step towards him, near enough to lift her face to his. He felt the warm moistness of her lips, the flutter of her lashes on his cheek, the pressure of her body against his. Her breasts were hard against his chest, her hands were behind his neck, bringing his face down closer to her.

Then the dam of his passion broke, and the waters, so long and so carefully guarded, broke loose and he was swept away by the fierceness of the wave of fire that passed through him. His lips, impatient at the soft pressure of hers, pressed hard against her mouth. His hands, contemptuous of strings and ribbons, tore the dress from her shoulders, ripped the gold gauze into shreds, clutched the thin linen undergarments and stripped them from her until his hands, rough and calloused from the reins of his horses, encountered the perfumed softness of her flesh. His fingers closed around that softness, straining her to him so completely that he felt she was a part of himself. His arms, crushing her even more tightly, lifted her from the floor and carried her to the bed; then he felt her soft body under his own.

In everything he did, she responded. His lips never left hers, until finally she drew her mouth away to speak. Mario did not want words – not even words of love – but she denied her lips to him until he let her speak.

'Mario, my Mario! You do not have to prove your love to me, beloved. Come, let this, our first moment of belonging to one another, be one of studied joy, not one of haste. We are no slaves, stealing a moment in the garden, hurrying to some ill-matched climax which neither of us can enjoy. Must you spend yourself in the twisted folds of your *djellabah* while I am fettered by the torn ribbons of my dress? Come, Mario, let this be love and passion together, not passion alone.'

He released her slowly, freeing her from the weight of his

body, and let only his hand rest upon her. He swallowed hard, trying to force words through the dryness of his throat.

'Zaydah! This I cannot believe. I seem to be in a dream and I must make haste before I awaken. But you are right. There is no reason why I should seek my marriage bed shod in *babouches*.' He kicked the slippers from his feet, watched them arc through the air and heard their soft fall on the marble tiles.

'Nor, my Mario, do you need your *djellabah* for protection from the cold night air.' She plucked at the thin wool which covered his chest.

'How true, for now I have you to keep me warm.' He raised himself on one elbow and looked at the guttering candles. 'Surely, my love, the moon shining through the window would be more welcome than this smoke of wax.'

She gave him a little push. 'There is no moon tonight, but what need have we of moon or candles? Snuff them out, my Mario.' She pushed him farther towards the edge of the divan.

He swung his legs over the edge, walked to the tall brass candlesticks and snuffed the candles out one by one. As the last one flickered out, she called to him.

'Do not forget the *djellabah*, Mario. Let it warm the cold tiles of the floor, for you shall have no need of it with me beside you.'

In the darkness, he pulled the robe up over his head, stretched his hands out, blindly groping for the bed, encountered the twisted pillars with their tatters of silk, then lowered himself to the arms that were waiting to enfold him.

Suddenly all the other women that he had felt beneath his body became as nothing. He was a young boy again, fresh, innocent and vigorous. All of the mystery which once long ago he experienced for the first time returned, and this new ecstasy, recaptured from the distant past, erased all the other bodies which had writhed under his embraces. For the first time, his lips touched love; for the first time, his hands cherished instead of merely fondled; for the first time the fire of his passion burned with the oil of gentleness.

He did not demand, he sought. He did not force, he entreated. He did not overpower, but allowed himself to be conquered. Zaydah's half-audible mouthings were answered by his own low moans. Her gentle hands with questing fingers searched, found and marvelled. His strong hands, which only a few moments before had gripped and bruised, now became tender.

The pulsating rhythm of life encompassed them slowly and rhythmically, lifting them and moulding their separateness into one being, one breath, one heartbeat, one inexorable force that neither of them could control. Like a current of water that forms itself together in the depths of the ocean, gathering force as it nears the shore, their love enveloped them, carrying them on its crest, lifting them higher and higher until its self-propelled mightiness built it up to a towering height, only to crash, splintering into tremulous fragments of foam that trickled into nothingness on the ivory-tinted beaches of their bodies.

With the ebbing of their desire came peace and quiet contentment that asked only a gentle touch of reassurance. It was enough to entwine a finger through a tendril of hair, to let a hand slip in soft caress over a cheek, to brush lips tenderly together, to lie in mutual surrender to the blind tempest which had raged through them and had now spent itself. They lay beside each other, not speaking, only listening to each other's heartbeats, hearing them become quieter and more regular, until they were able to breathe without a frantic drinking of air into empty lungs, but only a quiet, controlled evenness that betokened rest.

Zaydah moved, letting the cool air pass between her body and Mario's. In the darkness she straightened the silken sheet under her, smoothing its wrinkles. She leaned over Mario, letting her hair fall over his face.

'And you, my beloved, have you found satisfaction?' Her lips were close to his ear.

'For the moment,' he whispered back.

'Only for the moment? Then, my dear, for that moment, let me see you. The only glimpses I have ever had of you were stolen ones. Never have I had the chance to feast my eyes on you, to stamp every lineament of your face and body in my mind. This then is what I desire for that precious moment. Let me see you, so when that moment passes I may, even in the darkness that comes after, see you continuously!'

'Which means,' he said, laughing, 'that the candles, which you pushed me from bed to snuff out, must now be relighted.'

'You see' – she nibbled at his ear – 'what a silly wife you

have. She is really a giddy weathervane, which wants one thing one moment and something else the next. First she wants the lights out and then she wants them burning.'

Again she pushed him to the edge of the bed and once more he swung his legs to the floor. The tiles were cold to his bare feet and he ran across the room to where his *djellabah* made a white smudge in the darkness. He fumbled in the sleeves for his flint box, found it, ignited the small wax taper inside and shielded the tiny flame with his hand as he carried it to the nearest candlestick. One by one the candles flared up. With their full light, he turned and faced the bed, reaching out his arms to Zaydah.

But she, her eyes blinking in the sudden light, looked at him with horror. Her hands shielded her eyes as if to blot out some terrible vision, and Mario could see, through the screen of her fingers, the repugnance that she was trying to shield. He walked slowly to the bed, gently drew her hands from her eyes and lifted her face up to him.

She shook her head in despair and would not meet his gaze, lowering her eyelids so that she could avoid his look. Her hands struggled to free themselves from his grip. When he had once again managed to lift her face, he saw tears running down her cheeks.

'But what is it, Zaydah? What has happened? What have I done or said that has changed you? A moment before you caressed my body with your lips; now you shrink from me with repulsion. My God! What is it?'

She opened her eyes and stared at him.

'You say "my God", Mario.'

'It is an expression, nothing more.'

'But to what god do you refer?'

'I thought not when I uttered the words, Zaydah. They hark back to my days in Spain when *Dios mio* was a common expression. Yet you do well to ask "what god", for now I can answer you and answer you truthfully, because I have found God. There is only one God, Allah, and Mohammed is His prophet.'

'And yet you,' she said, 'do not carry Mohammed on your body. You carry Christ, and Him crucified.'

Mario looked down at his chest and saw the attenuated figure that hung there. It had so long been a part of him that he had forgotten it, and tonight, even after keeping it hidden for so long, he had lighted the candles without a thought of the picture on his body.

His hand stroked her hair. 'Yes, little one, I carry Christ on my body.'

She reached one hand up and touched the four points of the cross tenderly. As she did so, Mario went back in memory to that night the child Mohammed was born.

'You see, Mario,' she said softly. 'I am a Christian.'

'You, the wife of Adan, a Christian!'

'Yes. But Adan never knew it. Long ago, when I was in Spain, my grandfather allowed me to attend the convent there. The nuns taught me their religion. At first I would have none of it. I fought against it and I was loath to accept it, but in the end I did, and, with my acceptance of it, there came a great love for it. Now, although I am nominally a Moslem and must remain so in the eyes of all the world but you, I am really a Christian. Hidden in the corner of my room, under a loose tile, there is my crucifix. That is where I pray.'

'And you thought that I —'

'Yes – that you were really a Christian too.'

Mario sat down on the edge of the bed. He reached out his hand and she allowed him to touch her, although he felt that she shrank from the contact of his fingers. 'Oh, Zaydah.' He let his head sink to his chest. 'Must this difference between Moslem and Christian poison our love?'

She did not answer him.

He pointed to his chest. 'This, Zaydah, is what the Christians of Spain did to me. They branded me with their cross, not through any love or reverence for their Christ but that His cross upon my flesh might make me suffer even more. It was hatred, not love, that stamped this sign on me. How, then, can you blame me for hating it?'

Her hand slowly covered his. 'No, I cannot blame you, Mario, for I realize how much you have suffered.'

'But you do not understand, Zaydah. If this' – he pointed to the tattoo –'be your God, then why do you shrink from me because I wear it?'

'Because it is not right that we should lie together with such a holy sign between us.'

He threw her hand back on to the bed and stood up, the heat of sudden anger rising in his voice. 'Then would you have me flayed? Do you wish the skin stripped from my body? That is the only way I can rid myself of this!' He reached down and pulled her up so that she stood beside him. He grabbed her hand and placed it against his chest. Her fingers curled in protest and he flung her back on to the bed.

'I'll do it! I'll call the most learned physicians of all Isiam – the doctors from Cairo, from Istanbul, from Damascus, from Fez and even from Holy Mecca. Together they may know how to skin a man and yet allow him to live. If this skin that covers me is so hateful to you, I'll strip it off. See' – he pointed to the old scar on his side – 'once there was no skin covering this wound, but now it is covered. If an inch of a man's body can be covered anew, why not more?'

She shook her head sadly. 'No, Mario, you need not do this for me, even though it were possible, which I doubt.'

He ran to the pile of cloth on the floor which was his *djellabah*, rummaged in the folds and drew out a dagger from its silver sheath. With his left hand he gathered a fold of skin between his fingers and started to plunge the dagger through it. She ran to him, snatched the blade from his hands and threw it to the floor.

'No, Mario, no! I love you too much!'

His moment of anger was suddenly spent. He took her hands, folded them together tenderly and enclosed them in his own, and led her back to the bed. He knelt beside her on the floor and pillowed his head in her lap. She disengaged her hands and let her fingers wander through the curls of his hair.

'Oh, Mario! To think that I would spoil this moment we both have lived for! I am confused – I cannot think straight. You, with the mark of Christ upon you, are a Moslem. I, with the mark of Islam upon me, am a Christian. That which you despise I hold sacred. That which you consider holy, I deem as nothing. We must think, Mario. We must reason together. We cannot let this picture painted on your skin destroy us and our love for each other.'

'Then let us talk sense about it, Zaydah. Think now. Had I willingly put this mark upon myself and then repudiated it, you might blame me. But remember I had no choice in the matter. This Jesus whom you worship – He who was a prophet of love – would He consider this, which was born of hatred, something holy? I think not. Therefore consider it for what it is. Although the lines themselves delineate something sacred, it is not a holy thing. Therefore, my love, you can divorce it in your mind from whatever holiness it may signify. If you must look at it, think how human hate placed your Jesus on the cross, and then think how hate placed His cross on my body. Let not the evil that men have done to me come between the two of us.'

Her fingers crept under his chin and gently lifted his head so that his eyes looked into hers.

'You speak words of truth, my Mario. I am but a silly woman, surprised and horrified by the sight of you as you suddenly turned towards me. Where my thoughts had pictured only the perfection of your flesh, my eyes were suddenly confronted with the terrible picture you bear on your skin. For a moment I was startled, frightened and, yes, repulsed. I could not reconcile your body which had so recently loved mine with that picture it carries. But now I understand – at least a little – and know that that which has happened to you can have no connexion with my faith or yours.'

He smiled up at her and her fingers touched his lips, his eyes and his forehead. As his head nestled closer in her lap, she continued.

'But do not ask me to change my faith, Mario. I cannot. I can never repudiate the prayers that have brought you to me.'

'Nor do I wish you to. Long ago, Zaydah, when first I came to this land, the boy, Juanele, who befriended me, told me that his master did not wish him to change his faith to that of Islam. He advanced a very good reason, too.'

'Which was?'

'That Allah, delighting in the prayers of the faithful, is loath to grant them because they are a sweet incense to him. But the prayers of Christians are a stench in his nostrils. Therefore, he grants them at once so they will cease.'

'It sounds reasonable.' She smiled back at him.

'So then you, Zaydah, pray to your Christian God, and I shall remember that the God you pray to is also mine. And I, in my prayers to Allah, shall remember that my God is also yours. If it is the will of Allah that our prayers be answered, we shall not know which is the most powerful, for we shall both be praying to the same god. I shall honour your Jesus, Zaydah, knowing that you will honour my Prophet, and thus we can reconcile our beliefs.'

She did not answer. Her fingers continued to fondle his face. His head moved away from her hands and he stood up, walked across the room to where his robe lay on the floor. He picked it up, shook it out and caught the thin shirt that was entangled in it. He slipped it over his head and returned to stand in front of her, lifting her up until she stood beside him, her head pillowed against the white muslin that covered his chest.

'You see, Zaydah, it has disappeared. Now it is as though it never had been.'

'Yes, it is gone, Mario. I no longer see it.'

'Then banish it from your mind. Let it make no difference between us.'

'I shall try.'

'But, my love, even though we try to forget it and erase it from our thoughts, let it teach us a lesson.'

'And what might that lesson be?'

'Let the joining together of you and me be more than a wedding of two people. Let it presage the day when Moslem and Christian can live together, side by side, in peace and harmony. Let it put an end to the sword that has split two peoples – the sword of misunderstanding. You continue in your faith, and I shall in mine. You guide yourself by the precepts of the gentle Nazarene, and I by the teachings of the wise Mohammed. In so doing, Zaydah, we both reach the same goal, although we travel by different roads. This perhaps will be a small beginning, but through our secret compact we may be able to lay a foundation for generations to come so that Moslem and Christian may live together and work together to banish all cruelty, all misunderstanding, all wars between us.'

Her hands reached up, clutched at the open neck of his shirt and with one downward motion, ripped the thin fabric, baring his chest. Her fingers gently traced the outline of the tattoo, and then she slowly leaned over and kissed the four separate points of the cross. When she straightened up there was a calm peace in her eyes.

'We do not need a layer of cloth to hide this now, my Mario. All the evil and hatred which conceived it has gone. I shall no longer fear it, for now it has become a sacred thing, dear to me. It will always remind me of what you have said. Perhaps you and I, through this deeper understanding on our wedding night, can reach out and help those who need our help and love. This we cannot do in a moment or in a day or in a year, only little by little. But perhaps as time goes on and the reins of government fall into your hands, you can lighten the burdens of those poor wretches who slave on the walls and through them, the burdens of all Christian slaves in Morocco. And I, who am doomed to spend my life in the *hareem*, can ease the lot of the women there. Together, Mario, we can teach the young Mohammed to govern wisely, without hatred or prejudice for Christians, while yet he upholds the doctrines of Mohammed.'

Mario's arms reached out to encircle her, and they were gentle with love and tenderness. His kiss was a mere brushing of her lips. Together, as if impelled by some common purpose, they walked to the window, threw open the fretted shutters and looked out on the midnight of Marrakech.

The moon which Zaydah had previously denied them now rode high in the sky, silvering the tower of the Koutoubia, whitewashing the walls of the palace with a dim light, creeping into the courtyard below to disperse the drifts of violet ashes that covered the cobbles. As they watched from the window, two figures, sharply etched in black and white, crossed the courtyard. Mario noticed their shoulder-to-shoulder nearness. He recognized them as Ramon and Juanele, and he knew from their slow steps that each of them had found peace.

His hand lingered on Zaydah's shoulder and the warmth of her skin penetrated his fingers. Then he felt the back of his hand become warm with the tight, constricting grip of a palm placed over his – a hand that was warm and moist and strong. The hand seemed to close tightly over Mario's and Zaydah's. It was not the hand of Zaydah, for the strength in the fingers was the strength of a man. Mario turned in the darkness to look behind him, but saw only the shadowy outlines of the room. He understood.

'Thank you, Adan,' he whispered as he led Zaydah from the window to the dark shadows of the tumbled bed.

CHILD OF THE SUN 5/-
Kyle Onstott and Lance Horner

When Varius Avitus Bassianus became Emperor, even the voluptuaries of ancient Rome recoiled in horror. His perverted desires, his sadism, his degeneracy and his evil influences could only end in violence.

MANDINGO 5/-
Kyle Onstott

Mandingo blood was the finest slave strain available. The Maxwells of Falconhurst treasured it, bet on it, boasted about it. But it tore their plantation apart, bringing death and dishonour.

DRUM 6/-
Kyle Onstott

A giant saga of three generations. A story of slaves and slave breeding—of the inhuman, shameful deeds burnt into the history of the American South.

MASTER OF FALCONHURST 6/-
Kyle Onstott

The Civil War strikes the rich Alabama slave plantation. To save it, Drummage, born a slave and loyal to the land, must become Master of Falconhurst and of the ruthless, sensual woman who rules it.

SANTIAGO BLOOD 5/-
Lance Horner

The Santiagos, the proudest and wealthiest family in Cuba. An age of fierce appetites for both passion and slavery, and a violent obsession with revenge. Another magnificent novel.

These and other advertised PAN books are obtainable from all booksellers and newsagents. If you have any difficulty please send purchase price plus 6d. postage to PO Box 11, Falmouth, Cornwall.